A STORY OF DURHAM

A Story of Durham

*Told the
Wright Way*

CORA DARRAH

ACKNOWLEDGEMENTS

First and foremost, I want to thank my husband Jay, who was willing to endure years of listening to the unfolding of this story.

I want to thank my brothers Rob Hawkins and Bill Hawkins for their willingness to support this endeavor.

I want to thank Debbie Zaccardelli, my editor, for her incredible ability to work with the details.

I want to thank my daughter, Hannah Darrah, for her artistic flare and willingness to take this manuscript and transform it into a work of art.

I would like to thank Joy Rubenstein for being willing to read the many rough drafts and assist me in the development of the story.

I would like to let the staff at the Rubenstein Library know how much I appreciate their hard work in preserving Richard Harvey Wright's archives.

This project couldn't have been possible without Jean Bradley Anderson's book *Durham County, A History of Durham County, North Carolina*.

Robert Durden's book *The Dukes of Durham* was also a valuable resource.

I am grateful to C. Eileen Watts Welch for her encouragement to include her maternal great- grandfather, Aaron McDuffie Moore in my book. Her niece, Blake Hill-Saya's book *Aaron McDuffie Moore* was a true inspiration in the portrayal of this incredible man.

Thank you, Ann Wright and Mary Pearson, my newly found relatives, who have made this journey alongside me.

Lastly, but most importantly, I want to thank God for giving me this family, and the ability to spin a story that will hopefully live on for generations to come.

CONTENTS

WRIGHT

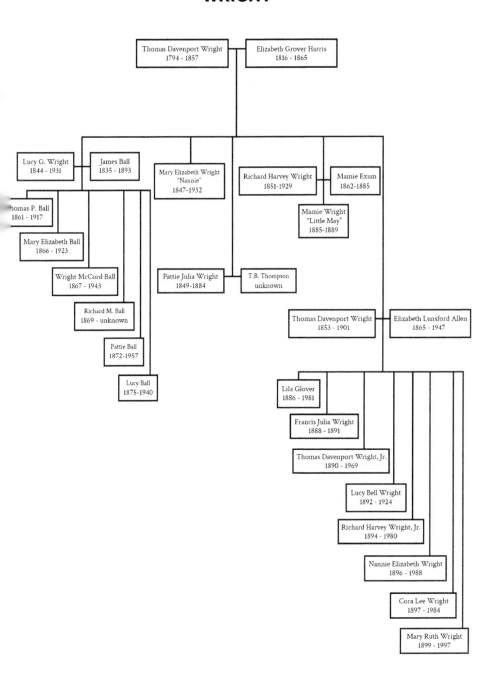

Thomas Davenport Wright
1794 - 1857

Elizabeth Grover Harris
1816 - 1865

Lucy G. Wright
1844 - 1931

James Ball
1835 - 1893

Mary Elizabeth Wright
"Nannie"
1847-1932

Richard Harvey Wright
1851-1929

Mamie Exum
1862-1885

Thomas P. Ball
1861 - 1917

Mamie Wright
"Little May"
1885-1889

Mary Elizabeth Ball
1866 - 1923

Wright McCord Ball
1867 - 1943

Pattie Julia Wright
1849-1884

T.B. Thompson
unknown

Richard M. Ball
1869 - unknown

Thomas Davenport Wright
1853 - 1901

Elizabeth Lunsford Allen
1865 - 1947

Pattie Ball
1872-1957

Lucy Ball
1875-1940

Lila Glover
1886 - 1981

Francis Julia Wright
1888 - 1891

Thomas Davenport Wright, Jr.
1890 - 1969

Lucy Bell Wright
1892 - 1924

Richard Harvey Wright, Jr.
1894 - 1980

Nannie Elizabeth Wright
1896 - 1988

Cora Lee Wright
1897 - 1984

Mary Ruth Wright
1899 - 1997

DUKE

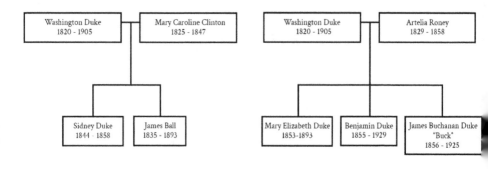

Washington Duke 1820 - 1905	Mary Caroline Clinton 1825 - 1847

Sidney Duke 1844 - 1858	James Ball 1835 - 1893

Washington Duke 1820 - 1905	Artelia Roney 1829 - 1858

Mary Elizabeth Duke 1853-1893	Benjamin Duke 1855 - 1929	James Buchanan Duke "Buck" 1856 - 1925

BLACKWELL

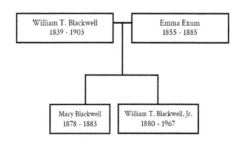

William T. Blackwell 1839 - 1903	Emma Exum 1855 - 1885

Mary Blackwell 1878 - 1883	William T. Blackwell, Jr. 1880 - 1967

MERRICK

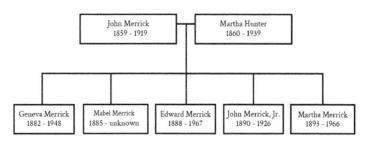

John Merrick 1859 - 1919	Martha Hunter 1860 - 1939

Geneva Merrick 1882 - 1948	Mabel Merrick 1885 - unknown	Edward Merrick 1888 - 1967	John Merrick, Jr. 1890 - 1926	Martha Merrick 1893 - 1966

MOORE

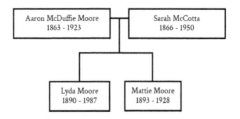

Aaron McDuffie Moore 1863 - 1923	Sarah McCotta 1866 - 1950

Lyda Moore 1890 - 1987	Mattie Moore 1893 - 1928

Author's Notes

The low brambles, along with the wild weeds, wrapped around the base of the cement structure, claiming it as its own. The large mausoleum loomed above all the other tombstones and grave markers, voicing an importance which had faded with time. It was here, at this place on the corner of Kent and Chapel Hill Street in Durham, North Carolina, that my journey began.

An old brass key forged in 1912 was placed inside the original lock and opened as easily as the day it was first used. Once the door was opened, I was welcomed by spider webs, along with the marble angel stationed in the back corner, to protect the bodies lying inside their vaults. Each marble slab declared the names of my distant family members, a family which centered around a man who placed his mark on the lives of each person within these marble walls.

The story of Richard Harvey Wright has been of interest to Durham historians, and rightfully so. Many have written about him as a founding father of this great city, while others have charged him with getting in the way of the formation of the American Tobacco Company. All of this is true. He was a ruthless, determined, and driven businessman, but he was also known for his great generosity toward his family members, a generosity that was felt long after his death.

As a small child, I had no idea who this man was or his significance to the city of Durham. My mother rarely spoke of her father's uncle and I didn't know the questions to ask. A half century passed before my curiosity was piqued and a passion burned within me to discover everything I could about, not only my great-grand uncle, but the city in which has been my home for the majority of my life.

If you have recently made Durham your home, or have lived here your entire life, you are blessed to live in a city with a rich history that is screaming to be told. This city is ever evolving and has changed drastically in the last few decades. As a small child, I often rode the bus from Lakewood Shopping Center to Main Street to take sewing lessons or purchase items from the few existing shops. As an adult, and living through the transformation Durham has recently taken, I have found a treasure trove of historical remnants at every turn.

If nothing else, my desire is to help others awaken to the history that makes Durham one of the most intriguing cities in this country. Even though I am writing this book through the eyes of my own family, my hope is that if you dig down just a little, you'll find a personal history just waiting to be told.

This book can be classified as historical fiction. It is based not only on the people that held significance to my great-grand uncle, but also those who contributed to the foundation of the city of Durham, North Carolina. I have tried to hold as closely to the facts as possible, but as all stories go, there are places in which I've taken the liberty to create.

Prologue

Dr. Bartlett Leonidas Durham would probably look up to the heavens and laugh at the thought of a city, the size of Durham, being named after him. Bartlett was first a businessman, and second a physician. In 1847, Durham purchased one hundred acres of land due to its location near the road that joined Raleigh to Hillsborough. The intent of his purchase was to build a store that could easily be accessed by the growing population in the area. After owning the property for one year, Durham was approached by the railroad company and asked if he would be willing to donate four acres for the sole purpose of building a railroad station. Durham was happy to comply and the rest is history.

Bartlett Durham was known for his flamboyant lifestyle. Being over six feet tall and weighing over two hundred pounds, he was a presence to behold. He was known to enjoy drinking and entertaining women. On the other hand, Durham took his responsibility as a physician seriously, some saying too much. It was known by his close friends that if he couldn't save a patient, he would become depressed and wash down his sorrows with a strong drink. At the age of thirty-five, Bartlett Durham developed pneumonia and never recovered.

Of course, the history of Durham did not stop with the death of this man. It just so happened that Dr. Bartlett Durham went into business with Malbourne Angier in 1852. They had opened a general store north of the railroad tracks. Of the many items that were sold, it was spirits that brought people into their store for conversation and good laughs.

In 1869, it was recorded that Angier, alongside Washington Duke and eight others, used a plow and two mules to create Main Street. They began at Angier's store and ran east through an old field. When finished, there were two furrows on either side of the street and plenty of gawkers yelling out how foolish these men were to believe that Durham would ever prosper beyond the few structures standing on either side of the railroad tracks.

In the next decade, not only would Durham grow beyond the furrows of Main Street, but it would become a bustling city known for some of the best tobacco in the world. With increasing demand for the bright leaf circling the planet, two companies forced the best and worst out of each other, for the rights to be called king of tobacco.

At the center of this evolution were a few men who rose to the top: Washington Duke, James Buchanan Duke, William T. Blackwell, Julian S. Carr, and Edward J. Parrish. But alongside of them was a determined orphan who, when he made up his mind to do something, come hell or high water, made it happen. He never gave up on a business deal, and he never gave up on Durham. This is the story of that man.

| 1 |

Richard (1865-1875)

Richard knew the smell of death. How could he ever forget the pungent odor that had arisen from his father's body as it lay stretched out on the rickety bed? He shuddered as he remembered the parade of mourners muttering their condolences to his mother and patting him on the head. Family members and friends had taken turns sitting beside the body until the coffin was finished and the grave made ready. He had been only six when his father died but now, as a young adolescent, knew he would never forget the look of the stoic face that had brought him such joy during his short life.

The following years grew more difficult with Richard's father gone and his mother preoccupied with survival. War had crept closer to their homestead in Franklin County, and food was in short supply. Daily, Richard watched young virile men walk down the dusty road situated in front of their home, called to fight a cause muddled in gray. As the years passed, the Confederacy lowered the age for enlistment, recruiting boys only in their mid-teens to make the walk toward the battlefields across the south.

The war dragged on and life was being squeezed of all hope for the young teen. Crops were sparse and it wasn't uncommon to have soldiers walk through and take any bit of food left in the fields. Richard's family worked from dawn to dusk with little to show for it, so it was natural for Richard to question God when the accident occurred.

It happened on a cool spring night in Franklin County with clouds billowing up in the sky. The family was visiting their Aunt Polly, a spinster, who occupied a house built by her father, Griffin Wright. The house was only a few miles away, as the crow flies. Aunt Polly was a strong independent woman who opened her home to everyone in need. She was known to teach anyone, no matter their color, to read and write. Aunt Polly was highly respected by most in the community. The two sisters had grown close since the death of Richard's father and her home was a place Richard always felt welcome to visit.

Richard's mother had been sitting next to the fireplace with her sister, Polly, nearby. She was stitching patches onto the children's clothes and enjoying the company her sister provided. A storm was brewing and thunder could be heard in the distance. As the women began to hum a hymn from church, a bolt of lightning shot down the fireplace, ricocheted off the andirons and struck Richard's mother. One moment she was sitting in her chair, and the next she was lying on the floor.

Richard was upstairs, playing with his siblings when he heard his Aunt Polly scream.

"What happened?" Richard cried, as he slid down the old staircase.

Once he came into the hallway, he saw his Aunt Polly hunched over his mother, crying. In that moment, he knew his mother was dead. Her eyes were still open but her motionless body looked lifeless. "How could this happen?" screamed Richard out loud. "God, how could you do this to us?"

Richard's brother, Thomas, followed close behind. His gasp could be heard as he fell to his knees. His sisters, Pattie Julia, and Mary Elizabeth, known to her family and friends as Nannie, came from the kitchen and made their way to their mother, staring at her body in disbelief. In that moment, Richard took a deep breath, leaned over, closed his mother's eyes and, ever so gently, lifted her body into his arms. His siblings trailed behind him as he carried her body to the back bedroom.

The following day, under a brightly shining sun, Richard and his brother, Thomas, dug into the Carolina red clay underneath the Maplewood tree where their father's body had been placed. The brothers' backs were sore as they wiped the stinging sweat from their eyes. As Richard pounded down on the hard soil, anger welled up inside of him. Happiness had long disappeared and the young teen had to fight off the bitterness that wanted to swallow him up. But as dismal as it all seemed, with each pounding of the shovel, Richard couldn't shake off the sensation of a better future life. It was a pervasive feeling that filled him with an uneasy peace and a determination that he wasn't going to let this life beat him down.

The feeling didn't leave him, even when the casket was placed in the ground, and the red clay covered the last of the pine box. It stayed with him as the mourners spoke their empty sympathies, got back in the horse-drawn carriages, and rode off with dust puffing up into the air.

After everyone had left the small cemetery, and Richard stood alone staring down at his mother's grave, he swore out loud. "Mother, I promise you this family will be taken care of. I don't know how, but I swear I'll do everything in my power to hold tightly to every child you have left behind."

With these words, he turned and walked toward the house where his siblings and distant relatives waited. Once inside, Richard noticed everyone sitting in chairs facing an older uncle with a letter spread out across the desk his father formerly occupied.

The weathered appearance of the man reminded Richard of his father and how he had appeared when he passed from this earth. Richard couldn't help but wish that he had been able to have more time with the man who meant so much to him. The old man looked up from the desk and directed his attention toward him. "Richard, please sit down. I have some information I need to share with you."

Though puzzled and curious, Richard stayed quiet and leaned his weight on the arm of the sofa where his sister, Nannie, was stationed. He looked around at his siblings and noticed their expressions of eagerness. All of them were waiting for the words their father had penned so many years ago.

The elderly uncle removed a paper from his pocket, adjusted the eye piece on his nose, and began to read. *"My name is Thomas Davenport Wright, and I am writing this with a sound mind and body. I have given this last will and testament a lot of thought. I wanted it read after my wife Elizabeth's death because I know she would be able to provide for our children. I love each child and hope that when this is read, you are doing well. I believe education is the best tool for success in this world. When our family arrived from England, my father, Griffin Wright, intentionally settled here in North Carolina because of the availability of higher education. I have similar beliefs so money has been set aside for my oldest son, Richard, for the sole purpose of paying for his tuition to the University of North Carolina. I have also enclosed enough money for my other children to be taken care of until they are married. Uncle James will serve as the executor of my estate. Richard, I am entrusting you with the privilege of an education. And my only hope is when you make decisions involving your personal and professional life, you will always place the affairs of our family at the forefront."*

Richard looked at his siblings and, for the first time in a while, began to feel a sense of hope. He cherished reading books and learning the reason behind how things worked. The idea of going away to school, to learn arithmetic and other subjects, excited him. He loved his siblings and knew if he had a proper education, he could eventually provide for them. Even though the responsibility his father left to him was daunting, something in his core made him believe he was up for the challenge.

Suddenly, there was a buzz in the air. Losing their mother was difficult for the orphaned Wright children, but the idea that their father had put into place a plan for their future brought a tinge of optimism which couldn't be ignored. Nannie reached up, took hold of Richard's hand and, with tears in her eyes and confidence in her voice, spoke, "Richard, I believe you will prosper."

"Thank you, Nannie."

"Now, once you make your way in the world, you come fetch me."

"Nannie, I will. I promise."

Richard looked toward the back of the room at his brother, who was sitting in a silent stupor. Since their mother's death, he had heard Thomas' quiet sobs and knew her passing had been far more difficult for him. Once the room had cleared, Richard approached his brother. "Thomas, I know how close you were to mother and how difficult it will be for you to take care of the farm. If you don't want me to go, I'll stay back."

"No, you need to go. Anyway, Uncle James has told me that he'll take us in if we need a place to stay. Don't worry about us. I know how much you want to go to school and once the crops have been harvested, you should leave."

Word was beginning to spread throughout the South concerning the possibility of an end to the war which had destroyed so much. Union soldiers could be seen rummaging through the newly planted tobacco fields and the remaining meager crops. There was news that Major General William T. Sherman of the Union was meeting with General Joseph Johnston of the Confederacy, at the private home of the Bennett family of Durham, to discuss the terms of surrender. Confederate President Jefferson Davis was not ready to yield to the enemy, but Johnston was aware that the confederates were outnumbered eighteen to one. And to make the situation even worse, weary men were deserting the Confederate forces in droves.

To complicate matters, word had reached the South that President Abraham Lincoln had been assassinated on April 14, 1865, by the well-known actor, John Wilkes Booth. Initially, Sherman was unsure how to proceed, but with word from Lincoln's successor, Andrew Johnson, he continued working through the terms with Johnston at the Bennett home in Durham. Time was of the essence due to the building frustration of the Union soldiers who were waiting in Raleigh for word. Riots were bubbling over and buildings were being torched. As each day passed, new threats of burning the city to the ground were becoming a major concern to the Raleigh citizens.

Finally, on April 26th, knowing he had to act quickly in order to get the best terms for his soldiers, Joseph Johnston met with William Sherman to bring closure to the war. The next day, with a codicil written by John Schofield, terms were agreed upon. The Confederate soldiers would retain their horses and, once they returned home, their private property. The Union soldiers would be able to return to their homes in the North and the South would once again fall under the jurisdiction of the United States Federal Government.

Union soldiers had never experienced the bright leaf tobacco that only grew in the Piedmont of North Carolina. The dense soil and unique curing process used by local farmers produced a sweet flavor the soldiers had never tasted. During the weeks leading up to the end of the war, bored soldiers with a desire for a good chewing tobacco, ransacked all of the bright yellow leaves and processed tobacco they could find. Local farmers around Durham could do nothing but watch, as their crops were stripped away.

As Richard turned fourteen years of age, with the war finally over, he had no idea that the destruction of the farmland by the Union soldiers would play such a large role in his future success as a businessman. As an adolescent, Richard's only thoughts were of leaving home after the harvest of his family's crops.

In June, Richard's oldest sister, Lucy, married Rev. James Ball and moved to Greensboro with her son, Thomas Mack. Once fall arrived, and Richard was ready to return to school, it became clear that the rest of his siblings would also need to leave their home in Franklin County. So, Pattie Julia and Richard moved in with their Aunt Polly so he could attend Davis High School in Louisburg and she could attend Louisburg College. Thomas and Nannie moved to Person County with their Uncle James and Aunt Elizabeth to live and help on their plantation.

Richard immersed himself into the high school's academic program. His determined spirit and desire to learn set him apart from the other students. Richard made several friends, but preferred a good book to lame conversations involving girls or puffed up stories that added no benefit to his future.

After graduation, Richard transferred to Horner Preparatory School in the small community of Tally Hoe where he was greatly influenced by his teacher, Mr. T.J. Horner. Every day, he would sit in class and absorb every bit of knowledge he could muster. Mr. Horner noticed Richard's desire to learn and provided him with books of various genres. Richard treasured each one of them, but particularly enjoyed the biographies of influential men in history.

Mr. Horner noted Richard's ability to not only learn the information presented to him, but to apply it to life. Over time, his admiration for this young man grew. Whenever he had time in his schedule, he would call Richard into his office to discuss business ventures and other topics he believed would assist Richard in his future pursuits.

Every few weeks, Richard sent a letter to his siblings to let them know of his progress. In return, they would write him back. It meant a great deal to him to hear his name during mail call. It gave him peace to know that they were doing well on Uncle James' plantation. Of all the letters from his siblings, he particularly enjoyed the ones he received from his sister, Pattie Julia. She had taken up writing poetry, which he found very soothing. Whenever he felt homesick, he would open her letters, read the poetry and get lost in her words.

Richard fully intended to continue his studies and follow his fellow students to the University of North Carolina in Chapel Hill. But, one day after class, Mr. Horner called him into his office. Richard walked up to the open door and observed the man who had come to mean so much to him. He knocked on the wall beside the opening and waited for Mr. Horner to look up. "Oh, Richard, come in and close the door behind you."

"Sir, you wanted to speak with me."

"Yes. Please sit down."

Mr. Horner motioned toward the seat in front of him and looked at Richard. "I hope you know by now how much I have enjoyed having you as a student. You have surpassed all my expectations.

I didn't want to be the one to tell you this, but your Uncle James contacted me and asked if I would share some news with you."

Richard wasn't sure what to think. "Is everyone in my family well?"

"Oh, yes. They're fine. But he wanted me to let you know that the money your father set aside for your education had to be used to pay off the family debts."

"What are you trying to tell me?"

"At this time, there's no money left to pay for you to go to college."

Immediately, Richard was consumed with a gut-wrenching feeling that made him want to get up and run. Ever since leaving home, he had been preparing to attend the University of North Carolina. All of his dreams were bound to an education in finance or history. Now, in a matter of moments, they had been taken away. He lowered his head and gazed down at the floor.

"Richard, I know this is crushing news for you. Before letting you know this, I contacted a friend who has a mercantile store in Oxford. He has agreed to take you on as an apprentice. Mr. Hunt is a smart businessman and can teach you a lot. I know it isn't the same as going to the university, but I do believe it would be an excellent chance for you to learn the art of becoming a proficient businessman. You have endured a lot in your young life and I believe you will make the most of this situation."

Richard looked up and said, with a broken voice that could hardly be heard, "Thank you, Mr. Horner. I appreciate how you have advocated for me."

The weeks that followed were difficult for Richard. Instead of spending time with the other young men headed off to Chapel Hill, he chose to lose himself in the books about men in history who had risen above challenging situations. After enduring graduation with his peers, he packed the little he owned and left the world that he had believed would provide for him and his family.

Richard traveled the thirty-nine miles to Oxford with a heavy heart. He tried to convince himself that the changed course would somehow be beneficial, but it looked so hopeless. When Richard arrived, he looked up at the mercantile sign and the whitewashed walls. This was definitely not where he wanted to be, but with no other options he took in a deep breath of air and walked through the screen door.

Richard stepped into the dimly lit room and noticed the dry goods stacked on shelves behind a long counter. Mr. Hunt was speaking with a customer and didn't notice the young man as he entered. Once the customer turned to leave, Richard made his way out of the shadows and walked up to the counter where Mr. Hunt was placing cans onto shelves. Mr. Hunt turned and faced Richard. "Can I help you?"

"Yes. My name is Richard Wright. My teacher, Mr. Horner, sent me here."

"T.J. did tell me that he was going to send a potential apprentice over to see me. He had very good things to say about you and how hard you work. Now, I want to be up front with you. I'm a very busy man and don't have time to be watching your every move. If I see that you're hindering my business, I'll ask you to leave. But, if you can be an asset to me, then I'll give you a place to sleep, food to eat, and a salary of $50 a year. I know it's not much, but it's what I have to offer."

Richard looked around the room, full of dry goods, fabric, boots, and other assorted items for sale. He breathed in the musty odors and watched as a long, lanky dog walked through the screen door and lay down in a corner.

"What will it be? I don't have time to waste on your day-dreaming."

"Yes, sir. I'm here to learn whatever you have to teach me. Thank you for the opportunity."

"Good. Now let me show you where you'll be sleeping."

Richard followed Mr. Hunt through a dark hallway to a small back room. There was a window that provided enough light to illuminate the space, allowing Richard the ability to see the small bunk bed and a nightstand with only a candle for light. Richard looked around the sparse room, fighting back the desire to run. But where?

Mr. Hunt turned to leave, then stopped and faced Richard. "There is one more thing." The older man reached over and opened a small chest, pulling out a book. "T.J. told me that you love to read. I discussed this with my wife and she thought you might like this book by a man named Longfellow. It's yours if you'd like to have it."

Richard took the book and gazed down at the cover of The Works of Henry W. Longfellow. At Horner's Academy, he had spent hours in his room reading every book that he could get his hands on. When he left, he thought he might not have the privilege of having possession of a book, and now had been given one written by his favorite author. Tears welled up in his eyes and he turned so Mr. Hunt couldn't see his expression.

"Dinner is at 6:00 p.m. sharp. We're up by 5:00 a.m. and the store opens at 7:00 a.m. every morning except on the Lord's Day."

"Yes, sir. I appreciate this opportunity."

For the first few weeks, Richard followed Mr. Hunt around the store and listened to every interaction the older man had with his customers. He noticed how the people would come into the store with only a few items on their list, then left with far more. Richard took notes on how his mentor convinced his customers to purchase all kinds of things and began to emulate him. After only a few months, Mr. Hunt recognized Richard's skills and entrusted him with more and more responsibilities.

As much as Richard enjoyed the challenge of sales, it was, in the dark of night with his candle burning, reading the poems of Longfellow and other inspirational works that he cherished the most. It was during these late-night hours of soaking in the writings of others, men who walked similar paths of destitution and had risen successfully, that Richard began to believe in his own path.

The three years of working for Mr. Hunt quickly came to an end and Richard had learned far more than he ever expected. He had developed a confidence in his ability to sell almost anything and found it enjoyable to sell the items that most found no need for. One afternoon, when the store was empty and the men were sorting merchandise, Richard broached a topic that had been brewing in his mind for some time.

"Mr. Hunt, I want to thank you for the opportunity you have given me."

"Richard, to be honest, I believe I have benefitted the most from this arrangement. Ever since you came here, my business has grown and I'm having a hard time imagining how the store will do without you."

"Mr. Hunt, I've been contemplating a solution that may profit both of us."

"Well, I'm open to hearing what you have to say."

"Several of our customers have to travel a far piece to come to the store. The community of Tally Ho is growing and could be a good place for a new mercantile."

"So, what are you suggesting?"

"I've saved some money, but if you could help finance the rest, I could go and start a store there. I'll split the profit with you until I can pay you back."

Richard observed Mr. Hunt to see how he would react to the idea. The older man was difficult to read and, for a moment,

Richard felt foolish. But, to his surprise, Mr. Hunt looked at him with a grin on his face. "I think that's a good idea. Let's do it!"

A sense of relief flooded through Richard's veins. "That's wonderful! I won't let you down, I promise."

Mr. Hunt exclaimed, "I'll hold you to it!"

Richard extended his hand out to the older man, grasping it with a firm hold. "I believe this will be a great partnership. Thank you so much for this opportunity."

In the following months, Richard worked hard to find a suitable building for his small enterprise. Once the location was found and the doors opened, people in the Tally Ho Community embraced the young man's efforts to stock a store with goods they previously had to travel many miles to purchase. Over time, the store made a nice profit and, for the first time in his life, Richard experienced what success felt like. But, as luck would have it, misfortune struck again.

| 2 |

Richard (1875-1877)

Throughout his life, small tragedies had plagued Richard. From the death of his parents to the lack of money to support his education, he had suffered and overcome. Now that his business was off to a good start, Richard was nagged with the thought that something bad must be looming.

The first incident was minor and gave Richard a story to later laugh at. On May 25, 1875, the Torchlight, a local newspaper, reported, *It Fired. Some eight or ten days ago, so we are informed, Richard H. Wright, while handling a loaded pistol at his store at Tally Ho, met with a misfortune by the weapon firing and the ball entering his hand.*

We are glad to hear that no bones were broken and that Mr. Wright is speedily recovering.

The next event was much more devastating and would have caused the demise of most men. But not Richard. His determined spirit to succeed and the words of a well-known speaker would push him past any thoughts of quitting.

One night, after Richard had locked the doors to his store, he traveled to Oxford to enjoy a meal. On the way back, he noticed a bright light above the trees. The closer he drew to the light, reality set in. He kicked the sides of his horse and raced in the direction of the blaze. After entering the clearing across the road from his store, he jumped off the horse and ran toward the water pump. But after taking a bucket and trying to douse out the flames, he knew his efforts were fruitless. The fire had destroyed most of the building and everything remaining was covered with soot.

Richard dropped to the ground and started screaming into the air. "I can't believe I didn't fill out the forms for renewing the insurance policy. Why didn't I complete them? How can I ever pay back my lenders? How can I ever get back the success I was experiencing?"

For the remainder of the night, Richard tried to save as much of his merchandise as possible. His face was blackened by the soot and his clothes smelled of smoke. The next morning, Mr. Hunt rode his horse over from Oxford to assess the situation.

"Richard, what happened?"

"I really can't say. I locked the door around 6:30 p.m. and rode to Oxford for dinner. I was on my way home when I saw the blaze."

"Well, the good thing is you have an insurance policy to cover the damages."

"Mr. Hunt, I've been meaning to renew the policy, but I was so busy with customers, I never got around to it."

Richard was horrified by the look on Mr. Hunt's face. It was clear that he wasn't going to make this easy on him. "Richard, you know I trust that you will make this right."

"Yes, sir. Somehow, someway, I'll do my best."

Richard became depressed and, for the first time, he wasn't sure if he would be able to pursue his present course of owning a successful business. But he just couldn't let go of his ambition. So, after salvaging all the merchandise he could, Richard traveled to Raleigh to meet with some potential investors. He spent the day attempting to sell them on the business but, to his dismay, they all appeared blind to his plight. None of them were willing to give him money, and he just couldn't see a way out of the mess he had created.

As Richard walked down the streets of Raleigh, he passed a theater with a poster of Josh Billings, a famous speaker who he had heard his teacher, Mr. Horner, speak about. Richard knew that Mr. Billings was a successful businessman and an excellent motivational speaker. For some reason, Richard felt a glimmer of hope.

That evening, when the doors opened, Richard was one of the first people in the theater. He found a seat in the middle, eight rows back from the stage, and in good viewing distance from where Mr. Billings would be speaking. When Mr. Billings walked onto the stage and scanned the crowd, Richard looked straight into his eyes. Even though the entire theater was filled to capacity, Richard felt like he was having a private meeting with this famous speaker.

From the moment Mr. Billings began to speak, Richard was mesmerized. The words were like discovering gold in a mine shaft. But it was one particular sentence that would forever change Richard's life. Mr. Billings looked over the crowd and settled his eyes on Richard. "Young man, never grieve over spilt milk, but pick up your milk pail and go for the next cow." The hairs on the back of Richard's neck began to rise and adrenaline pulsated through his bloodstream. At that moment, he knew he had to find his next cow.

No more looking back. For the first time in his life, he understood how he was going to be successful.

The next day he met with new investors. This time, he came across as a confident young man with charisma. Before leaving, Richard convinced every man in the room that investing in him was a winning deal. Once he had the money in hand, he returned to Tally Ho and worked tirelessly to rebuild the store and pay back his creditors. As the store prospered, Richard became more convinced that he could succeed beyond Tally Ho and the mercantile business.

Richard had heard from his customers about how men in Durham were making money from the sale of tobacco. Names like Blackwell, Carr, and Duke kept coming up in conversations that piqued Richard's interest. After discussing his plans with Mr. Hunt, Richard made one of the most important business decisions of his life.

It had been twelve years since the end of the Civil War, and the small town of Durham was experiencing record growth due to the popularity of golden leaf tobacco. What had appeared to be a catastrophe when the Union Soldiers confiscated the farmer's tobacco, ended up being an unprecedented opportunity. When the soldiers returned home to their northern states and shared the tobacco with their friends and family, demand swelled for the sweet leaf tobacco grown around the small town of Durham.

Richard was entering his mid-twenties when he began researching the tobacco business. Every time a tobacco salesman entered his store, he would draw them into a conversation about the men in Durham who were finding success selling the golden leaf. Over time, with the tobacco business booming, Richard decided to move beyond the boundaries of being a store owner. With his debts paid, and investors believing in his ability to make them money, Richard decided to rent a building in Durham and open up his own tobacco business. He had no idea how his endeavor would play out, but he knew that it was time to milk another cow. So, with incredible self-confidence and an endless drive, Richard headed south to a town that would bring him both heartache and unbelievable success.

| 3 |

Bettie (1865-1884)

Bettie Allen never knew a life without Thomas. He had been living with her Aunt Elizabeth for as long as she could remember. Every Sunday, after church, her family would travel the short distance to her aunt's home, better known as the Harris Plantation, for Sunday lunch. Her Aunt Elizabeth had been married to James Harris for some time and, as the years passed, it became clear that they couldn't bear children. So, when Thomas and his sisters became orphans, Aunt Elizabeth and James brought them home to live.

Thomas was a quiet boy with a grateful spirit. He never asked for much and worked as hard as any man on the plantation. James and Aunt Elizabeth felt blessed to have him in their lives. It was a good situation for everyone.

Bettie had always been infatuated with Thomas. She had been born the year he arrived on the plantation. When she was four, and he sixteen, she remembered an incident that forever formed a fondness in her heart for him. It was on a Sunday afternoon, after the meal had been eaten and the children sent out to play. As Aunt Elizabeth was picking up the dishes, she told Thomas to watch the small children while the women cleaned up.

Bettie had run down to the creek with Thomas walking behind her. A heavy rain had occurred the previous night and water was rushing over the rocks that usually could be used as stepping stones. Bettie's dog, a cocker spaniel, had walked beside her, wagging his little stump as they descended toward the creek. She remembered turning around and seeing Thomas making his way down the rocky path. When she turned back, her dog took off chasing a squirrel.

"Prince, come back!" Bettie yelled.

The dog didn't respond and drew closer to the edge of the creek bed where a squirrel could be seen hanging on a branch swaying over the water. With his eyes solely on his prey, the dog leaped up to catch the squirrel, only to find himself caught in the clutches of the brisk current.

"Prince!" Bettie yelled.

Bettie was terrified as she watched the scene play out before her. As much as she desired to jump in after the dog, she knew she wouldn't be able to swim in the strong currents.

"Thomas, do something!" Bettie cried out.

Thomas ran down the side of the creek, picking up a stick as he went. Bettie followed, trying to navigate the rocks and stumps as she walked. When she made her way around a bend, she spotted the dog, stuck between an old log and a rock. Thomas jabbed a stick down beside the dog, to secure himself as he tried to reach for the scared pup. Bettie stopped and watched as Thomas stretched his arm into the water and pulled the soaked dog from the crevice. As she stood there watching the event transpire, she was filled with awe.

Thomas cradled the little dog, soothing him as he walked. He passed Bettie on the path and headed up to the house. Bettie tried to keep up with Thomas, but his quick stride made it impossible. Once they climbed the steep embankment and were on level ground, Thomas placed the drenched dog on the grass and watched as it lay shaking. Bettie ran up beside them and noticed the look of fear in her dog's eyes. "Is he going to be okay?"

Thomas looked at Bettie and then back toward the dog. "I think so. Why don't you run up to the house and get some rags to dry him off?"

"Okay. Thank you, Thomas."

"Sure. Now run on up to the house and I will watch him until you return."

As she ran toward the house, she glanced back at Thomas and her dog lying in the grass. The memory would forever be embedded in her mind.

Two years later, James Harris died. The Sunday afternoons continued at the plantation, but it would never be the same. Thomas had now taken on the role of man of the house and rarely interacted with Bettie. Between supervising the workers and handling the finances, Thomas wasn't interested in playing the games they had previously shared.

As the years passed, Bettie spent little time thinking about Thomas. She was busy helping her own parents with household chores or attending to her school work. One day, when Bettie was seventeen and Thomas twenty-nine, all of this changed.

The heat of the sun was beating down on Bettie as she rode her horse through the fields that lined her family's property. Lately, she had wanted to escape the routine of school and chores and loved the freedom that riding gave her. She kicked the flanks of her horse to get him to move from a canter to a gallop. As the horse sped up, her long dark hair flowed behind her. She was singing a song and enjoying the sensation of the brisk movement of the horse, when a small fox ran in front of them.

The startled horse reared up, throwing Bettie from the saddle. As she fell onto the ground, her leg caught under her and twisted in an awkward position. Immediately, Bettie knew she was hurt and would need help. She tried to call for the horse to return but, to her dismay, the horse galloped away, leaving her alone in the field. As she tried to stand and place weight on her leg, she realized she couldn't walk.

Sweat spilled off her neck and the heat of the sun caused her to feel dizzy. She placed her head down in the grass and closed her eyes. With no way to move, all she could do was hope that the horse would return home, alerting her family that she was in trouble. The pain was difficult to bear and, feeling sorry for herself, tears formed and splotched her cheeks.

As the sun began to dip below the horizon, she heard the sound of a horse approaching. At first, she didn't recognize the rider, but when she saw it was Thomas, a sense of relief swelled within her. He pulled the reins of his horse, halting him steps away from where she lay. He jumped off the steed and approached her.

"Are you okay?"

"No. I think I broke my ankle. My horse got frightened when a fox ran in front of us. How did you find me?"

"I've seen you ride out into these fields and thought I would look. Can you stand?"

"No. I tried, but felt faint and had to lie down."

Thomas appeared hesitant to touch her. "I need you to put your arm around my neck so I can lift you up."

Bettie placed her arm around the curvature of his neck and Thomas gently pulled her up and cradled her in his arms. As she leaned closer to him, she could smell the faint scent of lavender. She started to smile and couldn't help herself. "Thomas, do I smell lavender?"

He turned his head down and gazed right into her eyes. "Yes, I think you do. I was picking it for Aunt Elizabeth when we got word you were missing."

"I have to admit, it smells very nice on you."

"Well, enough about smells and flowers. Let's get you home."

As Thomas placed his foot in the stirrup and brought his legs close to Bettie, she was overwhelmed with a strange sensation. She leaned back into Thomas' chest and, after he took the reins, they trotted back to her house. Bettie wished she could live in this moment forever, but knew it would end as soon as they arrived home. So, she closed her eyes and enjoyed the moment in time. A moment that would be forever remembered.

Over the next year, Thomas kept his distance and made excuses to be away when Bettie and her family came over for Sunday lunch. It hurt Bettie and she wondered what she had done to push him away. She often asked her Aunt Elizabeth where Thomas was, but the older woman never had an answer for her.

When Bettie turned twenty, Thomas moved to Mebane to pursue a job opportunity that his brother, Richard, had set up for him. By this time, Richard had become successful and wanted his brother to join him in the tobacco business. Without Thomas living on the plantation, Aunt Elizabeth asked if Bettie could move into the large house to keep her company. Bettie accepted the invitation, hoping for an opportunity to see Thomas.

One summer night, when the heat made it difficult to sleep, Bettie took a candle and a book, and found a comfortable chair out on the expansive porch. The full moon's reflection could be seen across the small pond situated downhill from the house, adding a mysterious feel to the night. The backdrop created a mellow ambiance as Bettie immersed herself in the story she was reading. At first, she didn't notice the sound of hoofs in the distance. Only when the rider crossed in the light of the moon did she recognize Thomas.

He steered the horse to the barn and, after a while, walked up to the house. Bettie's heart was pounding. She had waited a long time to see Thomas and now was nervous about how the conversation would go. Bettie wasn't sure if he would ever care for her like she cared about him. All she could do was hope that, as she got older, the difference in their ages would no longer keep them apart.

Bettie's pulse quickened as she saw Thomas walking toward her. Unsure how he would react, she took a deep breath and commanded her nerves to settle down. As he ascended the steps, he looked up and smiled. "Well, hello pretty woman. What are you doing out so late?"

"I was too hot to sleep and decided to read my book." Bettie picked up the book and waved it in front of her. "I'm reading Jane Austen's *Pride and Prejudice*. If you ever have time, you should read it. I think you'd like it."

Thomas sat down in a rocking chair next to where Bettie was sitting and leaned back. "Thank you for being willing to come and stay with Aunt Elizabeth. She's told me how she truly enjoys your company."

"I've enjoyed it here. I care about her a lot. She's such a kind woman. I do believe the field hands aren't producing the same yield of crops that they did when you were here. It's good for someone to try and hold them accountable. I don't think they listen to me like they did you, but I do believe my presence makes a difference."

"I'll speak to Henry in the morning."

"So, tell me, Thomas, what has it been like to be working in Mebane?"

"Okay. I've been helping out on a tobacco farm that produces the leaves my brother has been using for his own brand of cigarettes. I'm not sure if I'll be staying there. Durham is where my brother has been doing most of his business, and he has asked if I would like to move there."

"I've only visited Durham a time or two, but it does seem to be growing, and people are prospering in the tobacco and textile industries."

"Enough about that. Tell me about you. What does a pretty woman like you enjoy doing in your spare time?"

"Well, I've returned to riding. It took a while for my ankle to heal and, of course, I was a little hesitant to get back up on my horse. But I was determined to push through my fear."

"I'm glad to hear that." Thomas began to clench his hands and appeared nervous. "Bettie, can I tell you something?"

"Sure, Thomas."

"When my mother died when I was twelve, I was lost. My father had set aside money for my brother to go off to school. Richard has always been ambitious and he left as soon as he could. Once he was gone, my sisters and I were left to tend the small farm. Lucy wanted to stay but she and Reverend Ball married and moved to Greensboro, leaving me and my sisters, Nannie and Pattie Julia. Life was hard on my parent's land and we barely raised enough crops to get through the winter. My Uncle James knew of our situation and asked us to come and stay on his plantation. Not long afterward, Pattie Julia was able to go off to school to study writing. Uncle James and Aunt Elizabeth became my family and they treated Nannie and I like their own. Given that Aunt Elizabeth is also your aunt by marriage, I considered you family as well. You were just a baby when I came here and I thought nothing of having a relationship with you. But the day when you fell off your horse, that all changed. I felt an emotion that was both exhilarating and full of guilt. And I guess the guilt kept me from pursuing a relationship with you."

Bettie tilted her head down, afraid to hear the words she was sure he would speak. "Thomas, you don't have to go on. Ever since the day you saved my puppy from the creek, I've cared for you. At first it was a deep-seated infatuation, but as I grew into adolescence, it became a young girl's crush. I've prepared myself for the day that you would come home and tell me you have a girlfriend. So, if that's what you are going to say now, go ahead."

Thomas leaned over and reached for her hands, lightly touching each finger. He looked down into her brown eyes and waited a moment. "Bettie, to be honest, I did court a woman in Mebane. I thought, maybe if I saw someone else, I could make sense of the feelings I have for you. Up until now, I believed I was just too old for you. But, after spending time with this woman, I realized that my heart was already taken."

It took a moment for Bettie to process what Thomas was saying. "What are you telling me?"

"I love you, Bettie Allen. I always have and I always will."

Bettie was overcome with emotion. She had dreamed of this day, and now that it was finally here, she was speechless. "Oh, Thomas, I love you, too."

And then, in the light of the moon with the stars as witnesses, Thomas leaned over and kissed Bettie.

| 4 |

Washington (1820-1880)

The cold wind was held at bay by the fire in the hearth. Women scrambled around with wet cloths while men sat outside on the porch with smoke curling upward from their pipes. Small children huddled in the corners of the room playing with their simple toys as the woman on the bed pushed another life into being.

Dicey was exhausted from the hours of labor, but elated when her baby was placed on her chest. She took the cloth from one of her sisters and wiped the blood away from the face of her newborn baby. "I'm going to name you Washington, after George Washington. How do you like that?" she asked the small infant who peered around at his new surroundings.

The small baby clung to his mother as the placenta was being delivered. Once the women finished cleaning Dicey up, they retreated to the table to enjoy a warm cup of coffee. The small children began to draw close to see their new sibling and make remarks about his appearance. Even though Washington was Dicey's eighth child, there was always something miraculous about a birth. "So, what are you going to do with your life, little Washington?" his mother asked.

There was no response except for a little gurgling noise as the baby settled into his mother's arms. Several of Washington's siblings leaned onto the bed and touched the baby, while one sister reached over and gave him a kiss on his forehead. Any observer watching the scene being played out would remark that what the family lacked in things, they possessed in love.

As a small boy, Washington and his siblings helped in the tobacco fields that lined the property. A mule pulling a plow was used to break up the soil, creating furrows in the field. It wasn't until Washington was thirteen that his dad, Taylor, would allow him to maneuver the plow on his own. The young boy found peace as he steered the animal up and down the field, humming a song from church or just talking to himself.

In late January, farmers in North Carolina planted seeds in a seedbed. After a month, the plants were thinned out. In April, hills were plowed for the fragile plants to be moved, then the farmer would pray for a soaking rain to moisten the soil. Once the tobacco plants were moved and became established, the farmer would spend hours each day tending the fields, topping and removing the suckers from the plants.

When the farmer wasn't cutting off leaves, he was inspecting the plants for hornworms, the most dreaded predator of the tobacco leaf. Finally, in late August or early September, the plants were cut off the stalk, tied to sticks, and placed in barns for curing. The curing process took up to six weeks. Once the leaves were fully cured, they were laid on the floor of the tobacco barn to sweat. Finally, after months of hard work, the tobacco would be sorted and readied to be sold.

Growing tobacco was in Washington's blood. Every year, he and his family followed the same routine from January to October. Life cycled around the growth of the crop and everyone knew it. It was exhausting work, but Washington recognized the importance of this plant for the survival of his family.

When Washington was twenty-two years old, he married Mary Caroline Clinton. She was only seventeen when they spoke their vows. Mary's father gave Washington land to farm and he, in turn, built his wife a home. Two years later, their first child, Sidney, was born, followed three years later by their second son, Brodie. The family appeared set for a life of farming and growing old together. But fate stepped in, and Mary died the following year, leaving Washington with two small boys to raise.

Washington spent the next five years raising his sons and tending to his tobacco fields. When he was thirty-two years old, love came knocking once more. Artelia Roney was considered the prettiest girl in Alamance County. After a short courtship, Washington brought his bride home to a new house he had built on his property. Though the four rooms were simple, the house was larger than most in the area and the chores were too much for his wife to accomplish on her own. So, three years later, Washington purchased a slave named Caroline, to help around the house. He never felt good about purchasing another human being, but he needed the help with his young family.

Being from a large family, Washington had his sights set on fathering a large brood to help him in the fields. So, it wasn't surprising to anyone when Mary Elizabeth was born the following year. Two years later, Benjamin was born, followed by their last child, James Buchanan, whom they affectionately called Buck. Now, with five children underfoot and a beautiful wife by his side, Washington appeared to have it all.

The summer of 1858 started like all others. There was a never-ending list of responsibilities for each member of the family as the sun rose higher in the sky and the temperature swelled, along with the humidity. Washington and his two oldest sons, Sidney and Brodie, spent their days in the tobacco fields, while Artelia and Caroline were tending to the three small children and completing the unending household tasks.

One hot day, when life seemed good, everything changed. Washington, Sidney, and Brodie were out in the fields checking each plant for hornworms. Washington was only a couple steps away from both sons as the sun beat down. One minute, he could see the boys' heads peeking above the plants. The next, after hearing a noise that sounded like a fallen branch, he turned and only saw Brodie.

"Sidney, where are you?" Washington asked, as he picked the top of a plant.

When he didn't hear a response, Washington moved back to where his son was last spotted and found him lying on the ground. "Sidney, are you alright?"

The boy quietly responded, "Dad, I'm not feeling well."

"Are you able to get up?"

"No. I really don't feel well." Sidney closed his eyes and his breathing sounded labored.

"Brodie, come over and help me carry your brother to the house."

"What happened?" Brodie asked, as he ran between the plants to where his brother was lying.

"I don't know. Your brother is burning up. Help me lift him."

Washington placed his son over his shoulder and, with a strength he didn't know he had, carried him the two hundred yards to the house. Brodie ran ahead and screamed as loud as he could, "Artelia, get some water from the well. Sidney's really sick."

Washington scurried through the plants, almost tripping under the weight of his son. Once he made it to the flat area between the fields and the house, he picked up his speed. He could see Artelia on the porch waiting for him. After he climbed the few steps and was on the porch, she opened the door. Washington's arms were numb, but he refused to give in to the pain. He took a deep breath and carried Sidney into the house where he spotted the children staring up at him. Before anyone could speak, he ran to the back bedroom where he laid him down on a bed.

Washington was sweating and out of breath as he called to Caroline, "Go fetch the doctor. Don't stop for anything."

"Yes, Mr. Duke." Caroline scurried out the door and ran across the fields in the direction of the doctor's house.

Artelia followed her husband into the room and stood beside him. "Washington, I know you don't want to hear this, but I've been hearing from neighbors about typhoid taking the lives of several people in town. If it is typhoid, I think it's best that you take the children and leave Sidney for me to care for. We don't want the other children to get sick."

"Are you sure?" Washington asked in a cracked voice.

"Yes. Now if you can fetch some water and the rags in the bin, I'll take over from here."

"Okay." Washington went out to the well, took the handle, and pushed down with all his might. Tears were brimming in his eyes and a helpless feeling burned in his soul. He knew better than to share his concern in front of the other children, so he took his dust-covered shirt sleeve and wiped the tears away as he ran back into the house.

The doctor arrived a couple hours later and went directly into the room where Sidney lay. After a short examination, he looked at Washington and Artelia and quietly spoke. "It doesn't look good. Keep his fever down the best you can and try to make him as comfortable as possible. At this point, he's in the Lord's hands."

Artelia spent the next two days at Sidney's side, trying her best to keep the boy's fever down. But, just when they thought the fever would break, it would spike once more. Sidney became delirious and his breathing labored. The morning of the third day, with Artelia's head lying on the edge of the bed, Sidney passed from this world. When Artelia opened her eyes, her stepson was gone. She began to sob so loudly that Washington came bursting through the door. He ran to his son and held him close. His first born was gone.

Washington's grief was almost too much to bear. He reached over and closed his son's eyes and covered him with a blanket. Without a word to anyone, he walked out of the house, grabbed a shovel, and made his way to the small cemetery where Mary was buried. Into the night, Washington ripped the hard clay up from the ground to prepare a place for his son's body.

Washington's sorrow blinded him from the frail condition of his wife. When he walked past Artelia the evening they buried his son, he wouldn't accept that she had also fallen ill. But when she didn't rise from her bed the next day, he knew that typhoid had claimed her as well. With nothing to do but wait, Washington stayed close by her side into the wee hours of the night.

"Artelia, do you remember when I brought you home? I have to tell you I didn't think you would take me as your husband, me being ten years older and all. So many young men wanted to court you. I fell in love with you the moment I saw you. You were so sweet to give me time to finish grieving for Mary before accepting my proposal for marriage. I know we've only had six years together, but the love we shared is enough for a lifetime. Now don't worry about us. Your sisters and Caroline will help out. I just want you to know that I'll always love you, my dear."

The tears blinded Washington as he closed Artelia's eyes, kissed her on the forehead, professing his unending love. After realizing that his wife was gone, he refused to get up. He wanted to hold her hand and kiss her forehead for as long as possible. Finally, in the dark of the night, he rose and returned to the small graveyard where Mary and Sidney were laid. Into the night he dug the grave where his beloved Artelia would be buried.

Grief had wrapped its fingers around Washington so tightly, it was hard for him to breathe. In the days that followed, he hardly spoke. Artelia's sisters took turns coming to the house and assisting Caroline as she took over the tasks Artelia had left behind. As much as he didn't want to ignore his children, Washington couldn't face them without fighting back tears. So, instead of spending time at home, he chose to labor in the fields among the green sticky leaves that demanded his attention.

Over the next few years, life cycled around the tobacco leaf and making sure everyone was provided for. Washington's four children were kept busy in the fields or learning how to read and calculate numbers. Buck, the youngest, had been too young to experience the sorrow of losing his mother. The grief the other siblings experienced was foreign to him. Buck was particularly intelligent and strong-willed. If he wanted something, he seemed to find a way to manipulate the people around him to follow his wishes. Mary and Benjamin were weaker than their brother and were often taken to their bed. They preferred learning over being in the fields, but were willing to help when they could. Brodie, the oldest, was a very thin boy, but still preferred working in the fields alongside his father.

Even though Washington needed as much help as he could get around the homestead, it bothered him that Caroline was not a free woman. He had heard discussions among the other farmers regarding slavery and how the people in the North were becoming more opposed to the practice. His conscience rebelled against the idea of owning another person, and wouldn't allow him the peace he desired. He knew it was not right to keep Caroline from her own family and, even though it would be a hardship, he made the decision to free her.

One night, after everyone was asleep, he asked Caroline to join him in the sitting room. When Washington heard her soft steps coming toward him, he looked up at this woman who had come to mean so much to his entire family. "Caroline, please take a seat in front of the fire. I've something to discuss with you."

Washington took out his pipe, lit it, and stared toward the burning embers. "Caroline, you've been a part of this family for four years. You've been steadfast in your work and have never been consumed with gossip. I know you have a family up north. I've overheard you speak of them and seen your tear-stained cheeks. I can no longer keep you here against your will. I have discussed your situation with a friend who is headed north tomorrow morning."

Washington handed Caroline a folded piece of paper with instructions and money. "Everything you need to know is on this piece of paper. I wish I could offer you more, but I want you to know if there is ever a day when slavery is abolished, and you'd like to return, I'll be glad to hire you as a housekeeper."

Washington looked out into the distance. The light of the fire created a silhouette of Caroline. Her body seemed to draw higher in her chair as she absorbed this life-changing information. Washington inhaled the smooth fumes of his pipe as the two sat together for a while, neither willing to break the spell of this final night. After some time, with the embers in the hearth cooling down, Caroline rose from her chair and walked through the door, never to be seen again.

Once Caroline was gone, the children were told not to discuss her disappearance with anyone. After a few weeks, life on the homestead took on a new normalcy. The children were becoming less dependent on the adults and took on more chores. Artelia's sisters continued to rotate their time to help meet the needs of the Duke household.

Discussions of secession from the United States was on everyone's lips. Washington didn't believe in the South's viewpoint and wanted no part in a war that could only bring heartache for the many soldiers yanked from their families. At first, Washington wasn't too concerned about his sixteen-year-old son, Brodie, and never even considered that he, a middle-aged man of forty-one, would ever experience war.

But in September 1862, the upper age limit of the draft was raised from thirty-five to forty-five. Washington was now forty-three and Brodie, eighteen. The day Washington received notice that he was to report for service was dreadful for the Duke family. Many tears were shed and concerns were voiced. But he knew he would place his family in danger if he didn't leave. So, after making sure his children were cared for by friends and family, he packed a small bag and made his way to Charleston, South Carolina.

Soon after Washington's departure, Brodie received his own orders to report to Salisbury, North Carolina, to serve his time as a guard in a Confederate prison. Given Brodie's thin stature, he was kept from going to the battlefield, but was not protected from the demons that come from a war camp. Later in life, the effects of living through such hell would haunt Brodie until his death.

After several months in Charleston, serving in the Confederate navy, Washington was transferred to Richmond to man artillery batteries on the James River. It was here that Washington was captured by Union troops and placed in a Union prison. Thankfully for Washington, the surrender at Appomattox Court House took place shortly after his imprisonment, and he was released a week later.

Washington was transported by boat from Richmond to New Bern, North Carolina. He was given fifty cents and told to walk the rest of the way. So, with little in his pocket and a desire to return to Durham, Washington walked the one hundred thirty-seven miles back home. Other men shared the walk with him but, for the most part, Washington walked in silence. When he arrived back in Durham County, he was greeted by barren fields and uprooted tobacco plants. Rumor had it that all the work of the local farmers had been destroyed by roaming soldiers from both the Confederacy and the Union.

After walking through his fields and seeing the damage done to the small plants, Washington approached his house. Mary Elizabeth was sweeping the porch when they made eye contact. "Daddy! Everybody, come quick! Daddy's home!"

Before he could catch his breath, Washington was surrounded by his three youngest children. His sister-in-law followed and watched as the children embraced their father. Everyone was laughing and crying all at the same time.

Washington walked through the door and was escorted to a seat at the kitchen table. Mary Elizabeth began warming up some coffee and biscuits. After Washington consumed as much as he could, he sat back and beamed with pride over his children. It had been two years since he had left and all of them had grown so much. The clothes they wore were practically threadbare, but no one seemed to mind.

Washington looked at each child and then turned toward Brodie. His shoulders were slumped and the familiar grin had been replaced by a scowl. "Son, how are you?"

Brodie had trouble raising his eyes to meet his father's. "I'm fine."

Washington rose from his chair and walked over to where his son sat hunched over. He softly lowered his hand and placed it on his shoulder. Washington had seen many men with the same demeanor and knew it was best to demonstrate comfort without many words. "Brodie, I'm here for you. Anytime."

Washington returned to his chair, took a long sip of coffee and a bite of biscuit. He wiped his mouth and turned to his children. "I saw the fields while coming in and the soldiers ransacking other farms. What's going on?"

Benjamin spoke up. "The soldiers from both the North and the South were congregating in the area as they waited for the South to surrender and the papers to be signed at the Bennett place. There's no tobacco to be found and word is that a plug of tobacco is costing up to $500. The Union soldiers have been particularly ruthless. All the cured tobacco is gone."

"So, what you are saying? Do the Union soldiers like our tobacco?"

Buck spoke up. "Dad, they really like our tobacco. We should try and grow more this coming year and process it for selling. John Green, a farmer near Durham, has discovered a new way of curing his tobacco that makes it particularly sought after. I figure we find out what he's doing and try it."

Washington sat back and contemplated the words his sons had shared. "I believe you two have been giving this a lot of thought. Now that the war is over, we can start fresh. We might not have a lot of money but we know how to grow tobacco. There's no harm in hard work. If we're willing to put the plow to the ground, I believe we might just be able to make a living."

The following year, after the tobacco was harvested and cured, Washington, with the help of his children, beat the tobacco with sticks, sifted it, and packed it into small bags. The family then traveled throughout the country, selling the tobacco with a mule-drawn cart. Once it was all sold, they returned home and, instead of growing the tobacco in the fields, they spent their time processing all the cured tobacco they could buy from other farmers. Washington named his product "Pro Bono Publico" which meant for the public good. Over the next six years, the Duke family produced over one hundred twenty-five thousand pounds of tobacco.

After working in a small tobacco factory on their own property, it was time to move their enterprise to a larger building in Durham where they could be closer to the railroad for transporting their product. Brodie was the first to make the move where he occupied an old log hut that was located on Main Street. After several months, the rest of the family joined him. At this time, word was spreading about the quality of their tobacco. But even with the increased demand, they needed financial assistance to improve the process and fulfill all the orders.

Gerard Snowden Watts, a successful businessman from Baltimore, also had his sights set on the tobacco business. His son, George Washington Watts, had studied business in college and worked alongside him for several years. Seeing his son's potential, Gerard paid the Dukes $14,000 to obtain a twenty percent interest for his son to join their tobacco business. With this financial support, as well as Watts' business knowledge, the company became incorporated under the name of W. Duke, Sons and Company.

Washington was now in his mid-fifties and W. Duke, Sons and Company, was expanding and changing faster than anyone would have ever predicted. After working so hard throughout his life, Washington was eager to retire, but his youngest son was just getting geared up. Buck saw lots of potential in the tobacco business and took over as president, making most of the decisions regarding how the tobacco would be manufactured.

While his sons ran the company from Durham, Washington enjoyed traveling around the country and spent most of his time selling the tobacco to as many mercantile owners as he could reach. It was on one of these sales trips in 1879, that Washington would come face-to-face with the only man he believed could replace him as the salesman for W. Duke, Sons and Company. If he could convince this man to buy his interest, Washington could retire and know his sales department was in good hands. But little did Washington know that his decision would come close to causing the demise of his family's company.

| 5 |

Richard (1875-1879)

Richard opened the door to the vacant building and looked from one corner to the other. The excitement of manufacturing the golden colored leaf sent shivers up his spine. Ever since he heard of the success of men like Washington Duke and William T. Blackwell, he knew that this was his destiny. It had been years since he had felt the red clay between his fingers and smelled the musty odor of the cured tobacco. But what Richard lacked in farming skills, he had in the ability to trade. Just the thought of selling a product that everyone was already asking for brought a smile to his lips.

A few months later, with tobacco bought from local farmers and employees in place to manufacture the golden leaf, Richard set his sights on the task of selling his product. With lots of experience selling merchandise out of his store in Tally Ho, Richard decided to visit local stores in nearby counties.

One cool autumn day, Richard opened the door of a mercantile store in a local community and was greeted by the tinkling of a small bell. He glanced around the room, noticing the products on the shelves and the familiar items he had sold in his old store in Tally Ho. After browsing through aisles of articles of clothing, he made his way toward the back counter. Standing behind a long table was a large, burly man fumbling with his smoking pipe. Richard pulled out a match and approached the counter. "Can I help you with that?"

"This tobacco is hard to keep lit. It's the only kind I can get around here." The man continued to fumble with the pipe and, after having no success with lighting it, placed it down and looked in Richard's direction. "So, what can I do for you young man?"

Richard began to feel the familiar excitement that took over whenever he was ready to sell something. It was like a high that others might get with a drink or a drag of tobacco. "I believe the better question is, what can I do for you?"

The burly man gave Richard a peculiar look. "What do you mean?"

Richard pulled out a small bag of his recently cured tobacco, untied the knot, and shook some of the golden flecks onto the counter. "Let's get rid of what you have in your pipe, so you can take a draw of the best tobacco ever grown."

The man, eager to give this new tobacco a try, tapped the old tobacco out of his pipe, pinched some of the new flecks between his fingers, and pressed it into the shallow space. Richard lit a match and placed it over the pipe as the man inhaled. He closely watched the man's reaction to the taste of the tobacco and then stated, "Now, I can tell from your expression, that you're enjoying the fresh taste of Wright's Orange of Durham. There's nothing like it. Other tobacco companies might come in trying to sell you their brand, but what you're experiencing is the best you'll ever smoke."

"It sure is good," the man said between tokes of his pipe. "How much do you have? I'd love to sell this to my customers."

Richard smiled, reached into his pocket, and pulled out several small bags. "I have as many as you think you can sell. And I can assure you, when you need more, I can provide you with a never-ending supply."

For the next two years, Richard traveled by railroad and stagecoach to sell the sweet-tasting Wright's Orange of Durham. After every store he entered, he walked out with the jingle of coins in his pocket and a man enjoying the flavor of his tobacco. Richard was experiencing unprecedented sales, but no matter how much he sold, he never seemed to be able to compete with the budgets of Blackwell's Bull Durham or W. Duke, Sons and Company's Pro Bono Publico.

In 1879, with concern for his company swirling around in his mind, Richard made his way to Kansas City, Missouri, to sell his tobacco. It was on this particular trip that his career would take an unusual detour. For months, he had been traveling across the United States building his reputation as a strong salesman. He had sold so much that his competitors in Durham had begun to take notice. Even with all the great sales he had made, Richard wasn't making enough of a profit to justify his efforts.

The jostling motion of the stagecoach was soothing to Richard. He had been traveling all day, and the movement caused him to drift off to sleep. Thankfully, no one else occupied the space, allowing him time to ease his mind. Once the horses came to a stop in front of the hotel, he stepped out of the coach, brushed past the doorman, and entered the hotel lobby.

Once inside, Richard walked up to the counter and asked for an empty room. After paying, he gripped his bag, and ascended the stairs to the hallway where his room was located. Once inside, Richard was tempted to lie down, but knew he needed to eat before the hotel kitchen closed. He was exhausted and hoped to have a quiet dinner and return to his room as quickly as possible.

As he descended the steps leading into the lobby, Richard looked toward the floor, with thoughts of his business swirling around in his mind. He walked past a group of women, giggling under their breaths, and made his way toward the small cafe that was situated in the back of the hotel. As he looked around for a vacant table, his attention was drawn to a man seated in the corner. At first, he thought he must be mistaken. Why would this man be halfway across the country? And what was the probability that he would be staying at the same hotel?

Richard drew closer and peered down at the man with the dusty beard and dark suit. "Washington Duke, what are you doing here?"

"Well, I thought I was here to sell tobacco, but every mercantile I visit has your brand on their counter. I don't know how you do it, Richard, but you are one hell of a salesman."

"I admit, I am a phenomenal salesman."

"Richard, sit down and let's talk."

Richard pulled back an empty chair and sat down. A waiter walked up as he was putting his napkin in his lap and asked, "Sir, can I get you something to drink?"

"I'll have a cup of coffee."

Once the waiter left, Richard looked over at Washington with a curious expression. Washington leaned in. "I'm sure you know my story and how I got started in the tobacco business. When we began, we had nothing, but with God's grace, we're now selling all we can manufacture. Now that George Watts joined us, we have more capital to hire employees and purchase more tobacco. I know there are a lot of men trying their hand at this business, you included."

Richard sat quietly while Washington spoke. He wasn't sure where the conversation was headed, but was willing to listen. He'd always had respect for Washington and how he did business. But he wasn't so sure about his youngest son, Buck. Recently, Richard had been drawn into the same social settings and found Buck to be a little too arrogant for his liking. Even so, Richard's interest was piqued.

Washington continued. "As you may know, I have worked hard all my life either farming or selling my tobacco. My boys, and George, have stepped in and are doing most of the work. I'm getting ready to turn sixty next year, and I personally would like to retire and relax a little. But I'm not willing to leave my company without a competent replacement. I've been watching you and have to tell you how impressed I've been with your success. So, I have a proposition for you."

Richard took a sip of his coffee, sat back, and listened to what his competitor was saying.

"Richard, I'd like to sell my interest in my company to you. I believe your strong work ethic and your ability to sell anything would add a lot to the company. I also know that your company, along with so many others, is just not going to be able to compete with the price we can pay for the best of the golden leaf."

Richard sat back in his chair and tried to comprehend what Washington was proposing. He knew that working with such an established company could only benefit his career, but he also knew how much he had invested in the establishment of his own company. Before responding, he took a moment to reflect back on his interaction with the Dukes.

Months prior to this encounter, Richard had traveled to the auction house set up on Parrish Street. He remembered the muddy road and the smell of horse manure as he approached the entrance to the warehouse. Farmers were engrossed in conversation, as the men inside auctioned their product at the highest price possible.

The voice of E.J. Parrish calling out the grower's names and their asking price could be heard above the buzz of people milling around the tobacco. On this one particular day, Richard had his eyes set on a particular pile of cured tobacco, which took on the orange color he prized. As he was getting ready to bid on the tobacco, Buck walked up beside him and pointed down toward the pile. "This is some good-looking tobacco."

"Yes, it is," Richard stated in a calm voice. He didn't want Buck to know how much he wanted this particular pile. He turned to another heap of tobacco, hoping Buck would move on, but to Richard's dismay, his rival didn't budge.

"E.J., whatever the highest bid is on this tobacco, I'll add twenty-five cents over."

"Mr. Duke, you've got a deal!" E.J. called out.

As Richard thought back on that day, he knew the quality of his product wasn't ever going to compete with the smoking tobacco this man had to offer, potentially causing the demise of his company. Richard's thoughts turned back to the man sitting in front of him. "Washington, I must admit, I'm a little taken aback by your proposal."

"I really haven't discussed this with my sons. I thought it best to find out if you were at all interested before moving forward."

Richard wasn't sure if he could even afford the offer, and needed to know before the conversation could go forward. "Washington, now you know most of my capital is tied up into my company."

The older man looked Richard in the eye and slowly took a puff from his pipe. "I know you have property in Durham which I might be interested in. I'm asking for $23,000. We can make something work if you are serious about my proposal."

"Let me think about it. Once we get back to Durham, I can come over and meet with you and your partners."

"Sounds good."

Several weeks later, after returning to Durham, Richard walked into the W. Duke, Sons and Company building. Richard had given Washington's proposition a great deal of thought and felt prepared to confront the partners, particularly Buck. When he entered the massive building, he scanned the manufacturing floor where men were producing pipe tobacco.

Washington came alongside Richard, pointing in the direction of the Jewish men sitting at large tables, hand rolling cigarettes. He then pointed out where the cigarettes were bagged and made ready for sale. After going through the rest of the factory, Washington directed Richard upstairs. "Come up to my office where we can talk."

The older man placed his hand on Richard's back and ushered him upstairs and into his office. A massive mahogany desk was placed in front of a large window. Richard peered out the window, noticing W.T. Blackwell's building with the Bull Durham logo painted on the side. Buck came up beside him and said, "I can promise you, Richard, that sooner rather than later, that bull is going to be painted over! You mark my words."

Washington interjected, "Now, son, we're not going to talk about that bull right now. Come over and sit down. We have things to discuss."

Washington sat down and pointed to a vacant chair at a large oval table. George Watts, Benjamin, and Brodie Duke were already seated. Richard sat down and looked around at the men, whom he had always viewed as his competitors. Buck was the last to sit down, and finally sat on the opposite side of the table from Richard.

Richard wasn't sure what it was about this man, whom he found to be like a pebble in his shoe. He knew it was going to take a lot of convincing from Buck to let go of his company for theirs.

Richard opened up a leather satchel and reached in for a piece of paper and a pen. Everyone looked in his direction until Washington spoke up. "Now as all of you know, Richard has been establishing a solid company just across Main Street. He's been able to turn a profit while most of the smaller companies have had to bail out of the industry."

Washington stopped a moment, letting his business partners take in the significance of Richard's assets. He looked over at Richard and continued. "Every time I go on the road and open up a newspaper, I see an article declaring Wright's Orange of Durham to be the best tobacco. Richard, you have capitalized on the fact that you use Orange County tobacco and produce it in Durham. When I went through Memphis and Little Rock, I couldn't compete with you or your advertisement. There is no mistaking it, you are an excellent salesman."

Washington stopped and looked at Richard. "Everyone knows about our discussion in Kansas City. We've discussed it and would like to offer you an interest in our company."

Buck spoke up, "Richard, there is no denying your ability to sell your product. You have what our company needs. My dad has been sharing with us how you have outsold him in many of the western territories. He is now eager to stay home to spend time building up his philanthropies, along with enjoying time with his family."

"So, why should I come to work for you when I've been able to sell my own tobacco brand?"

Benjamin piped up. "We have a lot more capital at this time. And anyway, you are a natural born salesman. We can send you anywhere in the world and you can leave the manufacturing part of the business to us."

Richard took an assessment of the men sitting around the table. Washington Duke was sitting back smoking his pipe with a grin on his face. Buck appeared anxious and ready for Richard to consent to the arrangement. George Watts appeared agreeable and was nodding his head with affirmation. Brodie was the hardest to read. He seemed apathetic, and looked like he would rather be doing something else.

Richard looked from Benjamin to Buck before speaking. "As you may know, I've been traveling for the past three years and believe the market here in the United States has been saturated. I've always wanted to travel across the Atlantic and build upon the European's desire for a good chew or pipe of tobacco."

Buck looked at Richard and stated, "Before you take this position, I want to make something clear. If you purchase my father's interest in the company, it doesn't mean that you'll have the control over this business that you have with yours. I have ideas for how to advance this company and I'll be expecting your support."

Richard didn't like the tone of Buck's voice, and would have preferred to have no dealings with this man, but also knew this was an opportunity that he couldn't pass up. So, with a blank face showing no expression, Richard spent the rest of the meeting directing his questions to Washington and the other partners. After the legal documents were signed and everyone shook hands, Richard walked out of the building, an official partner of the W. Duke, Sons and Company.

| 6 |

William (1860-1884)

The summer day was particularly hot in the store located in the town of Roxboro. William T. Blackwell's shirt was drenched and perspiration was dripping from his forehead. The young man was looking forward to returning home where a cool drink and dinner were waiting for him. All he wanted was to get back to the house he shared with his family, eat his dinner, take an outdoor shower, and sit on the porch with his pipe of tobacco. He placed the last items on the shelf of his store, wiped his brow with a rag, and headed to the front door to lock up. As he reached for the knob, his friend, James Day, pushed the door open and walked past him. "James, I'm getting ready to close up. What do you want?"

James went up to the counter, hefted himself up, and with a big grin on his face, pulled out a small bag. "William, I have an idea that I want to run past you."

"What idea do you have now? Do you know how many hare-brained ideas you have conjured up?"

"No, William, this time I believe we can make some money."

"Okay. Let me hear it, but make it fast."

"This afternoon, I was approached by a man on the road selling chewing tobacco. I got to talking to him and he told me how much profit he had made in a week. He told me that he couldn't get enough tobacco to meet his orders. Well, I know my father's farm has plenty of tobacco that needs to be sold. So, I was wondering if you'd like to join me on the road, selling chewing and smoking tobacco. The man told me eastern North Carolina would be a perfect place to start."

William leaned up against the counter and stared ahead. He had to admit that this idea was appealing. He often daydreamed about leaving the store to explore the countryside. "James, I have to admit that you may be on to something."

"William, I thought you might like the idea. There's an extra wagon behind my father's barn we could take. If we can find a reliable horse or two, I believe we could be in business."

"Alright, let's not get too carried away. I'll need to talk with my family and see about getting someone to run the store. If I can, I think we might be on the road by the time the tobacco is cured."

The two young entrepreneurs worked hard prepping the tobacco for sale and, once it was ready, they headed east. With William's knack for selling, and James' knowledge of tobacco, the two began to see a profit. As time went by, William and James noted how some tobacco was enjoyed more than others. The most popular brand was manufactured by one of their friends from Person County, John R. Green. The two heard he had moved to Durham and purchased a building in the middle of the small township. They had heard word about how Green had come across a method of curing the tobacco that made the flavor milder than what people had been accustomed to. Green was selling it as "The Best Flavored Spanish Smoking Tobacco".

William and James had kept in touch with John Green during the war. They knew how his business had diminished since the University of North Carolina had dwindled down to fewer than a hundred students. Most of Green's business now came from soldiers coming through the area, but it was barely enough to make a living.

In April 1865, Green thought his business was over when the Union and Confederate soldiers located in the area broke into his building, and foraged for every speck of tobacco that they could find. He had never seen such an onslaught of men going after a taste of tobacco in his life. At first, he was devastated and believed he would never be able to recover financially. But everything changed when he started receiving postcards from up North. When the postcards poured in, Green realized that the catastrophe was, in actuality, a small miracle.

Early into the business, John Green knew he needed a brand name that would draw attention to his tobacco products. One day, he had gone over to Hillsborough to have lunch with his friend, John Y. Whitted. The two men were eating oysters and Green was rambling on about the need for a brand. About this time, Whitted stared at a jar of Coleman's mustard that was on the table. The mustard jar happened to be from Durham, England. As interesting as its location was, something else caught Whitted's attention. "John, I think I have the solution to your problem."

"What?"

Whitted turned the jar around so Green could see the bull's head. "How about a side view of a bull with the caption, "Genuine

Durham Smoking Tobacco". I believe it describes what you are striving to achieve."

"I like that. Durham definitely could use a different image and a bull is the perfect animal to describe this bullish town."

John Green hired a man from New Bern, by the name of James Berry, to paint the first bull. Believing the bull was worth paying for, he applied to the clerk of the Southern District of New York for the copyright on "Genuine Durham Smoking Tobacco", which included the logo of the bull.

Almost overnight, business started to accelerate and Green knew he needed help. He was looking for partners who understood the tobacco industry and had the drive to work hard. Green wanted men that had experienced their own success and knew how to sell his product. About this time, William and James opened a jobbing house in Kinston, North Carolina, and noticed how Green's tobacco outsold all the other tobacco in the state. So, when Green contacted them about buying half the interest in his company, the two men were eager to develop a partnership with him. Green sold the half interest for $1500 and stipulated that it would go back into the company. He also agreed that, after paying rent and other business expenses, the profits would be split three ways.

Green didn't live long enough to see the success of the "Bull" and how it would change Durham forever. After only four months of his newly formed partnership, Green died. With the death of their senior partner, and no ready cash, William and James contemplated selling the business. But William believed in the company and was able to find the money to buy out Green's interest from his estate, making him the principal interest holder. Business continued to suffer due to the lack of capital, and the two men knew they had to do something to turn things around. So, they advertised for a new partner in all the local newspapers.

John Carr was a local mercantile in Chapel Hill and had person-ally experienced the impact tobacco was having on the economy. He had witnessed the sales of tobacco in his own store spiral upward since the end of the Civil War, and believed that this was the time to invest his money in the industry.

After John Carr's son, Julian Shakespeare Carr, returned from serving as an officer in the Confederate Army, he left Chapel Hill and headed to Little Rock, Arkansas, and like his father, worked in a mercantile. His charismatic personality and number sense were perfect ingredients for success at being able to manage a business. When Julian's father, John, realized that his son could easily turn a profit, he knew that he wanted him back in North Carolina working in the tobacco industry.

After reading the advertisement in the newspaper, John Carr traveled the twelve miles from Chapel Hill to Durham to meet with William and James. After some negotiation, John purchased a third of the company for $4000. The plan was for Julian to take over the partnership with each man receiving a third of the profit. John and his son, Julian, agreed to split their third between the two of them.

Later, Julian Carr would resent the negotiations that took place without his input. During discussions, Julian's father only con-sidered the value of the business and neglected to see the value of the "Genuine Durham Smoking Tobacco" brand. Over time, Julian fared extremely well, but not having a piece of the brand would always be a thorn in his side.

Over the next couple of years, the bull was found all over the country in both small and large cities. Along with its popularity, came other corporations trying to steal the brand for their own. In order to keep the rights to their trademark, the company spent over fifteen years in the courts at a huge cost of over $100,000. But when all was said and done, the William T. Blackwell's trademark was rightfully theirs and theirs alone.

The next issue the company faced involved providing a warehouse for North Carolina farmers to bring their tobacco for auction. Virginia had a monopoly on buying the tobacco from farmers and Blackwell knew that in order to have the tobacco for production, the farmers needed to come to Durham.

So, in May 1871, the first auction of loose-leaf tobacco took place in a Durham warehouse run by the William T. Blackwell Company. A young man by the name of Edward James Parrish was known to have a gift for the role of auctioneer and he didn't disappoint. As he walked up and down the piles of tobacco, he was able to pick up cues from the buyers to determine the quality of the leaf laid in front of him. E.J. Parrish had found his calling and brought a hefty profit to the young company with the bull brand.

Julian Carr, William Blackwell, and James Day were experiencing record success. The bull was being painted on the sides of buildings across the country and even appeared on the side of an Egyptian Pyramid. But as effective as the paintings were, the noise made by the North Carolina Railroad that passed by Blackwell's factory, reminded everyone who was king. The train's steam calliope had been made to sound just like a snorting bull, and each day, as the train moved down the tracks, it could be heard by everyone in the small town of Durham.

Life was good, but as much as Blackwell enjoyed the success of his business, the company of a young woman by the name of Emma Exum soon took center stage. Emma lived in Hillsborough with her family.

One Saturday evening, William was having dinner at a local restaurant when he overheard giggles coming from an attractive young woman at a nearby table. William looked in the direction of the woman and found her sitting among a group that looked like a family enjoying their dinner. He listened in on their conversation, hoping to find some way to interject. It came when Emma mentioned the sound of the train to her father. "Dad, I've never heard a train sound like a bull before."

"Miss, I hope you don't mind me interrupting. I heard what you just said. My name is William Blackwell, and the sound you mentioned was created to sound like a bull, to advertise my company's tobacco brand, Bull Durham."

Mr. Exum stood up and shook William's hand. "You're William Blackwell. It's a pleasure to meet you. Please, we'd love to hear more about the bull sound and your business. Come join us."

William sat down in an empty chair across from Emma. As he looked over at her, he couldn't help but think how pretty she was. He immediately had an urge to place his fingers through her long, auburn hair and touch the faint dimple that appeared on her left cheek. William noticed how she was smiling at him and his hands began to shake. He couldn't remember the last time he became so nervous around a girl. William turned his attention to Emma's father. "Mr. Exum, I'm originally from Roxboro. My family owns a mercantile store. My friend, James, and I decided to get involved with selling tobacco at the end of the war and the rest is history."

"Well, I'm impressed with your success. Emma, what do you think of Mr. Blackwell's bull now?"

Emma, taken off guard by her father's question, said in a quiet voice, "I like your bull very much."

For some reason, everyone thought her comment was funny and Emma's sisters began to giggle. Emma's cheeks became rosy red from embarrassment. At first, William wasn't sure if Emma would become upset by the giggles. But then, to his delight, she also started laughing. William chimed in and looked directly at Mr. Exum. "If it would be okay with you, may I have the pleasure of Emma's attendance at a party next weekend? There's a social gathering honoring our contribution to the city. She'll be closely chaperoned and I promise I'll have her home at an early hour."

Mr. Exum looked at Emma, "I'm in favor of you going with Mr. Blackwell, but only if you want to."

For a moment, everyone was looking toward Emma to see how she would respond. Her younger sister, Mamie, chimed in. "Emma, say something."

"Yes, Mr. Blackwell, I'd like to join you next week."

"That's wonderful. I'll have a carriage sent to your house to pick you up at 6:00 p.m. Until then, it was a pleasure meeting such a nice family, and I look forward to seeing you again." William then pushed his chair back, took his hat, and left the restaurant. As he walked out into the cool night, he felt like skipping. It had been a long time since he had been in the company of someone who made him so happy.

Over the next couple of months, William and Emma were seen together at all of the company's social events. On Sundays, William traveled to Hillsborough to attend church with the Exum family. Afterward, William would join the Exums for a large meal and then retreat to the front porch for a smoke with Emma's father. At first, the discussions centered on business but, as time went by, the conversations gravitated toward Mr. Exum's expectations of how William should treat his daughter.

One particular Sunday, William and Mr. Exum were sitting on the porch. Both men had just lit their pipes and sat in silence. Birds could be heard in the distance and a dog was barking in a neighboring field. William was particularly nervous and his thoughts jumbled. As he looked at the man sitting across from him, he could tell that Mr. Exum wanted to speak his mind. "William, you know my family have all come to like and admire you. I know Emma has come to care deeply for you, and I must admit this concerns me."

William was taken off guard. He had wanted to speak of his intentions for quite a while but never seemed to have found the right time. "Mr. Exum, can you please explain what you mean? I've been wanting to tell you in the last few weeks of my desire to make your daughter my wife. I'm sorry I put off this discussion. I've found a ring and I was going to ask you today for your daughter's hand. Please forgive me for not speaking earlier."

For a moment, an awkward silence came between the two men. William wasn't sure what Mr. Exum was going to say and his heart began to pound. Finally, William noticed a grin form as the older man spoke. "I'm glad to hear this. I believe you'll be a good husband and provider for my daughter. I'll keep this between the two of us."

The next Sunday after service, Emma and William broke tradition and went on a picnic. William unfolded a blanket and laid it on the cool ground beside a brook. After sitting down, Emma begun unpacking a meal of fried chicken, deviled eggs, and coleslaw, from a large wooden basket. She was taking the last items out, when she looked up to see William getting down on one knee. He then pulled a ring out of his pocket and cleared his throat. "Emma Exum, will you be my wife?"

Tears sprang from Emma's eyes. It was clear that she was surprised by the proposal. After what seemed like eternity, William spoke again. "Emma, I'm sorry I've upset you."

Emma took a cloth napkin and dabbed at her eyes. "No, William. I just didn't know your proposal would make me so emotional." Emma took hold of William's hands, looked down into his eyes and proclaimed, "William Blackwell, I'd love to be your wife. I love you so much. You are the kindest person I know."

William reached over and placed the ring on Emma's finger, then gently took her in his arms and kissed her with a passion that neither of them knew they had. Once he pulled away, he noticed her eyes were still closed. At that moment, he felt a deep-seated love for this woman, and prayed that he'd have her in his life for many years to come.

The young couple were inseparable. Each day, after the bull snorted, symbolizing a successful day of producing tobacco, William would make his way home to his beautiful wife. Once he walked up the steps, Emma would open the door and lean into him, lift her lips upward, and the two would kiss with the same intensity they shared on the day he proposed.

William loved having Emma for his wife. She was beautiful and had a wonderful temperament. He couldn't imagine a fuller life until, one day, Emma took his hands and placed them over her round belly. "William, I have news."

"Emma, are you trying to tell me you're pregnant?"

"I am, my dear. We're going to have a baby."

"Emma, a baby. You're making me the luckiest man on earth. I love you so much!"

Over the following months, Emma grew in her beauty as her belly expanded. William was constantly pampering her and would wake up in the middle of the night just to make sure she was feeling okay. When the day finally came and their baby girl, Mary, was born, the couple was ecstatic. She was a beautiful baby who appeared happy and healthy.

A few years after the birth of their daughter, their son, William T., was born and their family was complete. Emma loved being a mother and dressing up both her children. She spent all her time doting on them during the day and tending to William at night. Life couldn't be better for the young family. William's business was doing well, and it looked like the family would enjoy a long and happy life.

Over time, Emma began to notice that Mary had a hard time overcoming simple ailments. A cold would turn into bronchitis or pneumonia and, instead of an illness lasting only a couple of days, Mary would suffer for weeks. When the little girl would fall ill,

William called upon the best doctors in Durham. But none of the medicines or procedures gave their daughter relief.

When Mary turned five, she developed a deep persistent cough that wouldn't go away. As the days turned into weeks, the little girl became feverish and weak. Night after night, Emma stayed close to her daughter, refusing to go to her bed. Each night, William tried to convince Emma to get rest, but she refused to leave her daughter's side.

One night, Mary became less responsive, and both William and Emma knew the end was near. William refused to leave Emma's side, as she held her small child, singing her songs, and talking about how much she loved her. As Emma hummed a lullaby and stroked her daughter's forehead, the little girl closed her eyes and breathed her last breath.

William looked over at his wife holding the little body and his heart broke for his daughter whom he loved so much. But, as hard as it was to witness his daughter's death, his heart ached more for his beautiful wife, and the grief that took hold of her, and wouldn't let go.

"William, she was so beautiful," Emma spoke through sobs.

"She was," he said with tears streaming down his face. "She was such a special child. I'll always love her."

Long after the candles burned down and the room turned dark, William sat with his wife as she hummed through her sobs. When Emma appeared to be asleep, he rose and had the doctor called. When the doctor approached Emma, she clung to her child and, with a desperate plea, asked William to stop him from taking Mary. "Emma, it's time. I'm so sorry. Please let the doctor take her."

Emma let go of her grasp and turned to William. "Oh, William, what are we going to do without her?"

William took her in his arms and carried Emma to bed where she lay face down and cried into her pillow. Later, after he had dismissed the doctor, William wrapped his arms around his wife's frail body, stroking her hair until she drifted to sleep.

As much as Emma wanted to move beyond the feelings that pressed so hard against her heart, it didn't appear possible. For weeks, Emma had no appetite and her face, that had been so full, was now taut and appeared without emotion. William was extremely concerned for his wife and hoped something could improve her depressive state.

It was at Emma's lowest that William formulated a plan that might help his wife. Emma was sitting by the window, still in her nightclothes, when he approached her. "Emma, I have an idea that I need your help with."

"William, I don't know. I just feel tired all the time."

"Yesterday, I met with Richard Harvey Wright. He's back from Europe. Anyway, I'd love to have him over for dinner and I thought you might ask your sister, Mamie, to come."

Emma looked up at William and, for the first time since Mary's death, he could see a spark of excitement in the deep green eyes and dimple he loved so much, form across her fair skin. "That would be nice. I believe Mamie would enjoy Richard's company. It would be so much fun to entertain once again."

| 7 |

Richard (1884)

Richard had always liked William. They had a lot in common and enjoyed many interesting conversations about their similar up-bringings and the trends in the tobacco industry. Even though Richard's partner, Buck Duke, referred to William as the enemy, he refused to view his competitors in this manner. So, when William invited Richard for dinner, Richard was pleased to accept. It would be nice to enjoy an evening with his friend and lovely wife, Emma. Richard knew they had recently suffered the loss of their daughter, and felt honored to be invited into their home so soon after their personal tragedy.

Richard arrived at seven o'clock sharp. A woman with a small, white bonnet and apron opened the door, took his hat and coat, and escorted him into a room off of the foyer. When Richard entered William's office, he was impressed by the number of books that lined the walls. Some of the titles he spotted on the reams reminded him of the years he'd spent in the back room of Mr. Hunt's mercantile store, soaking in inspiring stories that kept him hopeful about his future.

In the center of the room was a mahogany desk with a few papers scattered on the surface. An oil lamp cascaded light across the dark surface. William was sitting in a large chair leaning over the top of the desk staring at a picture. When Richard was announced, William looked up and a smile crept across his face. William pushed the chair back, made his way around the desk, and embraced his friend. "Richard, I'm so glad you could come. I can't wait to hear about your recent journey to South Africa. It's amazing to think about how far you've traveled."

Richard looked at his friend and stated in a sincere voice, "I'm so sorry for the loss of your daughter."

"Thank you. It's been particularly difficult for Emma. Thank goodness our son, W.T., is doing well."

"William, I'm glad you invited me over. I wanted to ask you about the recent sale of your shares in the William T. Blackwell Company."

"Richard, my family has required my attention more than the company. Julian Carr has taken over the position of president. He wasn't happy with my decision, but with Mary's illness, I believed I needed to free up some time to be home. Anyway, Julian works well with the men from Philadelphia and I'd like to take a stab at the banking industry. Durham needs another bank and there are a lot of people moving to town who need assistance."

"I hope the best for you." Then Richard paused a moment and continued. "I hope you won't be offended by me saying this, but you really underestimated the value of your shares."

"I'm sure others are thinking the same thing, but I have no regrets. Emma and the children come first and I'm excited about the change in my career path. Look, we can talk about this later. I had other reasons for your invitation. I'd like for you to meet someone. I know it's hard for you to find time to socialize with all your travels, but I have a hunch this woman will be worth meeting."

Richard felt a little uncomfortable. He hadn't dated much due to his busy schedule. He'd promised himself that if the right woman did come along, he would curtail his trips overseas. But since no one interesting had made their way into his life, he continued to spend time crossing the Atlantic to sell tobacco. "I'm not sure what to say. You know how busy I am. I'm not sure if I have time for a woman in my life."

William perked up. "Look, ever since Mary passed, Emma hasn't been herself. But when I told her that you'd be coming over, she actually became excited. She wants you to meet her sister, Mamie. So, I told her that I would invite you for dinner."

"I do think the world of Emma. If I can bring a little happiness into her life by being introduced to her sister, that's the least I can do."

"I believe they're waiting for us in the parlor. Let's go in and have a drink," William said, as he placed his hand on Richard's shoulder and guided him into the adjacent room.

Richard had met Emma on several occasions and found her attractive, and now hoped her sister would also have a pleasing physique. He began to feel a little anxious about meeting this young woman, but didn't want to appear so. Richard took a deep breath and intentionally lifted his shoulders, providing a confident impression.

William led Richard into the elaborately decorated parlor with gold-flecked curtains, a grand piano, and imported furniture. As Richard walked through the door, he was immediately drawn to a young woman sitting on the piano bench, gliding her fingers across the keys. The young woman was playing a song that Richard had heard multiple times, and was captivated by her grace as she hummed along with the music. Once the last note was played, the young woman turned toward the men as they stood motionless. In that moment, Richard was captivated by how beautiful she was, finding himself unable to speak.

The young woman stood up, placed the stool under the piano, and walked in Richard's direction. As she drew closer, Richard noticed her fair skin and slender figure. Her hair was auburn like Emma's, but short, complementing her facial features. She walked toward the men and stopped in front of Richard. With a faint smile on her face, she placed her hand out for Richard to take. He was spellbound and noticed his hand shake as he took her hand, placed it up to his lips and, ever so gently, kissed it.

William, seeing how spellbound his friend was, spoke up. "Richard Wright, this is Mamie Exum."

Mamie looked up into Richard's eyes and said in a soft voice, "It's very nice to meet you. I've heard some wonderful things about you from my sister, Emma. I hear you are a world traveler. I'd love to hear about your time in Europe and Asia."

Richard responded, "I'd love to share with you about my travels. To be honest, I've been to so many places it's hard to remember much."

Emma smiled at William as they both looked at the interaction that was taking place between Richard and Mamie. Emma spoke up. "Dinner is now being served. Let's continue this conversation in the dining room."

They walked from the parlor into a large rectangular room with a huge cherry dining table and a beautiful crystal chandelier hung in the center of the ceiling. Crystal glasses were at each setting, along with a lovely set of china with delicate flowers hand painted on each plate. Typically, Richard would have taken in the elaborate décor, but his eyes were solely on Mamie. As the servants came in and out of the kitchen with each prepared course, Richard said very little.

After the dishes were taken away, the four returned to the parlor and the women sat on a small couch across from the men, who smoked their pipes, and discussed Richard's recent travels.

Mamie looked over at the men and asked, "So, Richard, tell me what it's like to be a world traveler?"

"It sure isn't as glamourous as you would think. The food and accommodations can be questionable at times. But as time has gone by, I've made several strong contacts. I believe the more I go across the ocean, the better chance I have for future opportunities. As for the Dukes, they are busy figuring out ways to produce cigarettes without using so much manpower. Since the invention of the Bonsack machine, using it for manufacturing seems to be their way of becoming the most dominant cigarette company in America. The machine isn't perfect, but it's better than paying the Jewish men from New York to hand-roll each cigarette."

William took a long drag from his pipe. "That's interesting. I'm sure Julian Carr is trying his best to stay abreast of how efficient the Bonsack machine is. But, that's no longer my problem."

Emma whispered something in Mamie's ear and both women began to giggle.

Richard looked in the direction of the women and asked, "So can I ask what you are finding so amusing?"

Mamie looked at Richard and answered, "We were just imagining what it would be like to travel across the ocean on a rough sea and how people fare on those days."

"I assure you, it can be difficult. I've been blessed to have a tolerant stomach, but I know men that can't bear the motion of the ship and get sick every time they leave the port."

Mamie looked directly at Richard and asked, "Share with us about your favorite city that you've visited."

"Each city has its own distinct personality. But if I was to ever have the honor of your company, I would like to take you to England to see the castles and churches."

Mamie smiled up at Richard and with a quiet voice responded, "I think I'd like that very much."

For the next hour, the four sipped their tea and giggled over funny stories that Richard told about his travels. Before the evening came to a close, Richard knew he wanted to spend more time with Mamie.

When it was time for Richard to leave, he leaned over and, in a quiet voice, whispered in Mamie's ear. "It was very nice meeting you and I'm already looking forward to seeing you again."

Mamie smiled. "I'd love that."

Later that evening, in the comfort of his small home, Richard had second thoughts. He didn't have time for a woman in his life, particularly one like Mamie who might cause him to become emotionally deterred from his dreams. Richard thought about how hard he had worked for his success and wasn't going to let a woman career him off his path.

The next day, he walked down to the café that William often visited. Once he opened the door, he spotted William at a table surrounded by several local businessmen. It was clear from William's demeanor that he was selling them on the idea of placing their money into the bank he was starting. Richard ordered a cup of coffee and waited for the men to disperse.

Richard overheard one man say, "William, I'll get back with you. I need to speak to my partners. We do need a bank here in Durham that we can trust our money is safe in."

"Mr. Smith, you won't regret it. If it makes you feel better, I'm placing my own money in the new bank. I know you agree there is much to do here in Durham. If we have strong financial backing, we can get it done."

Richard waited until all the men had exited the café before winding his way back to where William was seated. He looked down at William as he worked on some calculations. "William, I need to speak to you."

"Richard, I wasn't expecting to see you today."

"William, I've been thinking."

"Would you like to place your money in my bank?"

"No. I have my money in Eugene Morehead's bank and I've been happy with the way it's been handled. No, I need to speak to you about Mamie."

"Richard, I haven't seen Emma smile for a long time. Just watching you and Mamie together made her so happy. I want to thank you for the little joy you brought to my family. Emma and I were talking about setting up a dinner party for next week. She wanted to make sure you were invited. You have no idea how grateful I am to you. It means so much to me to see the little bit of joy Emma is having because of your potential relationship with her sister."

"William, I'm just not sure if I have the time to be courting someone."

"Richard, I saw how you were looking at Mamie. I know a fire has been lit inside you. Now, why do you want to go and make things complicated?"

"William, they are complicated. You know my position with the Dukes includes a lot of travel. How can I treat a woman as wonderful as Mamie to the life she deserves when I'm gone so much?"

"Richard, you'll figure it out. Now, don't disappoint Emma. But, more importantly, don't let this opportunity for love pass you by. I can't imagine life without Emma. My wife is more important to me than all of this." William waved his hand over the books and papers scattered on the table.

"Okay. I'll come to the dinner party. Then I'll know if this relationship is worth pursuing."

"Now that's the man I know and respect."

Richard did attend the dinner party and found himself more attracted to Mamie than the first time he laid eyes on her. There was something about the young woman that he couldn't resist. Over the following months, Richard rearranged his schedule so he could spend more time with her. No matter if he was in Durham, or on a trip across the Atlantic, he couldn't stop thinking about Mamie.

When Richard was on the seas or in a foreign country, he would sit down and write Mamie letters, sharing about how much he cared for her. He found himself telling her things he hadn't shared with anyone else. He allowed her into his feelings about the death of his parents and how he had promised his siblings that he was going to take care of them. Even though he felt vulnerable, he also felt a sense of peace when he was with her.

Everyone Richard associated with could see the change in his demeanor. Instead of the serious man they were used to seeing, Richard appeared happy and easy-going. The topics of conversation had also changed. Instead of only wanting to discuss business, Richard was willing to let Mamie direct the conversation to subjects that previously bored him, but now, coming from her, he found entertaining.

The couple attended many of Durham's social gatherings and could be spotted taking long carriage rides out into the country. After only four months of dating, Richard became eager to ask Mamie to be his wife. On one trip to England, he spotted a ring inside a store he frequently visited. It was beautiful, but lacked the number of carats he desired. So, Richard paid a jeweler to have a diamond cut and placed in a similar gold setting.

In April, when Richard was home from one of his business trips, with ring in hand, he asked Mamie to join him for dinner. When she knocked on the door, his hands began to perspire and doubts clouded his thoughts.

"Mamie, please come in."

"Thank you, Richard."

"Please, come into the parlor. I have something to talk to you about."

"Richard, you sound so ominous. I hope everything is okay."

"Yes."

Mamie walked around the room, inspecting all of the furniture and objects that Richard had brought home with him from overseas. She stopped in front of a picture that was hanging above the loveseat. "Richard, tell me about this picture."

Richard looked at the picture and caught his breath. "I saw this picture in a store in China. When I saw it, I must admit I thought of you. You see, these women in their flowing dresses reminded me of the day we spent in Julian Carr's garden. The women look so free as they swing high above the trees. When I saw the picture, I thought of you swinging on the garden swing surrounded by all the blooming pear trees. I love thinking of both of us flying together above the troubles and worries of this life."

Mamie and Richard stood silent, both imagining flying above the ground. Richard reached down and took Mamie's hand in his own. For a moment they didn't say a word, neither wanting the moment to end. Then, ever so gently, Richard turned toward Mamie, went down on his knee and looked up into the face of the woman he dearly loved.

"Mamie, will you be my wife?"

Richard looked into Mamie's face and detected a tear falling from her eye. "Yes, Richard, I would love to be your wife."

Richard took a small package out of his coat pocket, opened it, and lifted the diamond ring out. Mamie gasped as she looked at the diamond setting. "Oh, Richard. It's beautiful. I've never seen a ring like this."

"When I saw it, I had one specially made for you."

Richard rose and both of them sat down on the loveseat. Mamie leaned over and kissed Richard on the lips. "Thank you, Richard, for making me so happy."

"Oh, no. Mamie, you have made me the happiest man alive. I can't imagine life without you."

The months of their engagement brought the best out of Richard. Even though he was known for his serious nature, when he was around Mamie, Richard was often seen laughing or telling her things to make her smile. He was deeply in love with her, and had hopes for a long life together.

On June 24, 1884, Mamie and Richard were married, surrounded by their friends and family. As he watched his bride walk down the aisle, Richard was consumed with such love that he wanted to burst. Five days later, the newlyweds sailed across the Atlantic to Europe. For the first two days, heavy wind and waves pounded against the ship and Mamie was unable to rise from her bed. By the third day, with calmer seas, Mamie was able to join Richard on the open deck. With no land in sight, and the breeze blowing through her hair, Richard took his wife's hand and kissed it. A joy welled up inside him that was hard for him to contain.

"Mamie, I never envisioned being with someone who I could love so much."

"Me either."

"When I was a boy, my father was the world to me. I loved him so much. Life was hard on the farm, but he was always there beside me, encouraging me to be whatever I wanted to be. At that time, my world was perfect. But then, he fell ill and died. The man that my world was built around was gone. After that, everything changed. My mother had become bitter and didn't have time to spend with us. Everything was centered on the crops and making sure there was enough food on the table."

"Oh, Richard, I'm so sorry."

"You see, Mamie, I lost what love looked like. A couple of years after my father died, my sister, Lucy, became pregnant out of wedlock. My mother was furious with Lucy and, at first, ashamed. But then, when Little Thomas was born, my mother turned her attention to taking care of him. I admit jealousy overtook me and, from then on, I was determined never to be that vulnerable again."

Mamie looked out onto the ocean, deep in thought.

"Mamie, I want you to understand how you have taught me how to love again. All the emotions buried deep inside me have been brought back to the surface. I was cautious when entering this relationship because I didn't know if I could love anyone, but you have changed me."

Richard placed his hand under Mamie's chin and turned her so she was facing him. "I love you so much, it almost scares me. I promise I'll take care of you and never hurt you."

"I believe you. I love you as well."

And ever so slightly, Richard brushed his lips against hers, turned, and gazed out onto the ocean.

Richard had made this journey across the open seas many times, but this time was different. He had never sailed with someone he loved, and wanted to soak in every moment of it. The young couple spent many days in their stateroom getting acquainted with each other's bodies. Richard would lie in the small bed, alongside his bride, trying to memorize every dip and curve of her youthful body.

And when they did make love, he was tender and gentle, making sure to bring her pleasure.

When they weren't in their stateroom, they were walking the upper deck or feasting on delicious meals served to them in an elaborate dining area. Every day, around three in the afternoon, they joined other passengers for cards or a reading in the library. Richard enjoyed the routine and found solace in the lack of business responsibilities.

On the eighth day, London could be seen from the bow of the ship. Richard and Mamie found a place to stand and watch as the vessel came into port. Mamie's excitement grew, the closer they came to approaching land, which made Richard laugh. "Richard, look. Isn't it beautiful?"

"Yes, it is my darling, but just wait until I take you out into the countryside and show you some of the castles and old churches."

"Richard, thank you so much for bringing me. I love you."

Mamie took hold of Richard's hand and squeezed it. After watching the boat come into port and be secured, the order to disembark was given. Mamie jumped up and down like a little girl. "Can we go now? I can't wait to see all the places you have visited."

Given the number of times Richard had visited London, he automatically took up the role as tour guide. It was difficult for Richard to keep the enthusiasm out of his voice as he led his young bride, with hands clasped together, to the Tower of London where they viewed the Crown Jewels. As they gazed at the incredible size and weight of the crowns, they found it funny to think about how heavy they would be, and pretended to stoop down with the weight.

Richard heard Mamie catch her breath as she entered Westminster Abbey. He waited a few moments as she took in the magnitude of the massive sanctuary and contemplated the number of historic events which had transpired there. Lastly, Richard directed Mamie over several of the famous bridges in and around London. As their horse-drawn carriage clopped across the different surfaces, Richard shared tidbits of historical trivia with her.

After each day of sightseeing, Richard would escort Mamie to a different restaurant, where they sat by candlelight and held hands. It was on such a night, as they sat overlooking the River Thames, with the sound of the water lapping over rocks, and the moon high in the sky, that Richard turned to his young bride, "Mamie, I never imagined I would be sitting here with such a beautiful woman."

"Richard, I'm the one who's blessed. I never thought I'd be in London, eating dinner beside the River Thames. You are so good to me."

Richard looked down, with tears welling in his eyes, and softly spoke, "I love you so much. It scares me." Richard said, more to himself than to Mamie "Every person I've ever loved has been taken away."

Mamie didn't respond right away. Instead, she reached over and held Richard's hand. "I'm not going anywhere. We have an entire lifetime ahead. Anyway, I've got plans for us, dear man, and several children to raise."

Two days later, the young couple left London, boarded a train, and then took a boat across the English Channel to Holland. They spent a day sight-seeing and walking the beach. Mamie loved the feel of the sand sinking between her toes. She persuaded Richard to take his shoes and socks off and run beside her. He had never done anything so spontaneous and freeing. It took him a few minutes to change his mindset, but in watching Mamie laugh, he was able to enjoy himself. After leaving Holland, the couple went to Belgium, and then into Switzerland, where Mamie couldn't get over the incredible snow-capped mountains and breathtaking views.

Every day was a new adventure for both of them. Even though Richard had been to many of the scenic cities, Mamie provided a fresh perspective he found refreshing. He had never smiled or laughed so much in his life. His love for Mamie only grew as the days passed. Neither of them wanted their honeymoon to end, but Richard knew he had to get back to the States. So, after visiting Italy, they took a train back to Liverpool, where they boarded their ship and sailed home.

During the final days of their journey back across the Atlantic, Richard started to question his motivation to work so hard. He had always been so driven by his pursuit of the next business venture that he had never experienced what it was like to be focused on another human being. Mamie's youth and eagerness to please him met a need that he didn't even know existed. So, when their ship docked in New York, Richard felt a sadness well up inside of him. For the first time in his life, he questioned his priorities. Since Mamie, everything had changed, and all he wanted was to be with the woman who had stolen his heart.

Before the honeymoon to Europe, Richard was notified that W. Duke, Sons and Company, was expanding north and needed Richard to be their main negotiator in New York. Richard was content with this arrangement, particularly since he preferred to keep his distance from Buck Duke and all his demands. Also, Mamie seemed to thrive among the social circles of the bustling city and had easily made several good friends.

The young couple found a large apartment at 6 Rivington Street near Washington Square, which suited both of them. It needed some work, which thrilled Mamie. After Richard left each morning for the office, Mamie would spend her days working with decorators and contractors. Every evening, when Richard returned up the stoop to the door, Mamie raced to greet him with a kiss and then, with a contagious enthusiasm, provided a personal tour of the changes to the apartment.

Both of them loved the nightlife in New York. Mamie particularly enjoyed the shows and other gala events that cluttered her calendar. Her youthful energy was contagious and Richard hardly ever denied his bride's wishes to leave the apartment to attend an event. On the evenings spent at home, they sat around the dinner table for hours, spinning dreams about their future family and enjoying each other's presence.

One day, when Mamie knew for sure she was pregnant, she sent the servants home early and prepared a special meal for the two of them. When Richard walked up the steps, he saw Mamie peeking through the curtains. He was just about to walk in the door when Mamie opened the door and locked her arms around his neck. "Richard, I'm so glad to see you."

He leaned down, looking into his wife's eyes, and whispered into her ear. "Mamie, you know every day all I can think about is coming home to you."

"I have some news, but before I share it, I want you to come in and enjoy the meal I fixed."

Mamie and Richard walked hand in hand through the foyer and into the dining room, where candles flickered light across the table. Mamie took Richard's hand and walked him over to his chair where he slid down. After she sat next to him, she held a crystal pitcher and poured each of them a glass of water. With an enchanting smile and giggles, she placed a large slice of roast beef onto his plate and reached for a ladle to serve him mashed potatoes. As she plopped the white cream down, a small glob of potato came off the plate and landed on Mamie's cheek. In that moment they started to laugh.

In between giggles, Richard asked, "Mamie, can I have the pleasure of removing the mashed potato from your lovely cheek?"

"Yes, you surely can."

Mamie pressed her body close to Richard and smiled down at him. He gently kissed the spot where the potato had landed. "These are the best mashed potatoes I've ever eaten."

"Richard, you are too much. Now eat your dinner and be good."

Richard took his knife, sliced a piece of meat, and placed it in his mouth. The meat was delicious and all he could think about was how lucky he was. He not only had a beautiful wife, but one who could cook a variety of meals. After Richard finished the last bite, he turned to Mamie. "So, what's this news you want to share with me?"

"Well, I haven't been feeling as well as I usually do. And then I got to thinking about the last time I had my monthly and it dawned on me. I must be pregnant. That was a couple of days ago and I wanted to be sure before telling you the news. Just today, I noticed how my clothes are tighter around my waist. Richard, I know I'm pregnant, and we're going to have a baby."

"Oh, Mamie. Are you sure?"

"I am."

"That's wonderful news! I love you so much."

"And I love you."

| 8 |

Richard (1884-1885)

Richard sat in his home office at 6 Rivington Street, New York, gazing out the window at the people walking past. Snowflakes began to fall as he rose to place another piece of wood in the small fireplace that kept the room relatively warm. It was two days before Christmas and he was struggling. A week ago, Richard had received word from Thomas that their sister, Pattie, had died after a long illness. Richard had so enjoyed his sister's company from childhood and treasured the poetry she had written. He knew Pattie had been sick for quite some time, but it was still hard to believe she was gone.

He was only able to make a quick train trip down South for the funeral and had arrived back in New York, greeted by a letter from Benjamin Duke that made him feel sick to his stomach. It was clear that the Dukes were using him for their grunt work and he didn't appreciate it. As he sat gazing toward the flames in the fireplace, he tried to shake off the negative feelings which were consuming every waking moment.

Mamie peeked her head around the door and softly knocked before entering. Richard knew she had seen the expression on his face, and quickly smiled up at his wife. She had such a positive impact on him and he couldn't imagine life without her. "Darling, what can I do for you?"

"Richard, I was hoping we could go shopping for a couple more gifts before the snow picks up."

"Oh, Mamie, there isn't anything I would rather do, but I just received a letter, or should I say a set of orders, that need to be addressed immediately."

"Don't the Dukes know that Christmas is in just a few days?"

"You would think so. Benjamin informed me that his wife just had a baby boy and he can't make the trip up North."

"Don't they know about Pattie and the loss you have recently suffered?"

"Yes, but they know I'm here in New York and think I should be willing to represent the company."

"Can't it wait until after Christmas?"

"Apparently, Benjamin Duke doesn't think so. It appears that the tobacco manufacturing company, Allen & Ginter, has been packing their cigarettes with paper labeled Duke Cigarettes. People have begun to think their cigarettes are the same brand as the W. Duke, Sons and Company. Benjamin wants me to meet with Major Graham, an attorney, to determine if we have any legal means to resolve this issue in a court of law. Apparently, dealers and consumers across the country believe that Allen & Ginter were the first to produce Duke Cigarettes. If we go to court and lose, we would have to invest a lot of money and time to prove otherwise. Money we don't have."

Richard gazed down at the four-page document on his desk. He noticed the letterhead with his name in the top right-hand corner. For the first time since accepting Washington Duke's offer, he wished he had no part of this company. "But it isn't so much dealing with this issue that's getting me irritated with the Dukes."

"Richard, if you don't feel comfortable talking to me about this, I understand."

"Mamie, if I didn't have you to talk to about such matters, I'm not sure what I would do. You have such a sensible perspective on difficult issues. Benjamin informed me that the company is very short on money at this time. They are opening a new factory in Chicago and hope to start production on January 1st. The cigarette rollers have begun work, and they are desperate for money. He had the gall to ask me to send him as much money as I could."

Mamie sat down on the small loveseat near the fireplace. She placed her hands out toward the warm embers and asked, "What are you going to do?"

"I'm not sure. I'll meet with Major Graham and with the president of May Brothers, the company that made the paper, but sending the Dukes money is out of the question. I've earned every cent that I've received. Ever since I joined this company, my opinions have been snuffed out and, lately, it seems like all I'm doing is extinguishing fires that Buck and Benjamin have created."

"Oh, Richard, I'm so sorry. I just want you to be happy."

Richard rose from his chair and walked over to where Mamie was sitting. He pulled her up and gently kissed her on the lips. "Mrs. Wright, you make me very happy. Just thinking about you, and the baby we're going to have, keeps me from going mad."

Mamie looked out the window and pointed toward the snow. "I guess it's snowing too hard to go out shopping. I have another idea if you can step away from all these business issues."

"And what would that be?"

"Just follow me upstairs, Mr. Wright, and I'll let you know how much you are appreciated."

"I think that sounds like a great idea."

In the following months, Richard was consumed with work and resolving the issues the Dukes placed before him. But as difficult as his professional life was, he could hardly think about anything but Mamie and the upcoming birth of their baby. One morning, still lying in bed, he gazed down at his beautiful wife. "Mamie, have I told you how much I love you?"

Mamie rolled over onto her side and looked up into Richard's eyes. "Yes, at least five times each day."

A serious look crossed Richard's face. "I never thought I'd ever find someone who completes me like you do." Richard took his finger and traced her protruding stomach. It was all too good. He only wanted to treasure every moment he could with Mamie. Then he lightly kissed her lips and pulled himself up. "I'd love to stay here all day, but I have to go to the office. By the way, what are your plans?"

Mamie yawned. "I have a doctor's appointment and then I'm having lunch with a friend."

"Please make sure you take care of yourself. I don't want anything to happen to you."

"Oh, Richard. You don't have anything to worry about. I'll be fine."

"Well, you know me. I just want the woman I love to be around for a long time."

The next couple of months passed quickly. Before Richard realized it, Mamie's pregnancy was almost full-term and she was having difficulty getting around. With each pound she gained, he found himself becoming more protective of her.

One night, as they were discussing their plans for the nursery, they heard a knock on the door. Richard and Mamie looked at each other, surprised to have a visitor at such a late hour. Richard called out to Clarisse, a woman they hired to help around the house. "Can you please see who's at the door?"

"I'll be glad to."

Richard and Mamie heard an interaction between Clarisse and another woman. Mamie could barely hear the woman's voice, but what she could hear, made her stand up from her chair. "Emily, is that you?" Mamie asked in an excited voice.

Clarisse moved out of the way, allowing Emily, Mamie's sister, to enter. When Richard saw Emily's grief-stricken face, he knew something was wrong. "Emily, please come in and take a seat."

With tears streaming down her face, Emily walked over and gave Mamie a hug. Mamie looked at her sister and asked, "Emily, what's wrong?"

"Mamie, I have some horrible news. Given your condition, I didn't want you to hear it from a telegram."

Mamie, now panic-stricken, asked, "Emily, tell me. What's wrong?"

Emily could hardly speak. "It's Dad. He died of a heart attack. I know how close you were to him. I'm so sorry."

Richard watched as Mamie took in a deep breath and then placed her head in her hands and cried. "When did this happen? How's Mom? She must be heartbroken."

Emily reached over and took Mamie's hand. "Mother is very upset. Her sisters are with her. Given your pregnancy, she was very concerned about you, which is why I took the train, so I could tell you in person."

"Have you seen our sister, Emma? How is she? She must also be heartbroken."

"When I left, she was okay. William has been wonderful and has kept a close eye on her. A couple of days ago, we had a funeral service in Hillsborough and everyone was there. I'm sorry you're only finding out now, but everyone was concerned and wanted me to be with you when you heard the news."

Richard got up and stood over his wife. "Mamie, I'm going to leave you and Emily alone. If you need anything, please let me know. And Emily, you're welcome to stay as long as you like. I'll get Clarisse to make the guest room ready."

Richard walked into the library and sat down behind his desk. He took a small bag of tobacco out of the drawer and placed it in his pipe. As he thought about his wife and her sadness over the death of her father, he couldn't help but remember the sight of his own father lying in the center of the room, surrounded by mourners. And, even though it was many years ago, the memory would forever be etched into his mind.

Richard wasn't sure how to comfort his wife, but having Emily here gave him a sense of peace that she was in good hands. The two sisters spent the next few days reminiscing about their dad and what a wonderful father he had been. There were lots of tears, but also laughter, when they told each other stories from their childhood.

After a week, just as Emily was talking about leaving, a telegram arrived. Richard took the folded piece of paper from the boy in uniform, unfolded it, and was instantly filled with disbelief. Thoughts of how God could allow such pain swept through his consciousness. Fear of how Mamie would respond to this news made him tremble. Richard thought about holding back the news, but knew it was best to let Mamie know what had happened.

Richard walked into the dining room where Mamie and Emily were talking about baby supplies and what they needed to get before the baby's birth. "Mamie, Emily, I have some news."

Richard sat down next to Mamie and took her hands. "Honey, we just received a telegram that your sister, Emma, has passed away."

Emily gasped. "But I just saw her a couple of weeks ago. She was fine."

"My dear sister. I can't imagine how William is doing. Oh, Richard, this is horrible. Emma was so young. She and William were talking about having another child. Oh, Richard," Mamie said through her tears.

"I'll send a telegram to William to see if he can give us more details. Emily, I hope you can stay longer."

"Yes, I can stay for a little while. Richard, can you send my mother a telegram, telling her that we're okay and that we love her?"

Richard nodded. "Of course, I will. Thank you, Emily, for being here."

Over the following weeks, Emily and Mamie spent every waking moment together. Richard returned to work and checked on Mamie throughout the day. He couldn't stop worrying about his wife and wondered how she would do once her sister left.

One day, Emily pulled Richard aside. "Richard, I don't want to leave, but I must. My own family is suffering and I need to get back to North Carolina."

"Emily, can't you stay until after the birth?"

"Richard, if I didn't have responsibilities at home, you know I would. I've been away too long as it is. I promise, I'll return after the birth to check on Mamie and the baby."

The next day, as Emily was preparing to leave, Mamie stood in her nightgown at the top of the stairs. Richard looked up at his wife and noticed how frail she appeared. Emily could be heard trying to console her sister. As the women embraced and sobbed in each other's arms, Richard was consumed with a feeling of helplessness. All he wanted to do was hold his wife and tell her that everything was going to be okay. But he didn't have it in himself to speak the empty words.

Once Emily left, Mamie fell into a deep depression. She stayed in bed for longer and longer lengths of time and Richard was at a loss for what to do or say to help her. Richard had several conversations with Mamie's doctor about the importance of a mother's state of mind during the birth of a child. Every day, Richard would bring in fresh flowers, or have Clarisse make one of Mamie's favorite foods. But no matter how hard he tried, Mamie became more depressed as the birth of their child approached.

On the third day of June, Mamie woke in intense pain. Richard knew this must be the beginning of his wife's labor. "Clarisse, go get the doctor. Hurry!"

In the hallway, Clarisse shouted back, "I'm on my way!"

"Honey, everything is going to be okay. I'm right here. I love you so much."

Mamie squeezed Richard's hand. "Please don't leave me."

"I'll never leave you. I love you so much. Now I'm going to get you a fresh washcloth and be right back."

Richard didn't know what to do to help Mamie as the pain intensified with every contraction. It seemed like hours before Clarisse came rushing up the stairs followed by the doctor. Once the older man rolled up his sleeves and took Mamie's pulse, he looked up. "Richard, I need you to go downstairs and boil some water. Clarisse and I will take it from here."

Richard was almost relieved to be pushed out of the room and given a task to do. But, over time, he was overcome with a sense of anxiety as he heard Mamie writhing in pain. Initially, her cries were strong and persistent, but as the hours passed, they sounded more like a whimper. Richard paced the floor and prayed to God for the health of his child and his beloved wife. Several times, he had to do everything in his power to hold himself back from knocking down the door that separated him from the woman he loved.

Finally, after the sun had sunk below the horizon, he heard the beautiful sound of a baby's cry. Like her mother, the cry was only a whimper, but it was clear to Richard that the baby was alive. After several minutes, the door was opened and Richard entered the room. Mamie was sitting up in the bed, holding her little baby girl. Richard rushed over to her and kissed her gently on the forehead. "Mamie, I'm so proud of you. I can't imagine how difficult this must have been."

For a few moments, Mamie didn't say anything, but smiled down at the infant leaning against her. In a soft voice, almost too quiet to hear, she said, "Richard, isn't she beautiful? I think she has your eyes and nose."

"Well, she definitely has your hair and complexion. Now, darling, we need to give our baby a name. Do you have any ideas?"

"No. What would you like to call her?"

Richard looked at the two most precious people in his life and said, "Her name will be Mamie, after the most beautiful woman in the world. But to keep it simple, let's call her Little May."

"Oh, Richard, that's so sweet."

Noise was heard from the foyer where neighbors and close friends had gathered. As the doctor left and declared that both the mother and baby were okay, a cheer rose up the stairs and into the bedroom.

"You have some friends here who would like to see you. I told them they had to wait until you thought you were up to it."

"I guess I can see them for a minute."

Richard left Mamie's bedside, walked over to the door and opened it up to a crowd of people. He looked back at Mamie, who was trying her best to smile. Before letting them in, he stated with a firm voice, "She's very tired. So please stay just a minute."

Several of the women approached the bedside and cooed and awed over the baby. Richard noticed Mamie grimace, which concerned him. "Okay, everyone, let's give her some time to rest. She'll be up and around in no time. Then we'd love to have all of you over to celebrate."

As the rowdy group left the room, one woman spoke up. "Mamie, you take care. If you need anything, please let me know. You have a beautiful baby."

Richard guided the woman out the door and escorted everyone down the stairs to the front foyer. Clarisse opened the large front door and everyone began to walk out. At that moment, Richard heard a strange noise come from Mamie's room. "I'll see you soon. I need to go up and check on my wife. Thanks for coming by."

As their friends were walking out the door, a sudden, rasping noise was heard from upstairs. Richard looked at Clarisse and the two of them ran upstairs, opened the bedroom door, and experienced the most horrific moment of their lives.

| 9 |

Richard (1885-1886)

It was hard to believe that Mamie was gone. The memory of that dreadful day was burned into the crevices of Richard's mind. It would be replayed thousands of times, always with the same outcome. His beautiful bride, the mother of his only child, was now lying in the cold hard ground.

Whenever Richard heard a guttural sound, his mind took him back to the stairwell that stood between him and Mamie. Maybe, if he hadn't escorted their friends out the door, he would've been there. To do something. Anything. Then maybe she would still be alive. If only?

Richard couldn't escape the haunting scene. It always began with the guttural sound and Richard lunging toward the staircase, each step a barrier between life and death. "I'm coming Mamie! I'm coming!" he yelled toward the bedroom door.

But once the door had swung open, Richard stood there in a state of disbelief. His beautiful Mamie was shaking all over with spew slipping out of her mouth. Her eyes were wide open, glaring at him. "Mamie, what's wrong? Clarisse, call the doctor! Someone, do something! Mamie, don't leave me! Don't leave me. Please, my love, don't go."

It was as if Richard and Mamie were on a stage, their group of friends watching from a distance, as Richard slumped over Mamie, weeping for the lifetime they were meant to have together. After an awkward amount of time had passed, Richard had to be pulled off the body. No one had ever seen him like this. Acquaintances, who had socialized together, were now worthless in this tragic circumstance, each one slipping away, not wanting to be a part of such a spectacle.

Richard was numb to everything around him. The only feeling was a cold chill circulating throughout his body, and he clung to it with his whole being. Nothing existed outside of his wall of grief. People would come and go, but Richard refused to let anyone come close or speak of the tragedy that he alone was living with.

His mind told him that he had a daughter who needed him, but his heart wouldn't allow him to draw close. The pain from Mamie's death had numbed his heart toward anyone, particularly a baby destined for suffering. He knew people would talk, but he just didn't care. He had sent a telegram to his sister, Nannie, to meet him at the train station in Durham.

As the train pulled close to the platform, with smoke swirling in the air, Richard spotted Nannie, standing alone. Just the sight of his older sister brought tears to his eyes, tears that were wiped away and commanded to never come again. He had to be strong and keep up the illusion of strength and power.

When Richard and Clarisse stepped onto the platform, Nannie walked up to them. "Richard, I don't have the words to tell you how sorry I am."

"Thank you for being here. I knew I could count on you."

"Miss Nannie, I'll be glad to stay as long as you need an extra pair of hands," Clarisse said.

"Thank you, Clarisse. I'd appreciate it if you could stay until the service and visitation are over."

Nannie took the baby out of Clarisse's arms and turned toward her brother. "Richard, I have a carriage here to take us to the house you purchased."

"Thank you, Nannie."

As they traveled to the house, Richard sat looking out the window. He knew this house would never be his home. He would set it up for his sister and his baby daughter. Nannie cleared her throat to get her brother's attention. "Richard, I need to let you know that Annie, Mamie's sister, came to see me yesterday. She was pleading with me to talk with you about her taking care of the baby."

"No. I don't want that. If you're willing, I want the baby to stay with you. I know you'll take good care of her."

"I appreciate you believing in me. Our sister, Lucy, also came to me asking if she could take the baby back to Greensboro. I told her I'd ask you."

"Again, no. I want you to take care of her. I'll probably be extremely busy in the near future and I want to know that my daughter is being cared for by the one person I trust the most."

"Richard, thank you for believing in me."

"No, thank you for being willing to put your life on hold and help me during this time."

When they reached the house, he climbed out of the carriage and walked up the steps. Once he opened the door, he looked at the dust on the furniture and cobwebs in the corners. A sinking feeling took over. This house was supposed to be where he and Mamie were going to raise their children. But, now it had lost all sentimental value. The house would work for Nannie and the baby to take up residence while he traveled for work, or until he could build a house that was more to his liking.

"Nannie, do you remember the night of Mother's burial?"

"Yes. There was a similar heaviness in the air. A wind of change had blown through then, as it has now. None of us knew then, as it is today, where the wind would carry us."

"Nannie, do you remember when you had me promise to take care of this family?"

"Yes, and I appreciate all you have done for all of us."

Richard looked down at the ground and had to brace himself. He was exhausted and knew he needed his sister's help. "I need you now. As much as I know I should be here for the baby, I can't."

Nannie sat still, causing Richard to wonder how the wind had come through, changing his course. Instead of living in New York with his wife and child, he was once again at a crossroads. But this time, the new direction was fueled by a burning anger; an emotion that needed to be directed at something or someone.

Richard hadn't been happy with how the partnership with the Dukes had evolved. Thoughts of injustice and being treated unfairly caused Richard to burn with anger. Spurred by the death of his wife, the grief, tangled with the actions of his business partners, caused Richard to react in a hostile manner which appeared totally out of character.

Bitterness had once again made its way into Richard's heart. Its tentacles wrapped around him, causing him to hold everyone at arm's length. Never again would he feel the hurt that the loss of

Mamie had provoked. He was finished with unnecessary emotions caused by others. Instead, he was more determined than ever to find his joy in business undertakings, which could be controlled and manipulated.

Richard had become fixated on leaving the Duke partnership. He no longer had the stomach to do business with Buck. He had spent the last four years traveling around the world selling cigarettes for the Dukes, and it was his turn to take the helm.

Richard's anger was sparked by the thought of the letter sent by Benjamin demanding that he contribute his own money back into the company. It appeared the W. Duke, Sons and Company was diversifying too quickly. Richard had no intention of putting another penny into the Duke's pockets. Instead, he would force them to buy out his interest in the company. If they didn't, he would look for another tobacco company to purchase his partnership, which would wreak havoc.

A fire had been lit in Richard's heart and, with the emotions of Mamie's death adding fuel to it, he made a decision that would change the course of his life. The day after Mamie's funeral, Richard arose, dressed in his business attire, and made his way to the W. Duke, Sons and Company building.

Walking through the door and onto the manufacturing floor, Richard noticed the men of Jewish faith hand-rolling cigarettes. He knew that cigarettes had become popular, exceeding pipe tobacco in sales. Even so, he didn't like that Buck hadn't sought his opinion, instead dictating himself the direction the company would take. And now, with the change from selling pipe tobacco to manufacturing cigarettes, more capital from the partners was needed; capital that Richard didn't want to invest.

As he climbed the steps that led to the offices, Richard sighed at the thought of the battle which would likely take place. The first door he approached was open and George Watts was sitting at his desk. He looked up and spotted Richard. "Richard, what are you doing here?"

"I had to come. There's nothing for me at home."

"I'm so sorry about Mamie. She was such a beautiful woman. I never would have expected that both Mamie and Emma would die so close together. You must be beside yourself with grief."

"Maybe so. But I've made a decision and wanted to approach you before I meet with Buck."

George Watts leaned back. "Why don't you pull up a chair and let's talk."

Richard sat down in the wingback chair that gave him a view of the train tracks and the W.T. Blackwell building. "You know that Buck and I don't see eye to eye on how this business should be run. I thought, by now, he would understand my views on the best course of action, but I can clearly see that he doesn't. So, this leads me to what I would like to ask you. Would you be willing to buy my interest in the company?"

George started to laugh. "That's so funny. Do you know I was going to ask you the same thing? I became a partner because my father thought this company would help establish my career. And it has, but like you, I don't feel that anyone listens to my advice, particularly Buck."

Richard stood up. "George, thanks for your honesty. I'm not sure what I'll have to do in order to dissolve my interest in the company, but I can promise you this, I'm going to do it."

Once Richard left George's office, he walked past Benjamin's closed door, then to the large office that Washington Duke had once occupied. Buck had redecorated the office to suit his taste, which, in Richard's opinion, was much too dark. Buck was sitting at his desk, dictating a letter to a young secretary. When he saw Richard leaning in the doorway, he addressed the woman. "Diane, you can go now. I'll call you to finish the letter in a little bit."

"Yes, Mr. Duke. I'll wait at my desk."

"Richard, come in. Given your circumstances, I didn't expect to see you for a while."

Buck could act the part of someone who cared about others, but Richard knew it was only a façade. He had heard him speak ill of too many people to trust his sincerity. "Buck, I've come to tell you that I want out of the company. I have sought representation and will do what I must to receive what I believe I'm entitled to."

Buck leaned back in his chair and took a cigarette from the desk drawer, lit it, and began to produce smoke rings. "These cigarettes have changed our position in the industry. A few years ago, we were barely able to sell our tobacco, and now we are becoming well-known throughout the world. Now, I know your willingness to go to all parts of the world to sell the cigarettes has helped our company. But it takes strong management for a company to succeed. You might not agree with my methods, but you know that I'm right when it comes to the direction we're taking."

"I've given my position in this company a lot of thought and have come to the conclusion that I can no longer work with you. I'm not going to justify myself to you or your family. I've given you my best, but I don't appreciate being told to give you money for a new factory. If you and your business partners are not willing to buy out my interest in the company, I'll find someone who will. I've been corresponding with several of your competitors. Maybe one of them will take advantage of my offer."

Buck looked right into Richard's eyes. His hands were clenched and Richard wondered whether the younger man was going to reach across the desk and hit him. "Have you lost your mind?"

Richard didn't flinch or take his eyes off of Buck. He was tired of being told what to do and, now that Mamie was gone, he didn't care how he was perceived. "No. Personally, I think I've finally awoken to the fact that I no longer want to work with you or anyone else.

I'll have my lawyer contact you about the terms I believe are fair to both parties."

Buck stood up and pointed to the door. "If you want to play it that way, I can't stop you. But I can promise you, like I've told all of my other competitors, I plan on putting every tobacco company out of business. So be prepared for battle. You can let yourself out."

If asked, Richard probably couldn't express why he felt so compelled to go after the Dukes through the court system. No matter the reason, he was determined to get the best settlement possible. If the Dukes wouldn't comply with his terms, he would sell his interest to someone who might possibly prevent the company from succeeding.

Richard's friends had never known him to act so maliciously. Even his sister, Nannie, couldn't convince him to drop the lawsuits. For months after Mamie's death, Richard couldn't be consoled or reasoned with. He had resolved to take revenge on the Dukes and there was nothing anyone could do to change his mind.

It didn't take long for word to reach other tobacco companies of the dissension between Richard and the Dukes. Peter J. Otey of the Lone Jack Cigarette Company in Lynchburg, Virginia, began sending postcards with invitations for Richard to come up and discuss a business arrangement. At first, Richard wasn't sure about the offer but, after several meetings, he began to see how this arrangement could benefit both parties.

Finally, after many months of negotiations between Richard's lawyer, John Hinsdale, and the W. Duke, Sons and Company, Richard received a check for $39,750 for his interest in the company. Immediately, Richard left Durham and moved to Lynchburg, where he became the primary shareholder in the Lone Jack Cigarette Company. Once again, Richard thought back on the lecture by Josh Billings and the words he'd spoken, "Young man, never grieve over spilt milk, but pick up your milk pail and go for the next cow." And that was exactly what Richard planned to do.

| 10 |

Richard (1886-1888)

In the months that followed, Richard became consumed with his newest venture. He spent less time in Durham, making his home in Lynchburg. With the W. Duke, Sons and Company in his rear-view mirror, and a fueled determination to succeed, he found it exhilarating to discover how effective he could be at the helm of a large company.

When Richard arrived in Lynchburg with the settlement from his lawsuit, he immediately started to think about how he could out-wit the Dukes. In 1881, James Bonsack had invented a rudimentary machine which could roll cigarettes faster than, and as effectively as, the workers hired to roll them by hand. The machine had its issues, but Richard believed it would dictate how cigarettes were going to be manufactured in the future.

The Bonsack Company was located in Lynchburg, Virginia. The company's president was D.B. Strouse, who owned the patent for the machine. Several of the individuals who held office in the Bonsack Company also held principal positions for the Lone Jack Cigarette Company. These two companies were known to collaborate on how to improve the effectiveness of the cigarette rolling machine.

Richard knew that this collaboration among companies would prove profitable for him if he could figure out a way to have access to as many machines as possible. But there was one major obstacle to overcome in order for this to happen. W. Duke, Sons and Company had already worked a deal with Strouse that gave them the right to the majority of Bonsack machines, as well as the expertise of a mechanic by the name of William T. O'Brien. Even though there were many flaws with the machine, O'Brien's ability to work out the flaws gave the Dukes an edge over all of their competitors.

Before leaving W. Duke, Sons and Company, Richard had had a conversation with Buck about the deal between Strouse and the Dukes. Buck told Richard that they had agreed to pay a royalty to Strouse of twenty cents for every thousand rolled cigarettes. During the conversation, Buck made it clear that all other tobacco companies should be charged at least twenty-five percent more. Richard wasn't sure how he would use this information, but believed it could benefit him in the future.

Now that Richard knew how much the W. Duke, Sons and Company was paying Strouse, he would do whatever he could to underbid it. As the principal stock holder of the Lone Jack Cigarette Company, Richard persuaded Strouse to agree upon a fifteen cents per thousand deal. As much as Strouse advised against the arrangement, Richard's persistence won out.

During the mid-1880s, the W. Duke, Sons and Company was selling the most cigarettes in the world. But Richard knew that Buck wanted more. Buck had his sights set on sucking up every small tobacco company, and believed the use of the Bonsack machine was the way to achieve that goal. In order to do this, Buck wanted to own as many Bonsack machines as possible to keep them out of the hands of other factories. This way, the W. Duke, Sons and Company could produce more cigarettes in the most cost-effective manner possible.

Understanding the importance of the cigarette rolling machine, Richard sent several letters to James Bonsack to discuss purchasing shares of stock in his company. A deal was set between the two men for Richard to purchase twenty-five shares at the cost of $125 per share. With partial ownership of the Bonsack Company, and principal shareholder of the Lone Jack Cigarette Company, Richard believed he was setting a solid foundation for his future.

In late October 1886, Richard plowed forward with business ideas humming in his head. Now that he was in Lynchburg, he formulated a plan on how to involve his brother, Thomas, in his business undertakings. One brisk day, they met in Durham at the tobacco warehouse owned by E.J. Parrish. Farmers from all over the Piedmont of North Carolina had ventured to this location, hoping for a good price on their product. As the two brothers walked by the hogsheads of tobacco, Richard stopped, never taking his eyes off of the piles of cured tobacco. "Thomas, now that I'm in Virginia, I need someone here in Durham to purchase leaf tobacco. I experienced success before I became a partner with the Dukes, and believe, with your help, that I can reestablish my own tobacco business. I want you to consider becoming a tobacco broker. Lone Jack Cigarette Company can be your first client and I'm sure that, with my name, you can find other companies that will hire your services."

"Richard, I really don't know that much about buying and selling tobacco."

"Don't you worry about that. You can learn all you need to know by spending time right here, listening and paying close attention to experienced brokers. I will finance building a prize house for storing the tobacco. All you need to do is solicit companies for your services."

"I think I can do that."

Richard picked up a golden-colored leaf and rubbed the rough surface between his fingers. "You can call the business T.D. Wright and Company. Most of the tobacco companies in the country will recognize our last name and trust your expertise."

As Richard turned to leave, he spotted E.J. Parrish walking toward them. "Well, if it isn't Richard Wright."

"Hello E.J., I'm not sure if you have met my brother, Thomas." E.J. held out his hand and gave Thomas a strong handshake.

Richard spoke up. "E.J., Thomas is going to open up a brokerage firm. If you can help him learn to spot the best tobacco, I'd appreciate it. I believe he'll eventually be an asset to, not only the Lone Jack Cigarette Company, but to you as well."

"Thomas, I'll be glad to assist you. Come back in the morning and I'll introduce you to the other brokers, as well as the farmers who have the highest quality leaf tobacco."

"Thank you, sir."

"So, Richard, how is Little May and your sister, Nannie?"

"Nannie is doing well. Little May continues to have a hard time. She's been seen by Dr. Glenn, a physician in Greensboro. He's concerned about her liver and has been treating her with mercury. I'm not sure if he is making her any better, but I need to trust Dr. Glenn. Nannie has been taking good care of her along with my sister, Lucy. And how about your lovely wife, Rosa. How is she doing?"

"Busy. She loves to be involved in Durham's civic activities. I can't say who is busier, her or myself." E.J. looked into Thomas' eyes. I'll plan on seeing you in the morning and we will give you an education in one of the most prosperous businesses today."

Thomas looked at E.J. and responded, "Thank you, Mr. Parrish. I'll be here."

For the next several months, Richard spent most of his time in Virginia, while Thomas strived to build his brokerage business in Durham. With information learned while being a partner with the Dukes, Richard began to work on a patent for a cigarette holder, similar to the patent held by Allen & Ginter. The holder would be unique, having a little piece of carbon on the end. The cigarette would ignite when the piece of carbon brushed up against a specially made box that was included with the purchase of the cigarettes. After a consultation with James L. Norris, a patent attorney in Washington D.C., Richard pulled back from going further with this project.

Over time, it became clear to Richard that The Lone Jack Cigarette Company could never compete with the W. Duke, Sons and Company. So, being the world traveler that he was, Richard adjusted his sales plan. Instead of selling cigarettes, he became an agent to sell the Bonsack machine. He knew that the Dukes had worked a deal with Strouse regarding the rights to selling the machine to other tobacco companies in America, but Richard also knew there was an overseas market. With a solid plan in mind, Richard approached Strouse with an agreement that included Richard paying his own travel expenses to countries around the world. Once a machine was sold, and the shipping costs taken out of the profit, the two would split the difference. Strouse believed it was a strong offer and agreed to Richard's terms.

Unlike most businessmen of the late 1880s, Richard had a transoceanic vision. The years he had spent traveling around the world for the Dukes had prepared him for this new chapter of his life. During his travels in the early 1880s, Richard had established contacts in South Africa, Egypt, India, and Asia. His resume also included a keen sense of interacting with different cultures, in addition to his relentless work hours. Everything he had accomplished so far had brought him to this pivotal point. So, with high hopes and renewed determination, Richard left Lynchburg for a life across the ocean.

Before setting sail across the Atlantic, Richard wanted to ensure that his daughter would be cared for and her medical issues addressed. His sister, Nannie, had taken her position as Little May's caregiver very seriously, but he was the one who pursued the opinions of different physicians to address the ailments that constantly plagued his young daughter.

Even though Richard had never truly bonded with the fragile child, he was willing to provide her the best medical care in the country. He had sought advice from doctors up and down the Atlantic Coast, discussing the possibility of institutionalization, but his sister refused to consider this option. Since Richard had limited knowledge of what was actually wrong with the child, he had to trust physicians who prescribed medicine and procedures, such as electrical shock, which ended up causing more harm than healing.

On one such visit, Richard had come to Durham to take care of loose ends before heading overseas. He had woken early to Little May's cries, but waited for Nannie to attend to her before getting up. Once dressed, he walked out of his room and toward the open door where the whimpering child lay in a crib. Staring down at the frail child, he felt a twinge of guilt that made him feel sick to his stomach. Instead of going over to provide some comfort, he chose to turn and walk out of the room. He made his way to the dining room and picked up a folded newspaper, which was placed beside his breakfast plate.

Richard scanned the paper and was shocked at what he read. He couldn't help but ask how a man like William Blackwell could be so stupid? Several years earlier, he had read an article in the The Tobacco Plant, dated November 1886, titled "One Million Pounds of Tobacco Burned". The story reported a fire that had started at Atwater's store in Durham and extended in every direction, crossing Parrish Street, destroying two beautiful homes. From there, the flames reached the tobacco warehouse owned by E.J. Parrish. People who witnessed the fire had shared with him how the blaze had no mercy, destroying over one million pounds of tobacco, of which eight hundred pounds belonged to Parrish.

As Richard read the current article "A Big Smash" in the Raleigh Signal, dated November 23, 1888, he realized that the fire had been the first step in the disaster that was now occurring in Durham. The pieces of the puzzle were falling into place. The article reported a recent mob attack and the unlawful expulsion of Mr. Jordan, a liberal-minded man running for office. Mr. Jordan and his family were vehemently taken from their home and forced to leave Durham, due to Mr. Jordan's Republican Party affiliation. The article also made reference to the fact that, prior to the attack, the Durham Bank had been losing money, and had sought financial support from northern investors. Those investors, livid with how Mr. Jordan had been treated, were now demanding the return of their money.

If the mob had foreseen the results of their actions, they would've left this man and his family alone. But the damage was done. The Durham Bank was folding, leaving over fifty businesses bankrupt. Everyone in Durham had been under the illusion that the president and founder, William Blackwell, was wealthy enough to back the investors' money in the bank he had started in 1884. Blackwell and Parrish, two of the wealthiest men in Durham, had been the primary investors in the failing bank. Even though both men had been successful in earlier years, the bank had now failed due to Parrish's financial loss in the fire of 1886, and the lenient lending practices of William Blackwell.

As Richard was reading the last of the article, he heard a knock on the door. He wondered who could be coming to see him so early in the morning. "Nannie, can you get the door?"

"Yes, Richard."

A few moments later, Nannie walked into the dining room with a man behind her. As she turned to leave, Richard looked up. He was shocked to see William Blackwell standing in front of him. "William, what are you doing here?"

"Richard, I wanted to speak to you in person and let you know how sorry I am for the loss of your $4000."

"I don't know if I have time for this. I told you that you practically gave your interest in the William T. Blackwell Company away to the McDowell brothers. Then, you and Parrish put all your money into leaf tobacco and what happens? The warehouse burns down. I see here in this article that you borrowed money from a Northern Capitalist, and now, because some narrow-thinking conservatives kick the Jordan family out of Durham, they are asking for you to return their money immediately."

William clenched his hat. "I've always wanted to help people out. You know how it feels to lose your loved one. Ever since my wife, Emma, died, I just wanted to feel worthy of something. So, when people who were in dire straits asked for loans, I just couldn't turn them down."

"Yes, I do know what it is like to lose a wife, but it doesn't give you a license to be stupid."

William lowered his head and glanced down at the floor. Richard looked at him with no sympathy. He used to have respect for William when he was working with Julian Carr. The William T. Blackwell Company was recognized all over the world and the branding of the bull was ingenious. But now, Richard was becoming more agitated with this man standing in front of him. How could a man, who once demonstrated so much business sense, lose everything?

"I'm sorry. I know I made some bad decisions."

"Save it. Several businesses are bankrupt because of your bad decisions. And to make it worse, the people they employ will have nothing to support their families with this winter. Think about that when you decide to lend good money to people you know are unable to pay off their debts."

"I'm sorry, Richard."

"What do you want? I hope you aren't coming to ask me for money. If you want a handout, maybe the Dukes will give you one. Don't expect anything from me."

"No. I just wanted to personally apologize."

"Well, you have. Now you can go."

William turned and walked out of the dining room, leaving Richard with a bad taste in his mouth. He pushed his breakfast plate away, opened up the newspaper, and sighed. "What in the hell was that man thinking?"

| 11 |

Richard (1888-1889)

If Richard was going to risk his life traveling to the ends of the world, he knew he had to put numerous revenue streams into place. For several months prior to his departure, Richard pursued tobacco companies with offers to sell their tobacco for a commission. After receiving enough offers to ensure a profit, Richard turned his attention to planning his trip. Using the contacts he had made while working for the Dukes, he set his sights on the ones that appeared most promising.

In early 1888, following the agreement with Strouse and the promised commissions from several tobacco companies, Richard sailed on an Italian shipping line to Alexandria, Italy, where he then boarded a train to Cairo. Upon arrival, he met with E.J. Manuk, a British subject who had made Cairo his home for over twenty years. Over a two-week period, Richard and Manuk formed an agreement for the purchase of several Bonsack machines, paying Strouse twenty cents for every one thousand rolled cigarettes.

After leaving Cairo, Richard went to the Cape of Good Hope in South Africa where he made another successful deal to sell more machines. Tobacco sales were also strong and Richard had every intention of going further, but he received word from Nannie that Little May had become deathly ill. As much as he wanted to stay on his business course, Nannie, along with his brother and sisters, persuaded him to cut the trip short and return home.

Once Richard arrived home, he walked to the far corner of the house where he found his sister slumped over a child-sized bed. Exhausted, and spent of all emotion, he looked over the scene, wrestling with why he had come. Just as he turned away, his sister looked back at him and called to the child, "Little May, your father is here." The fragile child didn't appear to hear her aunt's words and made no attempt to open her eyes. "Little May, your father came a long way to spend time with you."

Richard was overcome with the urge to flee from this scene with all its similarities to the death of the only person he had ever loved. He quickly rationalized how worthless it would be to stay, while there were so many business deals to be made. As Richard looked toward the child, he noticed her shallow breathing and lack of movement. It was then that he decided to leave. As he turned to go, Nannie called after him, "Richard, where are you going?"

"I'm leaving. There is nothing I can do here. I've provided the best physicians and medical attention known to modern medicine. Anyway, I have other important business decisions that need to be addressed. Call me when she passes and I'll arrange for the funeral."

"But, Richard, this is your daughter!"

As Richard walked out the door and closed it behind him, he could hear his sister calling his name. Her pleas for him to stay made him more determined to leave. To go anywhere. Anywhere but here. His first stop was the Lone Jack Cigarette Company, where he finalized some business dealings with Strouse, and then took a stagecoach to Craig Springs, Virginia. He had visited the small mountain town before and found it to be a wonderful place to remove himself from work and any unwanted stress. The hot water springs were known for healing almost every ailment but, for Richard, the feeling of the rushing water massaging his body allowed him to relax and focus on his business undertakings. It was here that he received word of his only child's fate.

On August 26, 1889, A.T. Powell, secretary of the Lone Jack Cigarette Company, wrote Richard, passing on the information he had learned.

Dear Sir:

I was inexpressibly pained to receive the telegram which I forwarded to you on Saturday last, advising you of the illness of your child, but was very much shocked to receive the telegram on Sunday advising me of its death. Being a father myself, I can appreciate fully the blow that has fallen upon you. I had to bury my first born, after having nursed it for nearly two years and allowed myself to become deeply attached to it.

These blows, when they come, seem hard, and it is almost impossible to reconcile ourselves to the words of comfort that are poured into our ears by those who take the Scripture as their excuse for everything. You did not mention before you went to the springs that your child was at all sick, but from what you have told me at various times, I suppose that it is best, as it is, for the little thing has suffered and is now at rest. I forward you today several letters, as instructed in your note, which I got at the hotel.

I assure you of both the sympathy of myself and wife in your bereavement.

I am,
Very sincerely your friend,
A.T. Powell.

As Richard finished reading the letter, he sighed and placed the letter back into the envelope. He picked up a pen and paper and wrote a letter to Nannie, informing her of all the arrangements he had put in place for the burial of his daughter. He then returned to the springs and spent the afternoon contemplating his next business endeavor.

Richard returned to Durham just in time for the funeral. The service was closed to the public and only a few family members attended. Richard didn't speak, leaving the words of eternal life and the scriptures to the minister. From that point on, Richard never spoke of his daughter and forbade any conversation regarding her to take place in his presence. Nannie found this to be extremely difficult, due to the fondness she had had for the child, and broke her silence in a letter.

Buffalo Station, Va.

September 12, 1889

My Dear Bro,

I've reached here, very tired, late dinner yesterday. Found a good many familiar faces to welcome me, but oh how my heart was bleeding out to have my little darling with me. Everything made me think of her so much. Everything I see is so associated with her. I don't see how I can go on and on living without her. My only comfort is she is so much more comfortable. So much happier than I could ever make her.

Though I did all that was in my power to do for her, it is a comfort to know I never left her, but to do something for her that I would not trust her nurse to do. I never thought of my own feelings where she was concerned. It seems as if I had supernatural strength all her life. For I was always so frail and weak myself that even the loss of a few hours of sleep would make me sick. But all her life, I would be up night after night, and day after day, with only a few minutes of sleep, now and then, when she would sleep and never seem to feel it.

It seems as if God gave me strength. I hope he will give me strength to take up the burden of my sorrow and go on, this with a broken heart, through the rough stormy pathway of life. Till He is done with me here, I know my precious little thing will be awaiting and watching for her old aunt on the other side. Oh, how sweet will be the meeting.

She is safe, safely landed, where there is forever more. Safe from all the sorrow and suffering of this world. The little thing's mission was soon ended, her career short-lived. But the good she accomplished while living, only eternity will reveal. We know how many souls that little frail innocent lamb was the instrument of leading back to the Savior's fold.

Now from the skies we see and hear a sweet childish voice saying "Come this way". A sweet childish hand beckoning this is the way, "Come this way." Oh, her little life was so short and she so afflicted. The good she did by living will live on till time shall be no more. "What I do then knowest not now, but shall know hereafter." We will know some day why she was as she was and why she was taken. But that little hand will ever be beckoning from the skies.

Mail is ready to start, must close. Mrs. Snow sends love, says she'll write in a few days. Says she thinks she'll feel better over time. I think I feel a little refreshed. Must close.

Your Sister,
Nannie

| 12 |

Washington Duke (1890)

Washington sat on the back porch of the house he shared with his daughter, Mary, and her husband. It was a beautiful spring day in 1890 and Washington was reading the paper, while sipping a cup of coffee, before heading to the office. The mornings were a perfect time to sit out on the screened porch and listen to the birds make their distinct mating sounds, all while he and his daughter discussed the news they read in the paper.

Life hadn't turned out the way Washington Duke had envisioned. He had hoped that, after selling his business interest to Richard Wright, he could rest easy and enjoy a quiet retirement surrounded by friends and family. But that was not to be the case.

After Richard had returned in 1885 from selling tobacco all over the world, he became incessant in his demands to have more say in how the company was run. Heated arguments ensued, leading to both parties obtaining legal representation. After Washington's sons informed him of the dissolution of their partnership, Washington knew he had to go back to work.

It had been five years since Washington returned to his office and to the board of directors for the W. Duke, Sons and Company. He had given over most of the responsibilities for running the business to his sons and George Watts. Buck's drive and determination to create a monopoly naturally put him in the position of president. All Washington needed to do was to show up and give his input when asked. Realizing he wasn't ever going to retire, the old man made the most of his role in the company.

Washington heard his daughter gasp and then looked up to see her walk around to where he was sitting. She took a section of the paper and placed it in front of him. "Daddy, look at this."

"What does it say?"

"People from all over North Carolina are singing your praises."

"Now, why would they be doing that?"

"Daddy, you gave $85,000 for the building and endowment of Trinity College. People in this area of the country have never known someone to be so generous."

"Now, Mary, I've been blessed and know that it's not right to hold onto my money. I believe the Lord wants me to set up a Methodist college to educate people with Christian values. I'm just glad to be able to ensure the college is going to be right here in Durham and not in Raleigh."

"You and Julian Carr make me want to laugh at your insistence of keeping Trinity College out of Raleigh."

"Julian and I don't see eye to eye on a lot of topics, but we can come together concerning the importance of building a college that will attract people with strong educational values to our city."

"I did hear from some of the women in my bridge group that he's trying to sell his interest in the William T. Blackwell Company for over $3,000,000."

"Well, I wish the best for him. But if your brother, Buck, has anything to do with it, I don't think his company is going to be worth that much."

"Why do you say that?"

"Well, as you know, we're no longer the W. Duke, Sons and Company. Just a couple of weeks ago, we bought out the tobacco companies of Ginter, Kinney, Emory, and Kimbrall, and are now incorporated as The American Tobacco Company. We now own more factories and have just contracted with the Bonsack Company for the exclusive rights of over one hundred cigarette rolling machines. No other tobacco company can match our production and eventually will have to concede or go out of business."

"So, I guess that means Buck is going to eventually get his wish of taking down the bull."

"It appears that way."

"Well, I doubt Julian is going to sit idly by while you bring down his company."

Washington took a sip of coffee and put the paper down. "What do you mean by that?"

Mary smiled at her father before speaking. "Well, you know that my bridge group doesn't just play bridge."

"I assumed that."

"Word has it that he has been corresponding with Richard Wright, encouraging him to return to Durham to help with growing our city."

"That's one man who I'd rather never see again. He's been a thorn in my side ever since we decided it was best for all of us to go our separate ways. I have to admit that I respect him for being willing to go to the far ends of the world to sell Bonsack machines, but his days are numbered. We're hiring the most competent mechanics for our factories and can pay them far more than he can offer to have them leave their home for the Philippines or Cairo."

"Now, Dad, don't get too worked up."

"I'm okay. Hopefully, he'll stay in Lynchburg or get on the next ship to Europe."

"So, getting back to your donation to Trinity College. Where's the college going to be located?"

"Word is that the land William T. Blackwell donated as a park will be used for the first couple of buildings."

"That's a beautiful piece of property. I can't wait to see it once it's complete."

Mary began to smile and Washington looked over at his daughter. "What's so funny?"

"Dad, I just thought of something."

"I can't imagine what thoughts are going on in that head of yours."

"Wouldn't it be amazing if one day you have a college or university named after you?"

Washington gazed at his paper and after a moment spoke, "Now, Mary, don't be foolish."

| 13 |

Richard (1890-1892)

Richard took his time walking down Main Street. He lowered his head when spotting familiar faces, trying his best to avoid any unnecessary small talk. In his mind, he was contemplating his newest venture and didn't want to be interrupted. For the last few years, he had been occupied with selling the Bonsack machine to foreign countries. He had successfully placed the machine in several cigarette factories in Africa and Asia, but was now responsible for servicing them.

The Bonsack machine was complicated, and its setup nearly impossible, without a trained mechanic who understood how the apparatus worked. Richard was fortunate to have worked directly with several of these mechanics in Lynchburg. One particular man, by the name of W A Hulse understood the intricacies of the Bonsack machine, and even more appealing, he didn't balk when asked to travel far distances to work on them.

The young man had no idea how long he would be gone or the challenges he would face, but with Richard's financial support, and the promise that his wife would receive a monthly check, Hulse boarded a ship and made his way to Malta, Cairo, Bombay, Shanghai, and other African and Asian cities. The travel was brutal, and the languages impossible to understand. Each destination had its own unique challenges, particularly when the machines were damaged or needed parts from America.

Hulse sent frequent letters to Richard's desk, asking for parts and other assistance to ensure the machine's success. As time went by, Hulse not only fixed the machines, but also created a crimping device which eliminated the use of paste.

When Buck Duke heard that Richard's mechanic, Hulse, was seeking a patent for the crimping device, he hired lawyers to interfere with the process. Buck was determined to deny Richard, or anyone working for Richard, the opportunity to develop a cigarette rolling machine with the application of the crimping device. To ensure that the American Tobacco Company would retain the rights to the machine, their secretary, William Butler, submitted a patent for the crimping device within days of Hulse's application.

Richard was furious over the interference, but had no time to sulk. He had been busy working on a different machine, one he believed could bring him the wealth and success he desired. With a patent in hand, Richard reached the entrance of The Fidelity Savings and Trust Company, swung the doors open, and walked in. A fluttering of emotion came over him at the prospect of his new venture taking shape.

The receptionist in the lobby greeted him. "Hello, Mr. Wright. What can I do for you today?"

"Hello, Dorothy. I'd like to speak with Mr. Angier."

Dorothy got up from her desk and knocked on the door behind her. "Mr. Angier, Mr. Wright is here to see you."

A muffled voice was heard behind the door. "Please send him in."

"Mr. Angier will see you now."

"Thank you, Dorothy."

Richard turned the knob and walked into the spacious office. Malbourne Angier got up from his desk and walked toward Richard, extending his hand. "Richard, I didn't know you were in town. I thought I heard from Julian Carr that you were visiting some exotic city abroad."

"Malbourne, as exotic as my travel may sound, it usually isn't. The food isn't what I'm accustomed to and the traveling can be exhausting."

"Well, Richard, what can I do for you?"

"Malbourne, I need some financing. As you know, I've been selling the Bonsack machine overseas. My sales are strong, but I'm not content to just settle on being a salesman. When I was in Gainsborough, England, I made a discovery that I believe will change, not only the tobacco industry, but other industries as well."

"Well, you've got my attention," Malbourne said, as he leaned over his desk.

"One day, I was doing some window shopping and I saw this." Richard pulled a small box full of cigarettes from his pocket. He passed it to Malbourne, who took the box and turned it over in his hand.

Richard waited a moment, to allow Malbourne to understand the significance of this small package. "Yes, the Dukes are now on their way to swallowing up all the small tobacco factories. Soon, Buck will take over all the manufacturing of cigarettes in the United

States. And, yes, they also have the rights to the domestic sales of the Bonsack machine. But, this little box will change how cigarettes are purchased, and I'll be the one who owns the rights to the machine that manufactures it."

"I've never seen anything like this. I like the idea of having a box that labels the cigarettes instead of using a small bag. I know I'd be more likely to purchase a pack of cigarettes verses a bag. So, what can I do for you?"

"When I was in Gainsborough, I met with William Rose, who engineered the development of the package. After some negotiation, I was able to make an offer to gain the rights to build the machine that produces it. I'd like to take out a loan to pay for the production of the machines."

"I'll need to speak with my partners in the bank, but I think we can work something out."

Richard waited a moment and then added, "This box has endless possibilities. I've spoken to a soap company that's interested in purchasing boxes for their product." Richard watched as Malbourne turned the package over and over in his hand. "And I can promise you that this is just the beginning of how this product can be used."

Malbourne sat back in his chair and Richard could see him pondering over what he had just shown him. "Richard, I've known you for many years and have seen how determined you are to be successful. I think this is a great idea and I'd love to provide a loan for your new business. Let me present it to my partners and I'll get back with you as soon as I have an answer."

Richard stood up and reached over to shake Malbourne's hand. "I'll get specifics for you and we'll go from there."

"Oh, Richard, I wanted to let you know about William Blackwell."

"You know my feelings about him. He had every opportunity to make a fortune when he sold his shares of the W.T. Blackwell Tobacco Company. I told him then, and I still believe it today, that he could've gotten at least $300,000 for his interest, instead of the $100,000 he received from M. E. McDowell and Company. And then, he was outright foolish to open a bank and use his own money to finance loans that couldn't be paid back. So many people in Durham were hurt when he had to close the bank. Just last week he sent me a letter asking for $1,000. Now, why he thinks I'd hand over my hard-earned money to someone who will just spit it away is beyond me."

"Now, Richard, I can understand your point of view, but I just heard from Julian Carr that William is deathly ill and I think it would be nice of you to go by for a visit."

Richard took a deep breath and grunted. "I do appreciate how he introduced me to Mamie. But after her death, and the death of his wife, Emma, I haven't had much to say to him. Anyway, I have no time for sentimental visits. My hands are full with taking care of my present business ventures."

And with that, Richard turned around and walked out of the door with Malbourne shaking his head.

For the next two years, Richard spent months at a time traveling back and forth to England to meet with the Rose Brothers. Once the majority of the kinks in the package machine were worked out, and the legal rights to the business in Richard's possession, he began to sell the machine to the many contacts he had acquired over the past decade.

As busy as Richard was with the sale of the package machine, he wasn't willing to settle down. He loved the hunt for new businesses and the endless possibilities of how he could experience the success his counterparts were having. Just thinking about the Dukes, and their newly acquired fortune, made Richard angry, but it also served as a poker to probe him to work harder.

For some time, Julian Carr had been corresponding with Richard, asking him to move to Durham and form a partnership.

Initially, Richard had discussed building another cotton mill, but Julian had other plans. After several incessant letters, Richard decided to explore Julian's proposal.

It was a difficult decision for Richard to make. He had established a solid reputation in Lynchburg from his work with the Lone Jack Cigarette Company, and was striving to get every red cent he could out of the company before it folded. He didn't want to admit defeat to the Dukes, but knew it was only a matter of time before the Lone Jack Cigarette Company, and all the other small factories, would be swallowed up by the American Tobacco Company.

But there was another reason why Richard wanted to stay in Lynchburg. A young woman by the name of Lizzie Winfree had made an impression on the middle-aged man. She enjoyed Richard's company, but wasn't interested in moving. He knew if he left, he would probably never see her again. It was a difficult choice, but Richard's determination to be successful outweighed his desire for love.

Once Richard returned to Durham, he couldn't help but notice the new development in and around the small township. Trinity College was being built, along with the new American Tobacco Factories. There were several cotton mills under construction and houses were going up everywhere. But what surprised him the most were the number of people who filled the streets. Both blacks and whites had moved to Durham, striving to claim their own piece of the pie.

Richard rode his horse down Main Street and headed toward Dillard Street, where Julian Carr's residence, Somerset Villa, had just been completed. He tied his horse to a post and walked up to the massive door. As he looked around, he imagined himself in a house just like this one, but with even more grandeur.

Richard knocked on the door, stood back, and peered around. The mansion that Julian had built was tastefully done. Julian had hired well-known architect, John B. Halcott, from Albany, New York, to design and build the house. He was standing in awe of the grounds when the door opened. A butler with a neat, clean suit stood in front of him. "Can I help you?"

"Yes. Can you please let Mr. Carr know that Richard Harvey Wright is here to speak with him?"

"Please, step into the foyer while I go and see if he is available to take company."

Once the butler slipped into the hallway, Richard looked around and noticed the large portraits hanging on the walls. A crystal chandelier hung from the ceiling and imported pieces of furniture were intentionally placed along the sides of the space. Julian walked around the corner and approached him. "Richard, what a nice surprise. Come into my office and let's talk."

Once they were seated, Julian opened up a bag and pulled out two cigarettes. After offering one to Richard he asked, "So, you have finally come to your senses and returned to Durham?"

"Julian, you know that I'm always open to a new project. Tell me what you have in mind."

"Richard, I know you have your mind set on opening up another roller mill here in Durham. Well, I must say that we lost money like a shot out of a shovel on our Mebane Mill. I think it had to do with poor management, but also we didn't have the right outfit."

Richard leaned in and asked, "So, if you don't want to invest in a roller mill, what do you want to do?"

Julian took a long drag off of his cigarette and looked at Richard. Before speaking, he exhaled the smoke into the air. "If you want, I can invest $1,000 into your roller mill. All of my ready cash has been depleted by my various investments across the state. I invested in the Atlantic Hotel in Morehead and put some of my money in Cherokee County, but neither have paid me back."

"Okay, Julian, I'm willing to look beyond the roller mill."

"Look, I want a bright, reliable, enterprising businessman like yourself to help me push Durham. Carrying the load almost alone, I've grown weary and tired."

Julian took a puff from his cigarette and continued, "Five years ago, the Durham Street Railway Company was formed to provide local transportation to the citizens of Durham. I've heard discussions about an extension of their rails north of Trinity College. At this time, the land is for sale and, I believe, if we acquire it, we can subdivide it and make a profit."

"I like what I'm hearing. Please continue."

"I'm proposing that we form a company for the sole purpose of taking over the land companies around Durham. I can take the $15,000 you are proposing for your rolling mill and make a heap more money than you are going to make out of a roller mill, and make it a heap quicker. Once we are profitable you can establish the mill, in addition."

"I like the sound of this."

Julian rose and looked out the window. "It'll take your $15,000 in cash to run the matter for six months, but after six months, I think we'll have realized over and above all the expenses, anywhere from $30,000 to $60,000. Eventually, I think we can build two factories, a good hotel, a bonded warehouse, a public schoolhouse, a Y.M.C.A. building and a hospital. Of course, once this happens, we will donate the hospital to the town."

Richard leaned in. He liked what Julian was proposing and was already thinking about how he could prosper from this arrangement. "So, what were you thinking about calling this new company?"

"The Durham Consolidated Land and Improvement Company. What do you think?"

"I must admit it sounds pretty ambitious."

"I'm sure it does, but once we start obtaining the land and selling it, we'll immediately see a profit."

"Julian, I've always been impressed with how you've done business and believe we can make a profit."

"Sounds good. Now tell me about your recent travels. Every time I see your sister, Nannie, at a social function, she tells me where you are. Is it true that you've been to Shanghai?"

"Yes. I've also spent time in Manila and Cairo. All beautiful places, but none of them can compete with what is happening right here in Durham."

"You're so right. Every day, people are moving here for the manufacturing jobs. With Trinity College beginning classes next year, there are endless possibilities of ways to prosper. As the president of The First National Bank and the Golden Belt Manufacturing Company, I have the financial backing and contacts we will need to move forward."

The two men began their business with the purchase of two hundred, eighty-six acres north of Trinity College. But after the lots were subdivided into fifty-six blocks, the development stalled because of the failure of the Durham Street Railroad Company to lay rails northward. Without transportation, the area sat dormant for longer than the two men had expected.

Over time, two very distinct neighborhoods were developed from the property purchased by the Durham Consolidated Land and Improvement Company. Initially, the large lots that lined the streets bordering the college were sold to college professors. Expensive homes with ornate features and large pillars lined the neighborhoods, and would later be referred to as Trinity Park. The second area of land was called Walltown, where poorly constructed homes were built for the influx of workers who came to Durham with very little money in their pockets and a need for a roof over their heads.

Initially, the Durham Consolidated Land and Improvement Company did not do well. With land development at a standstill, and the railway stopped due to litigation, it appeared that the men would suffer a loss on their investment. Richard and Julian knew that a form of transportation was needed to reach their undeveloped land, so they purchased a trolley system from Penn Construction Company. At the time of purchase, the trolleys were in need of repair and, even though Julian wanted them refurbished, Richard wouldn't give up more of his money for the work.

After years of neglect to the trolley tracks, the city threatened Julian and Richard with removal of the tracks if they didn't fix them. Wooden wagon wheels were often damaged by the unsightly tracks that lined the streets of Durham. Richard made promises to comply, but never did. Finally, a compromise was reached between the city and the company. The company could keep the franchise if they would reorganize and operate an electric streetcar system.

In 1901, Julian and Richard deliberated how to incorporate the trolley system into their present business, the Durham Consolidated Land and Improvement Company. Given that their present company focused primarily on the purchasing and selling of land, they decided to dissolve it and begin a new company, which they called the Durham Traction Company. The development of a transportation system, as well as an electric company, could easily fall under this new title.

By this time, Richard had experienced both success and failure in the business world. Offsetting his failures was the success from the overseas sale of the Bonsack machine and his newest venture, the development of a machinery company that made packets for cigarettes, which easily covered his losses from a few poorly performing acquisitions.

When Richard left England with the rights to the machine produced by the Rose Brothers, he knew he was on to something. As he was returning from overseas, Richard was quoted as saying, "Coming across the Atlantic Ocean right now, gentlemen, are machines which will automatically package your tobacco in a protective attractive packet." And, sure enough, after selling his first machines to the P. Lorillard Cigarette Company, news spread and Richard obtained contracts from the most prestigious cigarette brands in the United States.

Richard's deep pockets didn't give him the peace he desired on a personal level. After leaving Lynchburg, and any possibility of love, he turned his attention to taking care of his family members. He believed, that by helping them, he would feel a sense of accomplishment that was lacking in his life. His support might also have come from a sense of guilt or been a way to establish power over others.

No matter the reason, Richard was known for his generosity, particularly among the men he saw potential in, as well as several of his relatives. His nephew, Wright McCord Ball, attended the University of North Carolina and was only able to stay in school due to Richard's willingness to pay his bills. McCord was a good student and his only focus was on becoming a physician. Even so, Richard expected complete honesty with how his money was being spent. McCord was required to keep an exact record of where every penny went and send letters to Richard with the details of his expenses. McCord didn't know how much he was at his uncle's mercy until he sent Richard a bill for the purchase of cigarettes. Richard was furious and threatened to stop sending money. McCord apologized profusely, stating the cigarettes had been bartered for time with a tutor.

McCord's sister, Bettie, also benefited from Richard's wealth. She had her sights set on living in New York and was only able to visit the big city with her uncle's assistance. This young woman had made a huge impression on Richard, which is reflected in his will from 1921. Instead of the $1000 per year that he willed to all of his other nieces and nephews, Richard specifically left her $2000 per year.

Richard also gave freely to other women in his life, even some who were no longer related to him. In October 1889, a letter was sent from Mamie's sister, thanking him for his gift.

Dear Bro. Richard,

I was prevented from writing to you every day while at Buffalo, although I thought of doing nothing with more certainty. I was right sick during the first four days of my stay there but after all improved a great deal. I have continued to gain strength since my return; I have a splendid appetite, and my digestion is perfect. I was perfectly delighted with Buffalo; the water was excellent, the fare was wholesome, nutritious and well served-while the honey was lacking, "the land flowed" with delicious milk. Mr. and Mrs. Mitchel, all the boarders, and last, but not least (under the circumstances) the servants were the personification of kindness.

Please let me thank you again and again for your thoughtfulness and generosity. I am under a debt of gratitude to you which can only be paid by love.

When will you sail? I trust this letter will reach you before your departure. How many a time I will think of you during your long absence and earnestly pray God to bless and prosper you and return you in health and safety to your friends and loved ones. If it is possible for Mr. Snow or I to serve you in any way, we will be most happy to do so-don't hesitate to call on either of us.

With love and many best wishes,

Yours hastily and sincerely,

Annie E. Snow

Richard knew he had done more than enough to ensure his brother, Thomas, a successful career. After the T.D. Wright Brokerage Company failed, Richard opened a bobbin factory for the cotton mills and placed him in a manager position. After only a few months of working in the bobbin factory, Thomas became deathly ill, and was unable to return to work.

Richard rarely visited his brother and didn't want to hear him go on and on about his miserable life. He believed his brother was weak and acted too much like a victim, instead of a victor. He had too many of his own business issues to deal with and didn't believe in coddling anyone, particularly a man who couldn't make a living for his family.

Finally, after months of Thomas being bedridden, Richard sought out a doctor in Raleigh who would treat Thomas for $40 per week. It was a lot of money, but Richard had no other choice. He knew that Nannie, and his sister, Lucy, would give him a hard time if he didn't come to Thomas' aid.

In January 1891, Thomas wrote Richard a letter from the hospital.

Dear Richard,

Dr. McKee was to see me a short while after you left and seemed to be surprised to see me looking so well. But I don't know whether he really thought it or thought it would affect my feelings. I notice but little change since leaving home. Except in my diet. Dr. McKee told my nurse to give me sweet milk, tea, light bread, cornbread, plain and in muffins, grits, oatmeal, corn meal batter cakes, celery, cold slaw with beef, chicken, cold ham, and Irish potatoes. I told him Dr. Glenn was very particular and didn't want me to touch potatoes.

Dr. McKee explained Dr. Glenn's reasons for his advice, but said it would not hurt me. Says good nourishing food was the medicine I most needed. And he prescribed a tonic to be taken after meals to aid digestion. I have eaten some of all the above articles. Feeling if they killed me, it would but shorten a life of misery anyway. For it seemed as if I would die. I have suffered no inconvenience from the food, more than when I was eating chicken alone.

I would be pleased if you would run down to my house occasionally when you have leisure and check on my family. You don't need to anticipate any trouble whatever. The people in charge here are extremely kind and see to try to do all they can for my comfort. Will write you again soon. Shall be glad to hear from you when you feel disposed to write.

Yours very truly,
Thos. D. Wright

| 14 |

Bettie (1885-1892)

Thomas and Bettie were married in a quaint church in Person County surrounded by friends and family. After the ceremony, the guests and wedding party attended a reception held at the Harris Plantation. Thomas' brother, Richard, was also present, but was noticeably quiet. Bettie appreciated Richard's willingness to travel from Lynchburg to attend his brother's wedding. She was well aware of the pain he was experiencing over the sudden death of his wife and decided to tread lightly in his presence.

Thankfully, Bettie's friends and family brightened up the occasion. Children were running around in their Sunday go-to-church outfits, while their parents were sitting on the front porch sharing stories from her childhood. Aunt Elizabeth's broad smile and giddy tone displayed how ecstatic she was to see her and Thomas exchange vows. The two women had become extremely close in the months leading up to the wedding and Bettie felt like she was not only going to have a husband, but also inherit a second mother.

Once the reception was over and the two women were in the kitchen cleaning up, the older woman put her dishrag down and looked at her niece. "Bettie, I've always wanted the two of you to get married. I've had several conversations with Thomas over the years. He has always loved you, but because of your age difference, didn't feel right to court you when you were in your teens. He's a hardworking man who will do everything he can to provide for you."

"I believe that's true. As for you, Thomas and I want to make sure you will always be taken care of. Thomas appreciates how you and Uncle James brought him in and gave him a home. He loves everything about the country, from the freedom to ride for hours without seeing another person to working with the soil between his fingers."

"I know he does." Aunt Elizabeth sighed. "I hope the two of you can stay here, but I'm thinking Thomas' brother may have other plans for him."

The two women hugged and Aunt Elizabeth made her way to the back bedroom. Thomas came in from having a smoke on the porch and stood against the door frame of the kitchen, watching Bettie place the last dish away. Bettie looked up and smiled at Thomas. "So, Mr. Wright, are you ready to go to bed?"

"I think I am, Mrs. Wright."

"Would you like for me to carry you across the threshold?"

Bettie began to laugh. "Thomas, that won't be necessary."

Thomas moved across the room and pulled Bettie close to him. Before she could react, he lifted her up into his arms and carried her up the stairs.

A couple days after the wedding, Richard came to the Harris Plantation to speak to Thomas and Bettie. When his carriage arrived, Bettie greeted him at the door. "Richard, come in."

"Thank you, Bettie."

"I hope all is going well in Lynchburg. How is your sister, Nannie, doing as the primary caregiver for your daughter, Little May?"

"Nannie is truly enjoying her role as a mother to Little May. She left the other day to go visit my sister, Lucy, in Greensboro. I recently heard that they have been arguing about how to best meet Little May's needs, but I've given Nannie the authority to act as she sees fit."

"I think that's a wise idea."

At that moment Thomas walked into the foyer and shook his brother's hand. "Richard, what brings you out to Person County?"

"I have a proposition for you."

"Let's go into the parlor and sit down."

"Sure."

Thomas leaned back in a chair across from his brother. "So, what are your plans for the Lone Jack Cigarette Company?"

"I've been giving the development of this company a lot of thought. I'm pursuing this opportunity for one reason and one reason only."

"And what is that reason?"

"The Lone Jack Cigarette Company is directly linked to the development of the Bonsack Machine. Both companies have been working closely together to make the Bonsack Machine as efficient as possible. If I become the principal stockholder in the Lone Jack Cigarette Company, I will have an inside line on the Bonsack Machine. I know the Dukes have leased as many Bonsack Machines as they can get their hands on and I want to put a stop to that. But in order to do this, I need someone in Durham to purchase tobacco for my company. That's the reason why I'm here. I'd like to offer you a position in my company."

"Richard, that's very kind of you, but I personally like the life we have here in the country."

"Thomas, I need someone who knows good tobacco when they see it. This person needs to be someone who will correspond with me when I'm overseas. Someone to write checks and be in charge when I'm away. I'd like for you to move to Durham and be my right-hand man. I'll make it worth your while."

"Thank you, but I'm not sure."

"Thomas, I need you." Richard looked around the room and continued. "This is an okay life, but I promise if you come to Durham, you'll be able to live a comfortable life that you and your young bride will thrive in."

Richard looked over at Bettie. "Wouldn't you like living in a town that has a market down the street and restaurants you can walk to?"

"That would be nice, but I'm happy here." Bettie paused and looked from Thomas to Richard before continuing. "But I'll support whatever Thomas decides."

"Well, I know I need you, Thomas, and I can promise I'll do everything to make sure you're successful in Durham."

Thomas looked over at Bettie before speaking. "Well, if you need me, I guess I can move."

Richard turned and faced his brother. "Good. Now that this matter has been settled, I'll send a crew to help move your things."

Richard stood up and walked over to the door. "I'll let myself out."

Once Richard left the house, Bettie turned to Thomas. "Honey, you know I'll support you with whatever decision you make, but are you sure about this? Richard can be very demanding and I want to make sure you're able to live the life you want, and not fall under your brother's domineering control."

Thomas reached over and took Bettie into his arms. "My brother can be opinionated, but I do believe he has our best interest at heart."

Bettie looked up into Thomas' eyes. "I'm going to trust you with this decision. I just hope it turns out as well as Richard believes it will."

Once Bettie and Thomas moved to Durham, their lives changed drastically. Being a tobacco broker was hard work and required a lot of traveling between Durham and the neighboring towns. Discovering high quality tobacco at a low cost was difficult, particularly when there were other brokers with more money in their pockets. Very early on, Bettie could see the toll this position was taking on her husband. Instead of the carefree man she had married, Thomas was becoming reserved and moody.

One night after Thomas came home, and barely ate a bite of his food, Bettie spoke up. "Thomas, are you sure this is worth it?"

"Bettie, my brother needs me and, after all he has done for the family, I believe I can do this for him."

"I just hate seeing you so miserable. Please, talk to me. What's the matter?"

Thomas was slumped in the chair and began to mumble. "Bettie, Richard expects me to find good tobacco, but he doesn't trust me enough to purchase anything without his consent. I've missed out on some good opportunities because, by the time I write him in Lynchburg or God knows where in the world he might be, and get a response, the tobacco is already sold."

It upset Bettie to see Thomas this way, but she knew better than to speak ill of Richard. No matter how difficult he was, Thomas was extremely loyal toward his brother. So, she decided to change the topic in hopes of cheering Thomas up. "Thomas, I received a letter from Aunt Elizabeth this morning."

"How's she doing?"

"She writes like she's well, but I can tell she misses us. To be honest, I miss her as well. With you gone all day, I believe it would be nice to have her here."

"Bettie, I must admit that I miss her, too. The last time I visited her I noticed the plantation wasn't being kept up to her standards. It appears the men living on the grounds are taking advantage of her. She isn't making the money she used to from the crops and her cupboards were almost bare."

"Thomas, I believe she can be a help here and, hopefully, her pleasant disposition can give us something to smile about."

On a beautiful spring day, Bettie and Thomas traveled to Person County to visit Aunt Elizabeth. After they ate lunch, Thomas brought up the reason for their visit. "Aunt Elizabeth, Bettie and I have discussed your present situation and would like to invite you to come live with us in Durham. We believe you can help us, particularly when Bettie starts having children. I can never repay you and James for taking me in when I had nowhere else to go, but I'd like to try."

"Oh, Thomas, I can't impose. I'm alright. My workhand, Henry, checks on me on a regular basis and his wife has been helping in the house."

Bettie looked around the room and noticed it wasn't kept in the manner she remembered. "Aunt Elizabeth, Thomas and I have given this a lot of thought. We both want you to come and live with us. We have more room than we need and want to make sure you are provided for."

"Now, you two. I'm fine. I wouldn't want to be a bother."

Thomas spoke up. "Aunt Elizabeth, you are no bother. You are like a mother to me and I want you in our lives."

"Are you sure?"

And, without hesitation, both Bettie and Thomas responded, "Yes."

"Well then, I guess I'm moving."

Thomas rose and leaned down to give Aunt Elizabeth a hug. "Now, why don't you and Bettie go pack what you need for the next couple of days and I'll have Henry bring the rest of your things."

Bettie spoke up. "Aunt Elizabeth, I'm so excited. There are several restaurants that I believe you'll love, and did I tell you about the stores right down the street where you can purchase anything you need?"

After Aunt Elizabeth moved in, the two women could be heard laughing in the kitchen or sitting in the parlor doing needlepoint. Thomas continued to work long hours, but made a sincere effort to be home each night for dinner. Not long after Aunt Elizabeth moved in, Bettie realized she was pregnant. It was wonderful to have a mother figure living with her as the months passed. On November 2, 1886, Bettie delivered a healthy baby girl named Lila. Two years later, Bettie became pregnant again, and delivered another little girl by the name of Julia. Not long afterward, their first boy was born and Bettie was adamant that his name would be Thomas.

Life was hectic, and became even more so, when Aunt Elizabeth began courting Old Man Stone, an elderly gentleman from Chapel Hill. Her seventy years didn't stop her from believing she wasn't too old to marry. Thomas and Bettie were skeptical of the old man's intentions and hoped that time would resolve the situation. When Thomas shared the news with his brother, Richard wrote several letters in response, clearly stating his disgust over the idea of his aunt marrying at such an old age.

Bettie and Thomas often spoke to Aunt Elizabeth about their concerns, but no matter what either said, she was determined to marry. Then, one winter day, while the two women were doing needlepoint, Bettie noticed that Aunt Elizabeth wasn't as jovial as usual. "Aunt Elizabeth, I haven't seen Mr. Stone lately. Is everything okay?"

"I really don't want to talk about it."

Bettie considered speaking further, but thought it best to sit in silence and hope Aunt Elizabeth would tell her what was bothering her. A couple of minutes later, the older woman stopped stitching and wiped her eyes. "I feel like such a fool."

"Oh, Aunt Elizabeth, I'm so sorry. I know that Thomas and I have gone on and on about you and Mr. Stone. Please, forgive us. We only care about your welfare."

"Well, you don't have to worry about that man any longer. He has made it clear he won't be coming by ever again."

"Why? I hope we didn't say anything to offend him."

Bettie looked over at the older woman and saw tears rolling down her cheeks. "Apparently, he thought that since Richard has so much money that Thomas would also be worth a lot. He wanted me to demand that Thomas give payment, with interest, for all the years James and I took care of him."

Bettie began to simmer inside but bit her tongue. She knew Mr. Stone was a scoundrel and now she had a reason to believe it. "So, what did you tell him?"

"I told him I would never ask Thomas to repay me a single penny. James and I took care of him because we loved him. Anyway, I know you two don't have the $6,000 he thinks I'm entitled to."

Bettie looked around the room with the peeling paint and creaky floorboards. Every cent that Thomas received from his meager paycheck was spent on their basic needs. She couldn't imagine how they would survive if Thomas had agreed to pay his aunt even a small portion of what Mr. Stone was demanding. Bettie put her head down and picked up her needle to continue stitching.

Aunt Elizabeth stood up and placed her hand on Bettie's shoulder. "I love you and Thomas so much. This situation has hurt me deeply, but I've realized how much this family means to me. Thank you so much for bringing me to Durham and making me a part of your family. I promise there'll be no more mention of Old Man Stone or anyone else."

Months passed by and Bettie felt truly blessed to have her Aunt Elizabeth living with them. She enjoyed the evenings when Thomas made it home in time for dinner. But mostly, she loved her three children and her role as a mother. Lila was five, Julia three, and Thomas Jr., just one year old. The small children loved to play with each other, and most of the time laughter could be heard streaming throughout the house.

On a cold day in February, Bettie was watching three-year-old Julia in the front room. Lila was visiting a friend and Thomas Jr. was down the hall, taking a nap. Thomas was at work and Aunt Elizabeth was away visiting a relative. A constant fire was blazing in the fireplace, providing just enough warmth to take the chill out of the air. Julia was playing with her doll and Bettie was reading a book. A cry from the back room broke the silence. Bettie rose, knowing Thomas Jr. must be ready for a diaper change. Before leaving, she looked down at her three-year-old daughter. "Julia, I'll be right back. I need to check on your brother."

Bettie rushed back to Thomas Jr. and found him soaked. "Oh, Thomas Jr., what am I going to do with you? Let me get a clean nappy."

As Bettie was cleaning the mess and placing the dry nappy in place, she heard a bloodcurdling scream from the front room. She placed Thomas Jr. back in his crib and ran to find three-year-old Julia jumping up and down, covered with flames. Bettie took her long billowing skirt and grabbed her daughter, rolling her to the floor. "Mommy, I hurt! Mommy, I hurt!"

Bettie lay beside her daughter and screamed out. Tears sprang from her eyes as disbelief over the situation sunk in. A sickening feeling in the pit of her stomach caused her to have difficulty breathing. "How could this happen? My beautiful girl." As she lay beside her daughter, not daring to move, she heard a small exhale of air, and then there was silence.

Hours later, when Thomas came home, Bettie hadn't moved from the floor. Even though she was in pain from her own burns, she was paralyzed with grief.

After walking through the door and seeing his wife on the floor covering something from view he asked, "Bettie, what happened?"

"I only left for a minute. Thomas Jr. was crying and had a dirty nappy. When I left the room Julia was playing with her doll. I told her to stay away from the fireplace."

Bettie clung on to the body, hoping that this was all just a bad nightmare. But when she heard Thomas gasp, she knew it was true. Tears streamed down her face and she began to sob uncontrollably. Then, ever so tenderly, Thomas reached down and slowly pulled the body from Bettie's grasp. Bettie reached up, trying to find her way back to her daughter. But her despair had paralyzed her and she couldn't move.

Bettie watched as Thomas turned and carried the toddler's body to the back bedroom. A few minutes later, he returned and helped Bettie to her feet. With his arm wrapped around her waist, they made it back to their bedroom where Bettie climbed onto the bed. Exhaustion overtook her and she fell into a restless slumber.

When Bettie awoke she could hear hushed voices in the distance, conversations just out of reach. She wondered who was taking care of her children and tried to rise but was just too weak. She hardly remembered the doctor coming into her room and cleaning her wounds. She took some medicine and fell back onto her pillows, praying to wake from this nightmare.

For weeks, Bettie walked through life numb with grief. Over time, she changed her focus from the guilt and grief she felt whenever she thought of Julia, to being consumed with getting pregnant. One morning, after Bettie and Thomas made love, Thomas rolled over and asked, "Bettie, are you sure you want to get pregnant? Thomas Jr. is so small and Aunt Elizabeth needs to be monitored."

"You know how much I love being a mother. If I can have another baby to hold, I believe it will help alleviate my grief."

For a moment both of them were silent. Bettie wasn't sure what Thomas was going to say but then he smiled and, with a chuckle in his voice, declared, "Well, you know I don't mind helping with the process."

"Oh, Thomas, I love you so much."

The year 1892 brought both grief and joy when Lucy was born and Aunt Elizabeth died. The family was experiencing a roller coaster of emotions as they welcomed a child and buried the woman who meant so much to them. Bettie tried to put her sorrow in the past and spent all of her time being the best mother and wife she could be. But no matter how hard she tried, she felt her husband was slipping further and further away.

As the years passed, Thomas became more and more insecure. Richard's micromanaging of his decisions had only increased, making Thomas feel like nothing more than a yes man. He loved his children and Bettie, but the stress of raising so many children on such a meager salary began to take a toll on him. He felt like he could never do anything right and Richard's demands had increased his work hours until late into the night.

One night, long after Bettie had gone to bed, Thomas entered the bedroom and caught his foot on a side table, waking Bettie. "Thomas, are you okay?"

"No. I just hurt my foot."

"I'm sorry. Where have you been?"

"Where do you think?"

"I don't know. It seems like you are coming home later and later."

"Well, if my brother didn't make such demands of me, I would be home earlier."

Bettie could smell alcohol on Thomas' breath. She didn't want to bring it up, but was concerned about him. "Thomas, I love you."

"I know you do."

Thomas turned to kiss Bettie, but she turned away. "Thomas, I can smell alcohol on your breath. I know you're upset by the way your brother treats you, but you'll never be able to stand up to him if you're intoxicated."

"Well, it's the only thing that keeps me from thinking about what a horrible businessman I am. I'm not cut out for this kind of work. I never even thought about drinking when we lived on the plantation. I loved digging in the dirt and growing crops. I don't care about trying to organize my brother's business affairs. And, as hard as I try, he's never happy."

"I'm so sorry. Thomas, you are a wonderful father and a good man. I wish your brother could see that."

"All he cares about is making a sale. No matter how hard I try, it's never good enough. I'm just so tired all the time."

"Come, get in the bed with me."

Thomas laid down beside her, but instead of giving her a good-night kiss, he turned with his back to her and fell into a deep sleep. As Bettie lay there, a sense of helplessness came over her. She wanted to help her husband, but she also felt trapped. The plantation had been sold and the income from Richard was the only thing keeping food on the table and a roof over their heads. If only Thomas could have the confidence to break away from his brother's grasp.

The next morning, Thomas didn't get up from the bed. His breathing was labored and he slept for most of the day. Bettie thought he might be depressed, but when the days turned into weeks with Thomas too weak to rise, she sent a letter to Richard asking for his advice. Instead of responding, he sent over a doctor to check on him.

When Bettie heard the knock on the door, she rushed to open it. "Come in. My husband hasn't been out of bed in weeks and I'm concerned about him."

The doctor followed Bettie into the back bedroom and walked over to the bed. "Thomas, this is Dr. McKee. Can you hear me?"

"Doctor, is he going to be okay?" Bettie asked.

"How long has his skin been this color?"

Bettie looked down at Thomas who appeared to be in a deep sleep. "I noticed it about a month ago. He's been running a fever and suffering with chills."

"This looks like jaundice to me. Does he drink a lot?"

"Just recently, he has been drinking more. But the symptoms only started when he began working at the bobbin factory. He is working with different machines as well as chemicals."

"I'm not sure how to treat it. You should try to get him to drink water and chicken broth. Monitor him and, if he gets worse, let me know. Bettie, I wish I had more to offer but if his liver is damaged, there isn't anything I can do but wait and see."

Once the doctor left, Lila came into the room and sat down on the end of Thomas' bed. "Is Daddy going to be okay?"

Bettie looked into her daughter's eyes. "I really don't know. Let's hope so."

Lila went over and snuggled up to Thomas. "Daddy, please get better. I love you."

Thomas murmured something that Bettie didn't understand. "Thomas, what did you say?"

"I love you, too."

| 15 |

Richard (1891-1893)

Richard rarely found time for any type of amusement, but when he felt troubled or just needed fresh air, he enjoyed riding his horse across the fields of northern Durham County. When Richard and his horse galloped through the apple orchards or beside the rocky streams of the Little River, he would become one with the animal underneath him. These long rides evolved into a spiritual experience, leaving all of the negativity of the world behind.

One warm day in March, just as the daffodils were beginning to bloom, Richard took off from the stables and headed across the grassy meadows that covered his property. It had been a stressful week, peaking in an argument with Julian Carr over the condition of the trolleys owned by Durham Consolidated Land and Improvement Company. Durham city officials had also come to his office demanding something from him. Usually, disgruntled men didn't bother him, but their visit, coupled with his brother's incompetence, caused him to be consumed with anger.

On this particular day, Richard rode across the pastures into the forest that bordered his property. As he began the ride, his only focus was on getting in stride with his horse. After a few minutes, his thoughts drifted from the difficult decisions that needed to be made, to the beauty that surrounded him. The idea of how far he had come in life consumed his thoughts and a smile formed across his face.

Richard had ridden to the riverbank and was getting ready to turn back, when his horse reared up, causing him to fall to the ground. The animal raised up again, then came down with his hoof landing hard on Richard's left foot. Immediately, Richard experienced a sharp pain that started in his foot and shot up his leg. He tried to rise up off the ground, but was unable to place any weight on his foot.

After calling his horse's name, the large animal walked over to Richard and stood beside him. As Richard looked up, he could swear the horse was peering down at him with concern in his eyes. Richard took several deep breaths, grabbed hold of the stirrup, and raised himself up off the ground. He stood on one foot and stroked the horse's neck until the horse had calmed down. Richard then lifted himself up, transferring the injured foot over the back of the horse and trotted back to the stables.

For the next week, Richard applied a salve to his foot and used a cane to walk. After two weeks, the pain eased up and he was able to get around on his own. During this time, Nannie pampered her brother and tried to get him to stay home from work, but Richard refused. He had too many things to do and wasn't going to let a sore foot stand in the way of his next business venture.

Over the following months, the pain and swelling lessened, but never entirely went away. All of this changed in September, when one morning, Richard was unable to get out of bed due to the swelling and intense pain. "Nannie, I need you to come into my room."

"Yes, Richard. What's wrong?"

"Recently, the swelling in my leg has gotten worse. It doesn't look good and the pain is excruciating. Please call the doctor for me?"

When Richard moved the bedspread off his leg, Nannie was shocked. "Richard, this looks horrible. Why haven't you had someone look at it sooner?"

"Nannie, in the past, the swelling has gone down on its own, but not this time. I just assumed it would get better, but apparently not. Please send for a doctor."

Once Dr. Clark arrived, he was escorted into the room. He took one look at the leg and then looked at Richard and Nannie. "Can you tell me what you believe caused this condition?"

"Last March, I fell off my horse, and while I was on the ground, the horse stomped on my foot. For months, the pain and swelling would lessen, but never completely went away. The other day, it began to feel different, but I just assumed it was temporary."

"By the looks of it, it appears to be a very bad case of gangrene. The tissue in your foot and lower leg has begun to die and infection is spreading up your leg. Richard, we're going to have to amputate your lower leg as soon as possible."

Nannie gasped, as Richard looked down at his leg in horror. "There has to be another way!"

"I'm afraid not. It has gone way too long without treatment. If it isn't amputated, the infection will spread and you will die."

Nannie asked, "When can you do the operation?"

"I'm not skilled in the area of amputation and will need to call on Dr. James McKee to do the surgery. As soon as I can get in touch with him, I will send word."

Early the next morning, Dr. McKee arrived and performed the operation. He was able to stop the infection, which had extended right below the knee, but the pain following the surgery was excruciating. Richard was unable to leave his bed and knew that something was wrong, but every time he asked Dr. McKee for advice, he was told that it would get better with time.

In the days that followed the surgery, Richard allowed Nannie to help take care of his needs. The pain persisted and Richard was unable to move about. As difficult as it was, Richard tried to forget the pain by reading and responding to the flood of letters that came from his many business associates.

During the following months, Richard was racked with phantom limb pain, followed by hours of insomnia. It was during these nights, as he lay on his bed, that Richard battled feelings of hopelessness or outright anger. He hated being unable to attend to his business responsibilities and knew that he had to ask for a second medical opinion. He had heard about a doctor in Baltimore who specialized in amputations and called for him to come to Durham. Once the doctor saw Dr. McKee's work, he knew that Richard would need to come to Baltimore for a second surgery.

In late January 1892, Richard received a second operation. Almost immediately, he felt relief from the pain which had caused him such suffering. But Richard knew his ordeal was far from over. He refused to think of being stuck in a wheelchair for the rest of his life and was determined to learn to walk with a prosthetic.

As much as Richard wanted to be back home, he knew he had to stay in the hospital to receive the necessary physical therapy for his leg, and to learn how to walk again. In order to do this, he needed to have someone in Durham he could trust to take charge of his business. As much as he didn't like to ask for assistance, he believed he needed to ask his brother to help him. Thomas had just recently recovered from a lengthy illness and needed to be put to work. So, he wrote Thomas a letter asking him to come to Baltimore so they could talk.

The day that Thomas arrived, Richard was learning how to use crutches. The initial crutches he had received were too long, making it difficult for Richard to place weight on his right leg. Thomas was just walking into the room, when the crutches slipped out from under him. "Someone needs to make this crutch shorter!" Richard yelled out, causing a nurse who was assisting him to tremble.

"Now, Richard, there's no need to yell at this poor woman," Thomas said, as he walked into the room.

"I don't need your opinion either. You have no idea how difficult this has been."

"Well, the fact that you have asked for me to come assist you, tells me that it must be extremely difficult."

Richard sat down on the edge of the bed and waved the nurse out. "I've never been so frustrated in all my life. But I can tell you, Thomas, this is not going to stop me from accomplishing my goals. I've overcome every obstacle ever placed in front of me and I'll be damned if my leg will stop me now."

It was several months before Richard was released from the hospital and allowed to return to Durham. Even in his own home, he realized how difficult it was to maneuver from place to place. On occasion, the frustration would get the best of him, and Richard would reach for anything close by and throw it across the room. During one of these tirades, Nannie came running into the room as Richard was getting ready to throw a book.

"Richard Harvey, we will have none of this!"

"Nannie, I'm so frustrated!"

"I know you are. We all are. Now, I know you're upset, but you need to fight through this just like you have countless other times."

Richard was quiet for a moment, letting her words soak in. "Nannie, you're so right. I need to get myself up and learn how to walk properly."

"Now, that sounds like the brother I love and respect."

"Thank you. My pain has gotten the best of me. Please help me up."

As Nannie reached down for her brother to place his arm around her neck, Richard begun to think about the losses he had experienced and how his sister had been there for him. "Nannie, I don't know if I ever properly thanked you for taking care of Little May."

"Richard, as hard as it was, I will be forever grateful for those years. I know I'll probably never marry and have my own children. Taking care of your little girl was one of the most gratifying experiences of my life."

Over the next weeks, Richard fought off the depression and loneliness that preyed on his mind and soul. He refused to give up on the idea of walking again and standing up to the world. Each day he began with Nannie by his side, helping him balance the peg leg and cane. Over time, the sound of the peg leg scraping against the wood floor could be heard from almost every room in the house. Even though the scratchy sound was irritating to the ear, it was music to all who heard.

After several months of working with his peg leg, Richard acquired the independence he longed for. It was extremely difficult to navigate stairs or uneven surfaces, but Richard refused to succumb to being in a wheelchair. He knew people would treat him as a cripple if he acted like one. So, he made a decision to work as hard as he physically could, in order to be as independent as possible. And for the remainder of his life, he never allowed his disability to stand in the way of the goals he set for himself.

| 16 |

Richard (1894)

Richard lowered his head and placed it gently onto his desk. Over the past few months, he had been riding on the unending supply of adrenaline that coursed through his veins. So much had happened in such a short period of time, and Richard knew he had to act quickly, or lose out on the prosperity that he believed was rightfully his.

Since moving back to Durham, Richard had witnessed the expansion of the American Tobacco Company, with its assets growing to over $7,000,000. Just the thought of the Dukes succeeding without him drove him to contact as many lawyers as possible, in order to obtain a piece of their fortune. Richard had no qualms about his tactics or never-ending pursuit of what, he believed, he was entitled to.

The coolness of the November night, with its dreary rain and shortened hours, didn't help. The oil lamp cast barely enough light to work by, but Richard knew he had to get a couple more letters ready for the morning mail. Just as he was about to fall asleep, he heard the light footsteps of his sister, Nannie, shuffling across the old pine floors.

"Richard, you're working too hard."

"Nannie, we've discussed this over and over again. A man can't make his way in this world by just sitting back and hoping for prosperity. We have to go after it and that's just what I'm doing."

"I know, Richard, but I hate to see you so hell-bent on seeking out your fortune. I wish you'd go listen to Sam Jones the next time he comes to town for a revival. Just about every man in town came out to hear him speak, and now when I'm around town, everyone is talking about Jesus being the answer to our problems, not the depths of our pockets."

"You can save your witnessing for someone else. I'm the only one in this family who has put food on the table and a roof over our heads. Not Jesus."

Nannie placed her hand on Richard's shoulder. "I know you've taken good care of all of us, particularly our brother, Thomas, but I'm concerned about you."

Richard placed a piece of paper into the Smith Premier typewriter and made sure the ink ribbon was set in place. He started plunking down on the keys to write a response to Theo Allen, an attorney in New York. Theo had helped the Dukes sell their goodwill trademarks from the W. Duke, Sons and Company, to the American Tobacco Company. As payment, Theo had expected to receive a portion of the profits the Dukes had made since the transaction, but to his dismay, none came.

Richard looked up from the typewriter and noticed his sister sitting across from him. "Nannie, you don't have to worry about me. I'm fine, and will be doing even better once I get my hands on what, I believe, the Dukes owe me. When I was a partner in the W. Duke, Sons and Company, they changed their contract with the Bonsack Machine Company and didn't tell me. I had only been told that the company had to pay the Bonsack Company twenty cents for every one thousand cigarettes rolled. I was never informed that the contract had been changed to ten cents for every one thousand cigarettes. The Dukes held back this information and their true assets. Theo Allen believes I have a case, given that the value of the company was not fully disclosed."

After Richard read over the letter for mistakes, he pulled the paper from the typewriter, folded it neatly, and placed it in an envelope. He looked up to see his sister staring at him.

"Richard, please go to bed. Whatever you have to do can wait until the morning."

"I guess you're right." He stood up and pushed the chair back. Nannie turned to leave when Richard asked, "By the way, have you been down to see Bettie and the children?"

"I went this morning. That woman has her hands full with her two little ones and making sure Aunt Elizabeth's needs are being taken care of."

"Nannie, to this day, I'm not sure what happened to Thomas. Growing up, he seemed strong and able to work for a good day's wages. But since moving to Durham, he's appeared weak and miserable. I thought he'd do well with his own tobacco brokerage company, but I guess I was wrong. I did everything I could to set up a successful business for him. Then, when it became clear that buying and selling tobacco wasn't in Thomas' skillset, I placed him in a managerial position at the bobbin factory. All he had to do was hire some competent workers, sit back, and watch the money come in. But what happens? He gets sick and hasn't been back to work in over a year, leaving me to support his family and pay his medical bills."

"Richard, not everyone has your ability to run a business. I know you were trying to help him, but I do believe he would've done better if he had stayed in Person County on Aunt Elizabeth's plantation. He seemed happy working the soil and growing crops."

"I'm not going to feel sorry for Thomas, particularly now, when he's being given the best care under Dr. McKee's supervision."

Richard looked up to see Nannie shaking her head. He knew this was her way of demonstrating her annoyance with him. He had learned that it was best to keep his thoughts to himself when they didn't see eye to eye on family issues. As he walked up the steps leading to his bedroom, he called out.

"Nannie, get a good night's sleep."

"You, too."

The next day, Richard was up bright and early. He had a meeting with Julian Carr and didn't want to be late. Ever since they had incorporated the Durham Consolidated Land Improvement Company, Richard had been busy wooing factories, and other companies, to come to Durham. Most of the businesses had rejected the idea of relocating, but there were a few prospects.

Since his move from Lynchburg to Durham, he occupied a space in Wright's Corner, the building he had constructed only a couple of years ago. Richard had relocated one of his tenants out of a corner office and had furniture imported from England to fill the space. He was proud of the craftsmanship of each piece and how it made a statement to everyone who entered the room. As he sat back in his chair, preparing for the day, Richard heard a knock on the door. He knew it must be Julian Carr and called out, "Come in."

Julian opened the door, walked into the room, and stood over Richard's desk. Richard looked up at the older man with the gray, bushy mustache, noting to himself how Julian had aged, giving him a more authoritative appearance. "Julian, pull up a chair and let's get down to business."

"Richard, I'm concerned we won't have the projected number of new residents coming to Durham to purchase lots near Trinity College."

"I've received a large number of postcards from interested people all over the east coast. Also, with the opening of new textile mills, people are bound to move here and need a place to build a home. I've also been talking to a lot of farmers who've sold everything, due to the price of crops being at an all-time low. Many of them are trying to find jobs in the cities. I know we can't compete with the industrialized Northern states, but we're doing more than most cities in the South."

Julian leaned back in his chair and looked over at Richard. "Well, keep up the good work. Now, I want to talk about the condition of the trolleys we received to transport people from one end of Durham to the other. They're in need of a good cleaning and many of the seat cushions need to be replaced. I believe that if we can get the trolleys looking as good as new, we'll have more business than we'll know what to do with."

Richard looked down at his mail, flipping through several letters before responding. "I personally think the trolleys look fine. People will be happy to have other options for transportation with or without new cushions. Anyway, once we hire conductors, they can be responsible for keeping the trolleys clean."

"Richard, I know you have a difficult time letting go of your money, but the trolleys need some work, and I'm not going to start using them until they look as clean as a shiny, new penny."

Richard sighed, "Okay, but don't spend too much money. We have other projects that need financial assistance. By the way, have you had any luck selling the W.T. Blackwell Company to the Dukes?"

Julian quietly sighed before answering. "No. I've been reaching out to a company up North that appears interested in purchasing it. The Dukes think $3,000,000 is too high. They believe the W.T. Blackwell Company will fail due to the number of cigarettes their own factories can produce with the Bonsack machines. Given the cost of the machines I would need to purchase to be able to compete with them, I believe they might be right. Anyway, I'm just thankful I've been so successful with other businesses around the state."

Richard looked over at Julian. "It makes me so angry to witness how many companies they're swallowing up, all due to the success of the Bonsack machine. I've been trying to purchase as many shares of Bonsack Company stock as I can. If I can get my hands on fifty-one percent of the company, I'll be able to put a stop to their scheme to monopolize tobacco. I was hoping more people would be willing to sell their shares to me, but I have inside knowledge that the Dukes are also trying to buy as many shares as they can, preventing me from making any headway."

"Well, good luck with that. With the amount of money they have at their disposal, I believe they won't be stopped. By the way, how is your acquisition of the packaging company in Gainsborough, England, going?"

"William Rose and I have been working closely together. He's finalizing the paperwork, so I'll be the sole owner of the company. I've been busy with, not only trying to sell more Bonsack machines overseas, but also acting as an agent for the sale of the Smith Premier Typewriter."

Julian started to chuckle. "I have always believed that if you want something to get done, you ask a busy man to do it. And, Richard, you are that man. I'm glad you decided to make Durham your home and work with me on promoting our city."

Richard stood up and looked out the window at the people walking by. All he could see was strangers with desperation in their eyes. Durham had become a mecca for farmers, who couldn't feed their families, seeking jobs in the tobacco factories or textile mills. "Julian, I know we've been striving to bring in the most educated and wealthy buyers to line the borders of Trinity College, but there must be a way for us to sell the northeast lots to some of these vagrants."

After a few moments of silence, Julian spoke up. "I believe it's time to auction off as many lots as we can. I received a letter from the Richmond and Danville Railroad informing us that they'll give a discount to all passengers headed to Durham on July 7th for the auction."

"That's good news. I'm hoping for good sales and, with the trolleys starting up, I believe people will see how easy it is to get from the northeast section of our property to downtown."

Julian stood up, turned, and walked over to the door. Before leaving, he looked over at Richard, who was busy typing a response to his nephew, Wright McCord. "Richard, it's been almost six years since Mamie died and you aren't getting younger."

"What do you mean by that?"

"My wife would love to introduce you to a friend of hers."

"Julian, I don't have time for that kind of nonsense. I've dated a couple of times since Mamie, but to be honest, I don't have any desire to spend my time courting a woman. Tell your wife, thank you, but no thank you."

| 17 |

John (1897)

The red and blue striped pole stood out among the other buildings on Main Street. As John Merrick approached the storefront, he couldn't help but rub his finger over the etching of the words "Barber Shop". As his finger traced the letters, he soaked in the knowledge that he was actually a business owner. The idea that a former slave now owned five barbershops caused him to grin with pride. Over the course of several years, John had opened three shops for black clients and two for white customers. He couldn't understand why men had to be segregated when they had their hair cut, but given that they did, he decided to take advantage of it.

John believed that progress had been made since the Civil War had ended. Whites in Durham seemed tolerant of blacks owning businesses. From his point of view, blacks were going to be able to share the wealth coming in from the tobacco industry. Anyway, John knew that all men, regardless of the color of their skin, had to get their hair cut. And, so far, there weren't any obstacles standing in the way of his making a good living.

Of all five shops, this particular location was the one John treasured the most. It wasn't just because of the appearance of the building, which had been whitewashed and freshly painted, or that it had the most current equipment, comfortable chairs, and a well-designed room. It was his favorite because of the clients who walked through the door on a regular basis. He particularly liked Tuesdays. That was the day two of his favorite clients came in for their weekly haircut.

This particular Tuesday, was no exception. At 8:30 a.m., the door opened and Mr. Benjamin Duke walked in with his close friend, John Sprunt Hill. Henry, his best barber, took their coats and hats, and the two friends sat down in adjoining seats. Like a well-oiled machine, everyone took on their individual roles, which had been occurring since the first day the two men had walked through the door and sat down.

Henry wrapped the gown around Mr. Hill's neck and made sure it was snug. He waited a moment, until John looked over to give him the signal to begin trimming his client's hair. John was happy to have Henry working for him. He was a quiet barber, which John found to be a perfect fit. Henry listened in on the conversations, but always respected his customers enough to keep the interruptions to a minimum. John could count on Henry to keep his opinions to himself, at least until the client had left the shop.

John wrapped the gown around Benjamin Duke's neck and, with a broad smile, exclaimed, "It sure is a beautiful day."

"It sure is. John, you always have a positive spin on life. It is truly refreshing."

"Thank you, sir. You know how much I enjoy speaking with both of you."

"John, I heard that you purchased some more property off of Fayetteville Street. What are your plans?"

"Mr. Duke, I keep hearing of black folk coming to Durham to work in your tobacco company. Now, you know they need a place to stay. So, I purchased the property to build more housing."

"Well, that's mighty industrious of you. Have you found the wood from the old tobacco building worth using?"

"Yes, sir. I appreciate you giving me the contract for demolishing the building. The wood has worked out for building houses for our growing community."

Benjamin Duke smiled up into the mirror that reflected John snipping away at his hair. "Well, it works for me."

Over the years, the three men had developed a relationship based on their common goal of making Durham a place that welcomed everyone. John always showed these two men respect and, in turn, Duke and Hill advised him on purchasing property and running a successful business. John particularly enjoyed Benjamin Duke's humble attitude and generous nature.

"John, you know how I like hearing your story. You being a black man and how you have prospered right here in Durham."

"You don't want me to bore you with my life story."

Benjamin Duke turned to his friend. "John, would you like to hear his story again? Every time I hear it, it gives me goosebumps to think about how far the south has come in only a few decades."

John took his scissors in one hand and a comb in the other. He then took a little of Benjamin Duke's hair between his fingers and cut the ends. John always took his time, enjoying the conversations which transpired between them. "Well, where should I start? My mother and I were in Sampson County when the war ended. At first, when we were freed, Mother didn't know what to do. She had only cleaned houses and didn't have an education."

Benjamin Duke looked over at his friend and interrupted. "John, can you believe this man was a slave?"

John Hill responded, "Looking at how successful he is now, it's hard to believe."

John Merrick slid right back into his story. "Well, when I was twelve, my mother decided to move to Chapel Hill. At the time, I wasn't in favor of the move, but now, as I look back, I'm sure glad she did. Anyway, I found work laying brick. It was good work and I thought I would be a brick mason for the rest of my life."

John Hill asked, "Aren't you glad that didn't work out for you?"

"Yes, sir. I sure am. After my mother got married and left, I moved to Raleigh to work as a brick mason. After I helped with the building of Shaw University, there wasn't much work. So, a friend of mine asked if I wanted to work as a bootblack in his barbershop. At first, I didn't know if I would like it, but then, after only a couple of days, I felt like it was where I belonged."

Benjamin Duke asked, "So how did you end up in Durham?"

"Well, my partner at the time noted the growth in population in Durham due to the tobacco business. He believed it would be the right place to move to. And now, as you know, I own five barbershops."

Benjamin Duke asked, "Now, as a successful businessman, how do you think you can help your community?"

John Merrick paused, and then said, "Well, you know I've been involved with an organization I started a couple of years ago, the Royal Knights of King David. The organization helps its members with the cost of burials. I don't know if you know this, but not many blacks in the area have life insurance. When one of their loved ones dies, it can be a real hardship."

John Hill spoke up. "I haven't really thought about that before. So, what do you want to do?"

"I'd like to take the same strategies used by the Royal Knights of King David and create an insurance company."

Benjamin Duke asked, "Is there anything we can do to help?"

"Mr. Duke, you and Mr. Hill have helped me more than you can imagine. I'll let you know if I need advice on the insurance business."

Just as John Merrick finished his story, the door opened and a middle-aged man walked in. Benjamin Duke looked in his direction and then stated, "Well, look who the cat dragged in. If it isn't Richard Wright. I thought you were overseas developing a new machine for packaging cigarettes."

Richard looked at Benjamin and John Hill. Then he turned his attention to John Merrick. "Do you have time to give me a trim?"

John wasn't as fond of Mr. Wright as he was the other two men. He had a tendency to be critical of his haircut. He knew that Mr. Wright had experienced a lot of loss, but it still didn't give him the right to be mean. "Yes, sir. I think I can fit you in as soon as I finish up with Mr. Duke."

John Hill looked over at Richard Wright and asked, "So what brings you back to Durham?"

"I'm checking on my investments and making sure my building on the corner of Main and Corcoran is being utilized in the manner I like."

"Well, by the looks of it, you are getting around very well since your accident," Benjamin called out from the barber chair.

"I am. I'm not going to allow something as trivial as an amputated leg stop me from working."

John Merrick brushed the hair away from Benjamin's neck and unbuttoned the gown. Benjamin turned in Richard's direction. "You know we haven't seen eye to eye on many things, but I have to admit that I respect you for your determination."

"Thanks." Richard paused and looked down. "Benjamin, I'm not going to apologize for how I conducted myself after Mamie died. I needed a fresh start and just couldn't work with your brother. I have no regrets about leaving the firm and am now finding my own success with the packaging company."

"Richard, I understand how Buck can be, and given your personality, I totally understand why you needed to leave the company. You must also know that you have been a thorn in our sides for many years. But, I have to admit that your agitation has made my family and our companies stronger because of it. Good day."

Benjamin and John Hill got up from the barber chairs and made their way to the door. John Hill turned to look at John Merrick. "John, speaking of business ventures, I wish you good luck with your new company. Please let me know if you need any advice." Then, looking at Richard, he stated, "Richard, please give Nannie our best."

And with that, the two men walked out the door.

Richard walked over to the barber chair and made himself comfortable. John straightened up his tools and asked, "So what can I do for you, Mr. Wright?"

"Please trim up the sides."

"Yes, sir."

An uneasy silence fell between the two men as John used his scissors to cut Richard's hair. Finally, Richard looked up and asked, "So what other ventures are you pursuing at this time?"

"I've started buying up property. You see, there are many black folk moving to Durham without much money in their pockets. I've been purchasing as many lots as I can on Fayetteville Street in the community we call Hayti. Have you heard of it?

"I've heard word that it's attracting your kind. I've been told that your people have settled there because it's not in the city limits."

"That's true. Anyway, I've worked it out with the Dukes to demolish their tobacco buildings and use the wood to build homes. I've also been working on some other projects that I believe will help my friends and family have a better quality of life.

"Well, if you need electricity, contact me at the Durham Traction Company. Mr. Carr and I have been busy supplying electricity to people who can pay for it."

John felt a prickle on the back of his neck. He wanted to respond regarding the large bank account he now possessed, but thought better of it. He hoped there would one day be a time when people didn't judge others based on the color of their skin, but knew that day hadn't arrived. "Yes, sir. I'll definitely reach out to you when I'm ready to purchase electricity."

"You know, John, I have to admit that I like your determined nature. Not many men of your color have found the success you've had in the barbershop business. I can tell from looking at this shop that you take pride in what you do." Richard looked in the mirror at his haircut and pointed to one hair that stuck up. "Now, can you take care of this for me so I can be on my way?"

"Yes, sir."

As John brushed Mr. Wright's neck and unwrapped his gown, the bell above the door tinkled and another customer entered the shop. John watched as Mr. Wright took his hat and coat off the hooks and, after tipping John with the bare minimum, walked out the door.

| 18 |

Aaron (1898)

As Aaron Moore dismounted his horse and lowered his foot, his leg sunk downward into the brown puddle of mud that surrounded him. Taking a deep breath, he placed his other foot down and allowed it to settle. The mud was over two inches deep, making it difficult to step forward without bumping into a root or other unknown object. Reaching for his bag, Aaron almost laughed at the thought of the day he had received his medical license from Leonard Medical School, a part of Shaw University. He had been so naïve, as he picked up his diploma, never imagining a pair of good boots would be the most essential article of clothing he could own.

Aaron had just laid down beside his wife, Cottie, when he heard a knock on the front door, after which a voice boomed out, "Doc, please come. My neighbor, William, has been injured. He needs your help." As much as Aaron desired the warmth of the comforter and the embrace of the woman he loved so much, he knew he had to rise and attend to the needs of his neighbor.

After dressing and putting on his jacket, Aaron slipped out the door and walked over to the barn where his horse was sleeping. He hated to disturb this creature, but it always seemed to understand. As Aaron positioned the saddle on the horse's back, he ran his fingers through its mane.

The night had a drizzly feel to it and the cold penetrated his coat, sending a chill straight through his body. To keep his mind off the elements, Aaron began to sing an old hymn he remembered from attending church in his home town of Sandy Plain, a small community in Columbus County, North Carolina. His mind took him back to the sights and sounds of the parishioners, as their voices rose to the heavens and their bodies swayed to the feel of the Holy Spirit. He embraced the memories and allowed the scene to play out over and over in his mind.

As he finally approached his destination, Aaron called out to God for guidance, strength of character, and the ability to administer medical care. His faith in the will of God and His divine intervention, provided him the strength and insight to keep going forward, even when his cause seemed so desperate.

Once Aaron had waded through the muddy water, he stepped onto the stairs leading up to the house. The house was poorly constructed and it was apparent by the gaps between the wooden slats, that the cold wind was not being held back, but slipping into the inner room. Aaron knocked on the flimsy front door. "This is Dr. Moore. I received word that William is hurt. May someone let me in?"

Seconds later the door was opened by a thin wisp of a woman holding a blanket around her body. "Please, come in Dr. Moore. I'm sorry to call you out on such a cold night. My husband, William, has a knife wound that won't stop bleeding."

Once the door was closed, Aaron looked around the one room that made up the entire house. An old gray pallet was in a corner where two small children huddled together. A fireplace stood on the back wall with a couple of dying embers struggling to stay lit. A large man was lying on a soiled mattress near the front of the room. Sweat covered his brow, making him shine against the light of a candle that was positioned on a nearby crate.

"I told him not to go out, but he just wouldn't listen to me." The woman's words drifted through the cold air. Aaron had heard these same words spoken time and time again. He wasn't there to judge, and even if he was to judge this man, what good would it do? No, he had to keep his thoughts focused on the healing and not the accusations that would come from others.

"Mrs. Jones, can you find me some hot water?" Aaron placed his bag down next to William and felt his forehead. The heat coming off his brow was a clear indication that the man had an infection. "Now, if you can also find me some clean bandages, I'd appreciate it."

By this time, the two children were looking up from their pallet with a mixture of fear and curiosity painted across their small faces. Aaron gazed across the room and smiled. "Mrs. Jones, I've missed seeing you and your family at church. I've purchased some new books for the children's ministry that I believe your two young'uns would enjoy. I can also make sure they have a hot meal waiting for them in the morning before Sunday school."

"Dr. Moore, I greatly appreciate that. I don't know what I would do without the generosity of the parishioners at White Rock Baptist Church. I used to attend on a regular basis." The woman sighed and tears began to form. She took the blanket and wiped her eyes before continuing. "That was before William started taking to drinking. Maybe now, with this injury, he'll decide to stop."

"I hope you're right. All we can do is pray for him and extend him the grace our Lord has extended to us."

The next morning, Aaron rose before his family stirred and reached for his tattered Bible. He rubbed the cover that had become worn after so many years of use. Aaron opened the book to Psalm 23 and began to read the familiar words. *"The Lord is my shepherd; I shall not want. He makes me lie down in green pastures."* He smiled as the words rolled off his lips. He reflected on the fact that the Lord was definitely opening up paths for him, and hoped that, one day, he would experience the feel of green pastures. But until then, he would give the Lord praise for his present provisions.

He heard the soft footsteps of his oldest daughter. "Lyda, what are you doing up so early?"

"I wanted to be alone with you."

"Well, come over here and let's talk."

"Daddy, why do you work so hard?"

"Lyda, the Lord has given me the gift of medicine. It's my way to serve the people here in Hayti. One day, you'll find your gift and you will discover how serving is a blessing."

"Daddy, I love you."

"Lyda, I love you, too. Now it's time to get ready for church. Afterward, Mr. Merrick is coming over with his family."

"Is Edward coming, too?"

"Yes, he is."

Lyda made a sound of disapproval. "Does he have to?"

"Now, Lyda, you need to be nice to Edward. You never know, once you are older, your opinion of him may change."

"I doubt it, but I'll try and be pleasant."

After the service was over, Aaron made his way to the basement of the church building, where a small library had been set up. Several children were looking through books and he recognized the two children he had seen the night before, crouched in a corner with a book spread out in front of them. A feeling of joy swept over Aaron as he observed the two children looking at the pictures and trying to sound out the words on each page.

Once he arrived home, John Merrick greeted him from a rocking chair stationed on his front porch. Aaron's nephew, Charles Clinton Spaulding, affectionately called C.C., was seated next to him, talking with John's son, Edward. As Aaron walked up the steps, he could hear the sound of laughter coming from inside the screened door.

"Well, hello, John. It's nice to see you."

"Likewise, Aaron. I've been excited about sharing some news with you."

"Oh, really. Does this have to do with the insurance company?"

"It does. It also has to do with you, C.C."

The young man turned from the conversation he was having with Edward and listened to what John had to say.

"I believe it's time for us to move forward with our plans to charter the North Carolina Mutual and Provident Association. I know we were both discouraged when our friends pulled out, but you know better than anyone the need for burial insurance. I believe we need to hire C.C. to be our first employee."

"John, I couldn't agree with you more. If the black men and women in Hayti can see the value in our product, I believe we can encourage them to purchase it. C.C., what do you think?"

"Well, I'd have to quit my job as manager of the grocery store. But if you two think I'm the man for the job, I'll be glad to do what I can to help."

John stood up and leaned against the railing of the porch. "C.C., I'm willing to invest the money to pay for your position. Ever since you moved here to live with your Uncle Aaron, I've noticed the forthright way in which you have conducted yourself." John paused a moment before continuing. "I can't stop thinking about the riots in Wilmington and all the people who were killed. People who didn't deserve to die. So many of them were laid to rest in pauper's graves with no way for their loved ones to identify them. As much as I hope and pray it won't happen in Durham, we just don't know. That's why I believe we need to act now."

Everyone on the porch grew quiet, consumed with thoughts of the injustices that had played out only a couple of hundred miles away. John spoke above the silence, "C.C., we know it will probably take some time to convince people to purchase a policy, but if anyone can persuade the people to buy our product, it's you."

Aaron looked over at C.C. and could see the young man was excited about the new challenge. "Well, I'll be willing to give as much financially as I can. My heart goes out to the people who have lost a loved one and have no means to bury them. I do believe that if we can deliver on our promise of providing the $100 for burial, people will purchase our product."

Just about that time Martha and Cottie walked out onto the porch with glasses of lemonade. "Now, what are you menfolk talking about?"

John looked to his wife, Martha, and answered, "Nothing you pretty women need to worry about."

"Oh, we aren't worried. Are we, Cottie?"

"No, Martha, I'm not worried. I don't have time for such idle thoughts. I trust my husband and yours to steer us and our community in the right direction. Just look all around us. Both your church, St. Joseph AME, and our church, White Rock Baptist, have grown in number and strength. I believe that if we put our faith in God and our community, we'll be okay."

Aaron smiled at his wife and declared, "Amen. I couldn't agree more."

| 19 |

Bettie (1899-1901)

As time passed, Thomas continued to drink as a way to relieve the pressure of living up to his brother's expectations. He didn't make it to bed until late in the night, and often didn't come home until after the children had fallen asleep. Bettie had tried to convince her husband to stop drinking, but she knew that, unless his relationship with his brother changed, it was useless. Now that Richard had become wealthy, he acted like he was an authority over everyone. And given his financial support, there was nothing they could do.

Bettie would never forget the letter that Thomas received from Richard in 1899. Richard had been home for ten days and, she had to admit, the children were very rambunctious. On the other hand, she believed that children needed a sense of freedom to express themselves and, if that meant they were perceived as a little wild, so be it. When Richard left for another business trip across the Pacific, she felt relief and thought that his absence would again bring peace to her home. But little did she know, that Richard would continue to cause hurt, even from the other side of the world.

Thomas walked in the door one day in early July with a defeated look that made Bettie want to cry. As he entered the parlor, he pulled out a letter from his coat pocket and placed it down on the seat beside him. Bettie walked over to her husband, picked up the letter, and began to read.

Honolulu June 24/ 99

Dear Tom,

We arrived here last night and sail at 5 pm today for Japan.

I must call your attention to the way you and Bettie are allowing your children to grow up- particularly Lila- who will in only five or six years be a grown woman.

During my ten day stay in Durham last, I did not see her with a book in her hand and don't recall hearing her practice on her piano, but twice. I carefully looked over the reports in the News and Observer and of the Durham paper of the graded school commencement and I did not see Lila's name mentioned at all, anywhere, not even in the list of the scholars who got 85 or better average. Other children of less influence were listed, but not Lila.

This is not strange when you and Bettie allow her to collect all the street Arabs for blocks around in your yard and yell and whoop equal to wild Indians to the discomfort and annoyance of all your neighbors and to run and tramp equal to a lot of wild Texas steers in a stampede. You have no right to bring children into the world and let them grow up that way. Use Your Head-Think! That is what your heart and mind were made for. Can you expect Lila to be anything but an ignorant Tomboy if you allow her to go on this way? Can you expect any culture or refinement or any social standing for her? Are you content to let her be another Pat Ball-Helpless, ignorant, unsavable, another source of shame and humiliation? Another niece to be ashamed of? If not, you and Bettie should take her in hand at once. Make her practice one hour, and read one hour, learn her studies one hour every morning and make her sew one hour, practice one hour, and read one hour every afternoon. This only takes three hours a morning and three hours an afternoon, only six hours a day.

Do you think that's any hardship? Do you expect any result from any less effort? There are plenty of girls ten and twelve years old who work in factories ten hours a day and glad to get the work to support their mothers. Go through the knitting and cotton factories in Durham and open your eyes and USE YOUR HEAD. You have no right not to do so! If she thinks it's irksome and rebels, whip the hide off her until she learns to like the three hours task morning and evening. It's a duty you owe me. You have no right to bring up nieces for me to be ashamed of. She has the capacity, if you and Bettie will use your heads and do your duty by her and she may be made a source of pride to the family. But you must use your head and the switch if necessary. Finally, I have this to say-if you and Bettie do not take strict and rigid measures to cultivate and properly bring up your children, I shall withdraw

*from the U.S. and take up my residence abroad and get away from
another coming batch of helpless, ignorant, uncultured kin. I want
no more kin to be ashamed of. Laziness is the cause of ignorance
and poverty-all of which go hand in hand together.*

*Wake up to the reality and importance and responsibility of
the situation and act now while you have the time and opportunity.
Lay down rules and make your children live up to them and bring
up a family you can be very proud of and who everyone will love
and seek the society of.*

*The two courses are now open to you and it's your privilege
to elect whether you will bring them up a lazy ignorant lot, which
can be done without using your head or any rules or disciplines, or
whether you will make them cultivate their senses and keep aloof
from street Arabs and associates with bad reputations.*

*I have done my duty in calling this to your and Bettie's notice.
Do yours!*

Very truly, etc.
R.H. Wright

Bettie rose and looked at Thomas. "He does not have the right
to say these words. He doesn't know how difficult it is to raise
children, particularly Lila."

"I know."

"Thomas, please do not take this so personally. He's a brute!"

"I need some time to think."

Thomas got up and left the room with Bettie gazing down at the
letter. She thought about tearing it up, but knew that would make
Thomas even more upset. So, she took the letter back to Thomas'

study and placed it on his desk. As she looked around, she saw Thomas sitting on the couch, with a drink in his hand.

Later that night, Bettie noticed that the door to Thomas' study was still closed. Once the children had been asleep for some time, she quietly opened the door and saw Thomas hunched over the type-writer. Beside her sleeping husband was a letter written on Wright's Automatic Tobacco Packing Machine Company letterhead.

Durham, N.C. July 10th. 1899

Dear Richard,

Your letter of June 24th from Honolulu came to hand today and contents noted with care. I am sorry you considered it necessary to write me such a rasping letter. I believe between the two, I would prefer that you would take a shotgun and blow my head off. I am of no use here. It would be better for me to be out of the way and you will then not have me here to be ashamed of. I am just as created and can't help myself. There are opportunities that might have been improved in days gone by, but the time has passed and I am now on the westward slope of life, too late now to make amends.

I have regretted a thousand times over that I had not taken up my abode in the country when I was first married, for that is my natural element. I am not fitted to live in town and try to move in society of nice people to say nothing of the society people. Still, I have tried to live a moral life and shall try to stick to it unto the end and I don't believe my creator will be ashamed of me. I have that assurance in my heart and I would not exchange it for all the social folly this world contains. I have often remarked to Nannie why she would wonder why certain people in town did not call. That it was because she was living with me. And that I thought best for her and you socially, and perhaps other ways, if she and you were to keep house there and let me and my humble family get a much less pretentious place. I truly believe it. When you write such letters as this they make me feel mean low down and I hardly feel as good as a common street loafer. I do not take exceptions at your letters, far from it. But they have a peculiar degrading effect that seems to drag me down to a level with the brute creation.

You say laziness is the source of ignorance and poverty, as a rule it is true. I may have been lazy, but I know I have always tried to work whether in right direction or not. Referring to Lila, not making any excuses for her, whatever, and knowing she has not applied herself as she should, still she got very good reports at school and each of her teachers speak in very complimentary terms of her. Lila is very young yet and you should make some allowance for that. It is characteristic of all children to want to romp and play with few exceptions, and when you find them otherwise it is unnatural. I shall try at all times to bring up my children as near right as possible, but fear I will never get them up to your ideal, such children are scarce. Miss Peay said she didn't wish the children to practice over a quarter of an hour morning and evening. To compel them to practice longer would most likely cause them to have a dislike for music. Lila does not read perhaps as much as she should, but I know I often see her with books she tells me she gets from the public library.

I will hold on and do the best I can until your return at which time I will do what you suggest in the matter. I would rather move away somewhere from Durham rather than stay here and be a source of shame and mortification to you. I don't want to run you from the U.S. on account of the ignorance and stupidity of my family. I would much prefer to go to some nook or corner of the state where none of us would come in contact with you. The circle in which you move would soon forget you had such kin, I presume, but few of them know we are in existence. But I am as anxious that Lila should succeed and make a lady that you or anyone else would be proud as you possibly can and I expect to do all in my power to accomplish that end.

Yours Very Truly,
Thomas D. Wright

As Bettie read the letter, she wanted to scream. She agreed with Thomas. They should never have left the country, the place where Thomas thrived as a man. But she knew it was too late to even consider a move back to Person County. That life was too far in the past. She looked down at her husband, crumbled and defeated. This was not the man she married. He had been so confident in his ability to run a farm. If only Richard hadn't placed his claws into him and drug him down to this!

Over the next year, Thomas' physical health rapidly declined. His skin color had changed and he would often wince with pain when getting ready for bed. Bettie encouraged him to visit several doctors, but after none of them could offer a diagnosis, he stopped going.

One Sunday morning, long after he would typically get up for church, he called for Bettie. "Can you come in our room?"

"Thomas, are you okay?"

"No. I think you need to call the doctor. The pain is worse and I'm having trouble breathing."

"Darling, I'll call for him right away."

Bettie went down the hall and summoned her eldest son.

"Thomas, I need you to go get the doctor. Your father is sick. Please hurry."

"Okay, Mom. I'll be back as quickly as I can."

Bettie returned to her husband's bedside, sat down next to him, and began to stroke his hand. "Thomas, what am I going to do with you? We have gone through so much together. Do you remember the time you pulled my little cocker spaniel out of the water? I was so scared, but you eased my fear with your calm demeanor. I thought you were the strongest person in the world. I will never forget the time you found me in the field with my sprained ankle. I loved leaning up against you as you took me home. It was then, on the horse, that my heart told me we were going to be together. And now, look at the beautiful family we created. Oh, Thomas. I need you. How can I ever manage without you? You have to be okay. Please be okay."

"Bettie, I love you, too. I have adored being your husband and the father to all our wonderful children. I hope I'll be okay, but if I'm not, I believe Richard will take care of you."

"Let's not talk about that. I know he has lots of money, but I want you. My God-fearing, compassionate man. You are my rock and my soulmate."

Thomas grinned and then a throbbing pain took over his body. Bettie leaned down and kissed his hand. "Oh, Thomas. Please be alright."

There was a knock at the door and an elderly man's voice was heard. "Mrs. Wright, it's Dr. Clark. May I come in?"

"Yes, please."

The door opened and Bettie could see her children in the hall-way, trying to get a glimpse of their father. "Now, Bettie, I'd like to examine your husband. I'll come get you, once I'm finished."

Bettie leaned down and kissed Thomas on the forehead. "I'll be right out here if you need me. I love you, Thomas."

Once Bettie closed the door, all of the children gathered around her. Four-year-old Cora tugged at her mother's skirt. "Mommy, what's wrong with Daddy?"

"Oh, Cora, I wish I could tell you. Hopefully, the doctor will have some news for us after he examines your father."

Thomas Jr. walked over to Bettie and, with tears in his eyes, asked, "Mom, what can I do to help?"

"I need all of you to be as quiet as possible. We don't want your father to be concerned about us. Now, go in the front room and find something to do while the doctor examines him. I promise I'll let you know something as soon as he leaves."

Bettie leaned her ear against the door and tried to make out what the men were saying. Every few minutes, Thomas would call out in pain. Bettie tried to keep the tears from coming, but her love for her husband, and the concern of what life would be like without him, frightened her.

After about an hour, Dr. Clark opened the door and shook his head. "Bettie, I wish I could give you good news, but I can't. He's having trouble breathing and I'm afraid that his lungs are starting to fill up with fluid. It appears Thomas has been suffering with a stomach ailment for a long time. I can't do anything for him. I recommend you try and make him as comfortable as possible."

Bettie gasped and began to weep. "What do I tell the children? They love their father so much."

"I would tell the truth and give them a chance to tell him good-bye. I'll leave some medicine for pain. Call me if you need me. I'm sorry, Bettie."

Dr. Clark let himself out and Bettie made her way to the front room where all of her children were playing. She took a deep breath and called them to join her on the couch. "Children, your father is very sick. I wish I could tell you that he will be getting better, but that wouldn't be the truth. It appears that the Lord is calling him home."

Four-year-old Nannie Bet spoke up. "Mommy, is Daddy going to be with Jesus?"

"Yes, Honey."

"Can I go with him?"

"No, Honey. Not now. Your daddy needs you to stay here with me and your sisters and brothers."

"But I want to be with Daddy and Jesus."

"Oh, Sweetie, I need you here with me."

Bettie gave her little girl a hug, and placed her next to her, as she addressed her children. "Now, I want all of you to let your daddy rest awhile. I'll let you know when you can go in and cuddle with him. I know he wants to be near all of you for as long as possible."

Ten-year-old Lucy raced down the hall and ran toward her room. Richard Jr., barely eight, teared up and put his arms around his mother and wept. "It's okay, Richard Jr. Cry if you need to. But once all the tears are gone, I want you to find something interesting to share with your dad. He always likes the things you bring in from outdoors. See if you can find a turtle or a frog from outside. I believe it will make him smile."

Bettie gave Richard Jr. a big hug and pointed toward the back-door. She looked over at Nannie Bet and Lila and told them to come sit close. "Okay, children. Let's make these the best days of your father's life. Go out and pick some flowers or draw him a picture. We're going to make your father know he's the best daddy in the whole wide world."

The children clung to their mother for a few minutes, and then, one by one, they climbed down from the sofa, and went in pursuit of gifts for their dying father.

On Wednesday morning, around seven-thirty, Thomas passed from this world surrounded by his family singing songs. Nannie Bet and Cora sang verses of "Jesus Loves Me" while the older children sang hymns from the hymnal. Bettie did her best to sing along while stroking Thomas' hand and whispering in his ear. "Thomas, it's okay to go. We'll be fine. You know that I have loved you all my life. You've been a great father. The children will never forget you. Now, go on my love, and I'll see you in our eternal home. Make sure to tell Jesus that Nannie Bet is excited about meeting him one day."

A tear slid down Thomas' cheek and, mustering up the last bit of energy in his body, he mouthed, "I loved you at lavender."

And he was gone.

The next day, among close friends and family, Reverend W.C. Norman conducted a service that Thomas would have been pleased with. People from Richard's social circle were present, as well as fellow parishioners from the church Thomas attended. After the church service, grieving mourners went to the city cemetery where Thomas was to be buried. All the children huddled around Bettie as she placed a flower on the coffin. Each child followed her example and then walked to the carriage that carried them back to the house.

For weeks, Richard and Bettie rarely spoke. Her anger was clearly directed at him, but he didn't think he had anything to be sorry for. She knew that Richard thought Thomas was a weak man who consumed too much alcohol. It was clear from Richard's actions that he had very little remorse over his brother's death. Bettie had noticed that, now that Thomas was gone, Richard tried to impart his paternal authority over the children living under his roof.

As the weeks turned into months, Bettie's children spent more time reading, practicing the piano, and completing their studies. Whenever they did have a chance to go outside, they would play in the yard, but rarely did a friend come over. Richard had made it clear that no one outside of their social circle was welcome. This didn't upset most of them, but Lila was clearly disappointed when the friends she had once played with never came to visit.

As harsh as Richard was with the oldest children, every once in a while, Bettie noticed a change in temperament when he interacted with Nannie Bet and Cora. She wasn't sure why, but maybe it had to do with the fact that the two girls were too young to be expected to read or practice the piano. On several occasions, she witnessed Richard watching them with an amused expression. If ever he was to attempt a smile, it would be in their company.

| 20 |

Richard (1902)

One day, when Richard was pondering how to drum up business for the Durham Traction Company, he decided to get some fresh air and walked outside of his house on Dillard Street. He spotted his young nieces, Mary Ruth and Cora, playing with their dolls on the front stoop. His first instinct was to reprimand them for sitting on the dusty bricks, causing their dresses to become smudged with dirt. But instead, Richard decided to engage them in a conversation. "Hello, girls."

Cora looked up into her uncle's eyes and responded, "Hello, Uncle Richard."

"What are you playing?"

Mary Ruth shoved her doll toward him. "We're playing carousel. Mommy showed us a picture of a carousel with horses and other animals. We're pretending to ride on one."

"Is that right?" Richard answered.

Cora chimed in. "There were pictures of a park with a carousel and a swimming pool. I would love to go swimming in a pool."

"What else do you think you'd like to do at this park?" Richard asked.

Mary Ruth leaned her head back and paused. Then, with a burst of excitement, she declared, "How about ride a carriage that goes up and down and around?"

"I like that. Anything else?"

Cora said, "Richard Jr. and Thomas Jr. like to watch people play baseball. It would be fun to watch baseball and eat hotdogs."

"Is that so?" Richard asked, thinking about his problem with the trolleys and a way to solve it. "You know, girls, I'd also like to watch baseball and ride on a carousel. How about if I built a park like that?"

Mary Ruth cried out, "That would be fun, Uncle Richard! Can we go now?"

"Not now, but I believe it can happen very soon."

Richard entered the office of the Durham Traction Company and found Julian sitting behind his desk, reading over some documents. He sat down in a chair facing Julian and waited until he received his full attention. "I think I know how to solve our problem with ridership on the trolleys. I believe our problem has to do with the lack of destinations. If we had a park that people would want to go to, then they would ride the trolleys to get there. We could create a park at one end of the city and a baseball field at the other."

Julian took his pipe and tapped it on the edge of the desk. As he got ready to light it, he looked up. "Richard, I think you have a great idea."

"Well, to be honest, I had the help of two imaginative girls with this one."

"Maybe we should hire them."

Richard laughed at the idea of hiring Cora and Mary Ruth. "Maybe in a few years when they finish school."

Julian peered over at Richard with a quizzical look, and then returned to reading the many documents that were scattered on his desk.

Later that year, once the land had been cleared, the swimming pool installed, and a carousel constructed, Lakewood Amusement Park opened its gates. Richard believed this project would make a difference to the Durham Traction Company's bottom line, but also give the common people of Durham an affordable weekend destination.

As much as Richard didn't care to go out in public with his unruly nieces and nephews, he knew it was the best way to be perceived as a family man by the people of Durham. So, on a beautiful Sunday afternoon in July, Richard walked Bettie and the children to the trolley stop on Main Street where they would ride to the new amusement park.

All seven children were filled with excitement over being a part of the grand opening festivities and couldn't stand still as they waited for the sound of the trolley car making its way down the track. Cora, Nannie Bet, and Mary Ruth were jumping up and down, trying to imitate the roller coaster ride they envisioned. Richard Jr. and Thomas Jr. were throwing a ball, and Lila was discussing with Lucy about the boys she hoped to speak with. When the trolley stopped, there were several dozen people already seated. The conductor, dressed in a creased black uniform, recognized Richard and looked throughout the car for enough seats for all of them, sending some passengers toward the back. "Mr. Wright, it's so good to see you. Business has definitely picked up since people have heard about Lakewood Amusement Park. Now, step this way. There are enough seats here in the front for your family to sit together."

Bettie and the girls sat down on the black cushioned seats, while Richard and his nephews took the seats behind them. As the trolley made its way through the city picking up passengers, Richard felt a sense of pride over the development of the park. With all of his accomplishments, he had never witnessed so many people be excited about one of his business ventures.

Once the trolley reached the end of the track, Richard, Bettie, and the children were ushered to a large platform with a ribbon tied to both ends of the stage. A local band was playing and people were gathering on the field surrounding them, creating a festive feeling among the citizens of Durham and nearby towns. Mayor McCown walked up to Richard and shook his hand. He then signaled the band to stop playing, turned to the crowd standing around the stage, and said in a loud voice, "Ladies and gentlemen, it is with great pride that I would like to introduce Richard Harvey Wright, the financial backer behind this wonderful new park."

After loud applause, Richard moved forward. "Thank you, everyone, for coming to the opening of the Lakewood Amusement Park. We at Durham Traction Company have great plans and hope you'll make our park a destination for your family and friends to enjoy on a regular basis. We are also pleased to welcome the Runkel Stock Company, who will be occupying our large casino." A shout came out from the crowd as the members of the stock company made their way to the stage.

Once the applause had subsided, Richard continued. "Many of you have taken advantage of the new baseball park at the other end of the trolley line. Local baseball teams have already impressed the hundreds of people who have attended their games. We at Durham Traction Company are honored to have your support and believe that Durham is the best place in the country to live. Without further ado, let's cut this ribbon and open Lakewood Amusement Park for all of you and your families to enjoy."

Applause erupted from the crowd as Richard took note of the familiar faces smiling up at him. For a moment, he relished the attention and waved back at several of his business acquaintances and local politicians. After a few moments, Richard moved back to his chair and tilted his head toward the mayor, signaling him to take the podium. Cora reached up and took Richard's hand. "Can we go on the carousel now?"

"In just a minute. As soon as the mayor finishes speaking."

Cora looked down and softly stated, "Okay."

A few minutes later, Richard led Cora through the crowds of people with his hand holding tightly onto hers. As they walked, a jumble of emotions erupted inside him. Feeling the small, soft hand of his niece stirred up feelings of sorrow over the death of his own daughter, remembering the times he had left her side for a business trip or social engagement. A gut-wrenching feeling of pain came over him and he had to stop and catch his breath.

The carousel loomed in front of them with beautifully painted horses, tigers, and giraffes. Clanging timbres, playing in a rhythmic motion, matched the movement of the animals circling around, and up and down. Once the ride stopped, and everyone got off, Richard leaned down and asked, "So, Cora, which animal would you like to ride on?"

"I'd like to ride the giraffe."

"Why the giraffe?"

"A giraffe has a long neck so it can look down on people and not be stuck near the ground."

Richard smiled as he lifted Cora onto the speckled, painted giraffe with its brown saddle. He placed the reins into her small hands. "Now, hold on."

Richard slid his hand down the side of the giraffe and was amazed at its beauty. It was hard to believe that all of this was created because of a need for ridership on his trolleys.

As he pulled back and watched the carousel begin to move, he turned his attention toward his other nieces and nephews. The two boys were rolling on a field and the older girls were laughing at a boy who had approached them. Bettie and the other girls were waiting in line to ride real ponies that were going around in circles. His first instinct was to pull the boys up and give them a good talking to, but he decided it would be best to have a conversation with them later at home.

The rest of the day, Richard stood back and observed Bettie guide her children around the park. He didn't agree with her mild temperament when it came to discipline, but also felt it was not his place to constantly intrude. He was sure that Bettie had read the letter he had sent Thomas close to three years ago. Even if she didn't share his views on how to manage her children, he knew she was their mother, a fact he needed to respect.

Richard had not imagined the impact that the opening of Lakewood Amusement Park would have on the city. The park provided a destination for people in Durham, and the surrounding areas, for three decades. Tom Folley was hired to oversee the park and took a lot of pride in his responsibilities. A casino was built that housed live music and entertainment from all over the country. A roller coaster was constructed and restaurants were opened on the grounds. On Sundays, church groups came for picnics and Tom would often eat with them. Tom also invited traveling circuses and carnivals to set up on the property. In its heyday, the park was referred to as the Coney Island of the South and drew people from all over.

Once cars became popular in the 1920s, the need for the trolley and its destinations was eliminated. The electric cars moving down Chapel Hill, Mangum, Main, Angier, and Kent Streets, were practically empty. People were now able to afford their own vehicles and could travel elsewhere on the weekends and summer vacations. In 1932, Lakewood Amusement Park closed its doors. Over a period of thirty years, a forest overtook the property, and it was almost impossible to believe that it had once been a place that so many people had flocked to. In the early 1960s, the land was cleared and Lakewood Shopping Center, a strip mall, was built on the exact location of this former prized jewel of Durham history.

While the park was a destination for all who lived in Durham, Richard rarely attended. He had more cows to milk, cows that would hopefully fill the void in his heart and take away the pain that he had ignored since the loss of his wife and child; a pain that took the form of anger and a need to control everyone in his life.

| 21 |

Washington (1905)

Washington Duke had enjoyed his retirement from the largest to-bacco company in the world. After handing over his responsibilities to Richard Wright, he spent time serving at the Methodist Church, working on committees geared toward the advancement of Trinity College, and trying to convince other wealthy individuals of the importance of giving their money toward the betterment of all people in the Durham community, both black and white.

Given the number of years he'd spent in poverty, Washington was well aware of the needs of people who had not been as fortunate as he had been. So, whenever a worthy opportunity arose, he was eager to extend a helping hand. A good example of this came from a time in the late 1800s, when he was approached by Dr. Aaron Moore to donate toward the building of a hospital for the black citizens of Durham. Washington fondly remembered the day that Lincoln Hospital was dedicated in 1901 as one of his most acclaimed achievements.

There was only one regret that the elderly man had lived with for two decades. It was the decision to have Richard Wright buy out his interest. Washington never would've imagined, at the time of the sell, that this young man would turn against his sons and the company in such a vicious manner.

As Washington's health declined, he felt the need to try to come to peace with Richard before passing from this earth. The anger and inability to forgive Richard had caused plenty of sleepless nights and diminished the peace he wanted before dying. So, Washington did what few men would have thought worthwhile; he wrote Richard a letter inviting him to his home.

One afternoon in the early spring of 1905, Washington was lying in his bed, surrounded by his grandchildren. He was having a particularly good day and was playing a card game with two of the children, when a servant filled the doorway. Washington looked up and addressed the servant. "Yes, George. What is it?"

"Mr. Richard Wright is at the door."

Washington took a deep breath and responded, "Please see him in."

He then turned toward the children who were gathered around his bed. "Can you please give your grandfather a few minutes alone with Mr. Wright?"

"Yes, Grandfather." Immediately, the oldest child stood and directed the others to follow him through the doorway, down the hall, and out the door to play. Once the children were out of sight, Washington rose from the bed and held on to the bedside table, pulling himself up. Slowly, the old man shuffled to a nearby chair and sat down. As painful as this was, he didn't want Richard to see him in bed.

Moments later, Richard entered the room and stood inches inside, leaning against his cane.

"Richard, come sit down."

Washington was amazed as he observed Richard maneuver his way around the room on his peg leg and cane. He thought about how Richard had overcome the loss of his leg, and so many other calamities, and persevered in a life directed toward a successful business career. "Richard, thank you for coming. As you can see, my health has declined quickly and, I must admit, I don't think I have much time left on this earth. But don't feel sorry for me. I believe my Lord is preparing a place for me with far more grandeur than all of this."

Washington looked over at Richard, who was staring around the room, taking in all the pleasantries the house had to offer.

"Washington, why have you called me over here?"

"Richard, I believe we have a lot in common. We both started off with not a nickel in our pockets. We both have had opportunities, and experienced the pain of losing the love of our lives."

Richard turned his head away and was clearly uncomfortable listening to Washington's words. "Washington, I have several pressing issues I need to take care of, so please get to the point."

"I'll never forget the day I saw you in Kansas City. During that trip, I hardly made a sale. In all my years as a salesman, I had never been turned down so many times by mercantile owners. I can't imagine the number of days you spent overseas selling our product. You weren't the least bit intimidated by the language barriers or cultural differences you experienced. I was proud of you and the choice I made to have you take over my position. When I looked at you, I saw a young, determined man who knew how to sell everything and anything. I knew you'd be my perfect replacement and, at first, I believed I was right."

"So, what are trying to say?"

"As you can see, my health is failing and I want to clear the air between us."

"I have no qualms with you. But, I must admit, the way your sons handled the building of the new factory in 1885 disturbed me. When they demanded that all of the partners put their own money into the company, I was furious."

"Richard, is that the real reason for all the lawsuits? During those years after you left the business, you acted like a man with a personal vendetta."

"I really don't remember. All I know is that I was hurting deeply from the death of Mamie. Maybe I misplaced some of that anger. I really can't say."

"Richard, if anyone can relate to the pain you were feeling, it's me. I lost two wives, whom I loved dearly, along with my first-born son."

Washington sighed and took a moment to catch his breath. He hadn't anticipated that this conversation would take so much out of him. He looked over and could tell that Richard was ready to leave. "Richard, I just want you to know that I'm not angry with you any-more. I respect you and what you have done for this city. I believe you're doing a good job raising your brother's children. That's all I wanted to say."

Washington leaned his head back against the back of the chair and closed his eyes. He hated feeling so tired, but was glad he'd had the chance to tell Richard how he felt.

Richard lowered his peg leg and, with the opposite hand, placed the cane down on the floor. After rising from the chair, he looked over at Washington and said, "Washington, I've always respected you. I appreciate you calling me over so we could properly say our goodbyes."

Washington wanted to stand, but didn't have the energy. He was overcome with exhaustion and closed his eyes. And, as he tried to catch his breath, he heard the peg leg hit the floor in a rhythmic movement and the sound of the door close behind this man who would never know real peace.

On May 8, 1905, surrounded by his family, Washington passed away. When word reached the mills and factories, operations were ceased, and the workers sent home to be with their families, where each could pay respect to the man who had done so much for Durham. Three years later, to commemorate their father, Buck, Brodie, and Benjamin, placed a statue of Washington Duke at the entrance of Trinity College. Today, one can find this beloved man sitting at the entrance of the East Campus of Duke University, where he greets all Duke Students and their families, no matter what culture or color they might be.

On the south face of the statue, the inscription reads: "Washington Duke/1820-1905/Animated by lofty principles he ever cherished the welfare of his country with the ardor of a true patriot; diligent in business he acquired riches, but in the enjoyment of them did not forget to share with the less fortunate; A patron of learning he fostered an institution which placed within the reach of aspiring youth the immortal gift of knowledge; and when activities of his early life and the sterner struggles of his maturer years had passed he entered upon a serene old age cheered by a lowly piety and sustained by an unfailing trust in God, who in all the vicissitudes of life had kept him single in his aims, sincere in his friendships and true to himself."

| 22 |

Bettie (1907)

Bettie could hardly remember what life had been like with Thomas. Everything had changed so much in such a relatively short period of time. The sound of children running around the house or neighbors coming over to play had been replaced by the sound of the piano and the silence of children reading books. Private tutors had been brought in and a strict order of conduct instituted, particularly when Uncle Richard was home from a business trip. Even if Bettie wanted to encourage the children to play, she knew her voice would be overpowered by the man who had total control of the purse strings.

The only sound Bettie could hear came from the clicking of the grandfather clock in the downstairs foyer. She opened her door, hoping for someone to beckon her, but was greeted by a hushed silence. More than anything, Bettie wanted to go downstairs and be with her children, but knew it was best to leave them alone while school was in session. Instead, Bettie walked down the back staircase, with its squeaky wood planks, and approached the door that led to the kitchen.

Once the kitchen door was open, she glanced around for some task that she could help with. Field peas had been purchased from the market and were strewn across the table. Several of the kitchen staff were sitting with bowls in their laps, opening up the pea pods and dumping the peas into their bowls. Right before Bettie opened the door, she could hear the women talking among themselves. She wasn't sure what they were saying, but knew it was a conversation that would stop once she entered.

The women, wearing aprons covering their simple dresses, looked up and, as expected, became quiet, causing Bettie to feel like an intruder. "Please, don't stop your conversation on account of me."

One of the kitchen staff turned her head down, while another woman spoke up. "Ms. Wright, can we help you? We're not quite finished with making lunch yet."

"Shirley, if it is okay with you, I'd love to help with the peas. You know, before Mr. Wright brought us into this big house, I would do all the cooking. I loved being in the kitchen with my children gathered around. Now, I don't know what to do with all of my time."

"I can't stop you, but I know Miss Nannie won't be happy if she finds you back here."

"I'll take my chances. Anyway, I rarely have the opportunity to go out and visit with others. Since my husband died, I haven't been out much. I promise I'll be as quiet as a church mouse. Please, return to the conversation you were having before I came in."

Bettie took a bowl from the counter and sat down in a chair near the door. As she started to peel away the silk from the side of the stringed pea, she hoped the women would resume their conversation. After a few minutes of silence, she said, "Shirley, I heard that your daughter is studying to be a nurse at Lincoln Hospital. You must be very proud of her."

"Yes, ma'am, I am. When Little Dorothy was a small child, she was really sick. We had no place to go and I thought I was going to lose her. Thank the good Lord for Dr. Moore and the others who worked tirelessly to build Lincoln Hospital. I'm so thankful for the good doctors that come to Durham to practice medicine. But, I'm even more thankful for my daughter wanting to be a nurse."

One of the other women chimed in, "Yes, Shirley, I agree. We're truly grateful for men of color right here in Durham who are working to make health care accessible to everyone."

Bettie remained quiet while the other women spoke about a world that seemed so foreign to her. She had heard of the poor housing conditions where these women lived, and felt foolish. Just as she was going to place her bowl in the center of the table, she heard a scream from the front room. Startled by the noise, she dropped the bowl, scattering peas across the floor. "Oh, I'm so sorry."

Bettie had just stooped down to pick up the peas, when the door opened and Nannie walked in. "Bettie, what are you doing? You need to get off the floor immediately!"

"I'm sorry. I heard the scream of one of my children and it startled me."

"There is no need to be concerned. Richard Jr. thought it would be funny to pull Nannie Bet's hair. She was taken off guard and turned around and hit him in the stomach. Richard Jr. is being disciplined and Nannie Bet is okay."

"I'd like to speak to them. They are my children."

"No need for that. Anyway, lunch will be served in a few minutes." Nannie looked around the room and then turned her attention to Shirley. "I'm expecting lunch to be served in fifteen minutes."

Nannie made a sound of disapproval and walked out of the room, leaving Bettie feeling like she had brought trouble onto these women. "I'm so sorry. I'll explain to her that it was my intrusion that caused you to get behind on lunch. Please let me pick up the peas and help prepare the meal."

Shirley rose from her chair and started gathering the peas from the floor. "Mrs. Wright, you need to get along now, so we can fix lunch."

Bettie rose, placed the empty bowl on the table, and walked out the door that led into the main dining room. She made her way across the large room with the beautiful mahogany table and leaned her head out of the door that led to the foyer. If she turned her body in just the right way, she could see Thomas Jr. working at a desk with a pen in his hand. Cora was in the parlor playing the piano. The sound of her small fingers hitting the black and white keys reverberated throughout the house. It was a pleasant noise that beckoned her to draw closer.

Bettie walked across the foyer and stood inside the doorway to the parlor, drawn by the familiar song that her daughter had played countless times. Cora turned and spotted her mother stationed near the entrance to the room. "Mom, please come join me. Miss Peay, you don't mind if my mother joins me, do you? Mom, we have been practicing a song that I believe you will enjoy."

Cora moved over and patted the cushion beside her. Bettie walked slowly over to her daughter and sat down. "Now, Mom, let's play the song, 'A Beautiful Lady in Blue'."

Bettie waited for Cora to begin, allowing her daughter to dictate the pace. When they were halfway through the song, Bettie noticed Nannie Bet and Lucy walking over, followed by Thomas Jr. and Richard Jr. Mary Ruth was the last to join them and tried to find space on the bench beside her mother. Once the song was over, the children applauded and asked for another song, one they could sing to. Richard Jr. called out from behind them, "How about 'I'm a Yankee Doodle Dandy'?"

Thomas Jr. responded, "Why would you want to sing that song? How about 'In the Shade of the Old Apple Tree'?"

Bettie fingered through the sheet music and found the song, placing it on the ledge above the keys. "Okay, is everyone ready?"

All of the children began to sing as Cora and Bettie played. The longer they played, the louder the children sang. Lucy started dancing and whirled Nannie Bet around the room. Bettie was lost in the moment and a sense of happiness wrapped itself around her like a warm blanket. As Bettie sat at the piano with her children all around, she hoped this moment would go on forever. But, as all dreams do, this one ended, with a crashing sound, followed by children yelling out.

Bettie turned around to see one of Richard's imported lamps shattered on the floor. "I didn't mean to run into it!" Lucy proclaimed. "Richard Jr. pushed me."

Trying to hide her feelings of horror, Bettie called out, "Now let's pick up the pieces and see if we can fix it." She rose from her place on the piano bench and leaned down on the floor, collecting as many of the broken pieces as she could hold in her skirt.

Bettie heard the opening of the front door and looked up to see Richard walking in, assisted by Nannie. They appeared to be glaring at her and taking note of the children's actions as they yelled at each other. Richard shook his head at the scene being played out before them. Nannie had a look of scorn written across her face as she yelled out, "Bettie, I never thought the day would come when I'd see you on the floor two times in one day! You need to get up and act like the mother God created you to be."

Bettie was without words. One minute she was happier than she had been in years, and now she felt like a disciplined child. As she picked up the pieces of the lamp, she heard Nannie call out, "Children, it's time for lunch. Please go wash your hands and meet your uncle in the dining room."

In that moment, Bettie was left alone to, once again, pick up the pieces of her broken life.

| 23 |

John (1910)

One morning, John Merrick woke and placed his arm under his head. He enjoyed this time of day, when no one was up and the silence served as a room for his thoughts. John spent some time reflecting on the days when he had been a brick mason in Raleigh. During those early years, he never would've entertained the idea of one day owning five barbershops and prime real estate.

As John thought about his many accomplishments, it was the insurance company, created by him and his partners that brought him the most pride. John knew that the company was not only making money, but was providing a basic need for his friends in the black community of Durham. He smiled as he thought about the first days of selling insurance, and how the payouts brought such relief and hope to his policy holders.

John suppressed a chuckle to hold back any noise that might wake his wife, Martha. He continued to ponder on the progressive direction that the town of Durham was taking. White men, such as Julian Carr, Benjamin Duke, and Richard Wright, had found their own path to success. Early on, John realized that the black man could also prosper. He knew if he worked hard, established strong relationships with all members of the business community, and never dwelled on his doubts, that success could be his.

As John lay in bed, he played out in his mind how Parrish Street had been transformed from boarded up buildings to a thriving area of town. The fire in 1886 was vivid in his mind. He remembered how it had destroyed several of the homes and businesses that lined the dirt street. One of the men most affected by the fire was E.J. Parrish, the man whom the street was named for.

Years earlier, Parrish had come into his barbershop for a trim and, while sitting in the chair, shared how he and his family had barely survived. John remembered how Parrish appeared optimistic, as he spoke of rebuilding the warehouses and making them better than they had been prior to the fire.

Several other houses and storefronts remained barren and, with the close of the Bank of Durham in 1888, there was little interest in this area of town that was known for such destruction. John remembered how he had kept the street in the back of his mind as a potential location for the insurance company. He knew that the number of black citizens moving close by would deter his white counterparts from building on Parrish Street.

In 1902, a mob, made up of white citizens, had burned down the building where his insurance company did business. When he first heard of the fire, John was angry but, over time, he began to see it as a sign to make a move to the street he had his eyes set on.

If anything, the attempt to place the insurance company out of business only fueled John's determination to proceed with his plans. With over 140,000 policyholders, The North Carolina Mutual Life Insurance Company wasn't going anywhere but to a larger building on Parrish Street. In 1905, the first black-owned building was constructed. By 1907, The Merchants and Farmers Bank opened its doors, followed by a drug store with a licensed pharmacist.

John knew he couldn't have gone forward without the core group of like-minded men like R.B. Fitzgerald, W.G. Pearson, Dr. A.M. Moore, C.C. Spaulding and J.E. Shepard. These men met often and their determination, combined with a strong faith in God, pushed them through the barriers the South was erecting to keep them, and all other minorities, in their place.

Once the insurance company was established, with other businesses to follow, this section of Parrish Street became known as Black Wall Street. Black advocates from all over the country heard about the success these men were experiencing and came to see if, indeed, it was worth recognizing. Booker T. Washington visited in 1910, praising the ambition and thrift of the residents of Durham.

John tried to stay still as he smiled at his success, but a chuckle finally slipped from his mouth, awakening Martha. She looked up at him and yawned.

"John Merrick, what in the world are you contemplating? I can tell when you have another idea simmering in that good-looking head of yours."

"Martha, don't worry. I was just thinking about my upcoming meeting with Richard Wright."

"Now, why do you have to meet with him? He is so gruff. I have to feel sorry for the man, with the loss of his wife so many years ago, but he doesn't treat you with the respect Benjamin Duke and John Hill do."

"I know. But we are opening up an electric theater on Parrish Street. People will come to experience motion pictures and other amusement. And Mr. Wright owns the Durham Traction Company. So, I have to work with him to supply electricity to our buildings."

"The electric theater does sound like fun. I have to admit that, since we've had electricity put in our house, we can stay up longer and enjoy the heat in the wintertime. What else do you have planned today?"

"I scheduled a meeting with Aaron Moore at White Rock Baptist Church. Lately, he has become more active in philanthropy. He wants to talk with me about the Baptist Orphanage in Oxford and his plans to open a library for the black community."

Martha leaned over and kissed John on the lips. "Have I told you how lucky I am to be your wife?"

"I believe you have."

"I can't believe how times have changed. It's been only fifty years since our parents were slaves, and now you're running the largest black-owned company in the state and maybe the country. I'm so proud of you. I love you, John Merrick."

"Now, Martha. You don't want me to become arrogant with all that talk. God has blessed us and I only want to make sure our friends and the black community are taken care of."

Later that afternoon, John walked into the Wright Building that stood on the corner of Corcoran and Main Street. Ever since it was built in 1884, the three-story building, with a mansard roof and dormer windows, stood as a reminder of the wealth Richard Wright had accumulated over the years. John felt a nervous tension as he walked to the back of the building and knocked on the closed door. An assertive voice called out, "Come in."

John took a deep breath and opened the door to a room he had visited only once before. He was overtaken with a nostalgic feeling of when Thomas Wright, Richard's brother, had sat in the chair now occupied by Richard.

John believed the best way to do business with Richard was to wait patiently for this man to acknowledge him first. Richard had his head down, signing several papers, before looking up. "So, John, what can I do for you?"

John didn't care for this man but appreciated his direct nature. "As I stated in my letter, I would like to purchase electricity for my businesses on Parrish Street."

"Yes, I do remember your letter. Why don't you pull up a chair and let's discuss the specifics. You know, if you were any other colored man, I wouldn't even entertain your request."

John felt a twinge of anger settle in the pit of his stomach. He knew his reputation and bank account should speak for itself. But he had been working with men like Richard for so long that he knew the game he had to play in order to receive what he needed. "Mr. Wright, I do appreciate your time."

Richard kept his eyes downward, sweeping over the many documents piled on his desk. "Just this morning, I read in the *Durham Recorder* how they praised you and your contemporaries on how your insurance company has more investors than any other company in this town and the state. Apparently, the white community is supporting your efforts."

"We have a solid product that has proven itself to be worth the investment. Just like you, I have learned to benefit from a need the people have. I respect your ability to identify a solid investment and make it profitable. I'm doing the same thing."

John could tell by Richard's expression that he didn't want to be placed in the same company as this man of color. Again, John knew it was best to hide his true feelings and proceed with his request. "Richard, we both have the same mission, to put money in our pockets and provide a service for our community. If we can work together, I can assure you that you will be paid for the electricity, and my business will encourage others to purchase electricity from the Durham Traction Company."

"Well, since you put it that way, I'll have a contract typed up and will send it to you by the end of the week. You can let yourself out."

Richard leaned his head down as a signal that the conversation was over. John stood up and walked out of the door and into the fresh air. He could only feel sorry for this man who only lived for the next deal. As he headed toward Parrish Street, he looked up to the sky and prayed for a forgiving attitude toward this man who could rub his nerves raw.

| 24 |

Richard (1913-1920)

Since the early 1900s, the Durham Traction Company had run electricity for the trolleys, street lamps, and the homes of wealthy people like his partner, Julian Carr. In 1913, Richard sold his interest in the Durham Traction Company to Henry L. Doherty Co., out of New York City. And just like all of his previous investments, Richard turned around and invested his earnings into, what appeared to be, the next most profitable venture, the Interstate Telephone and Telegraph Company.

It was at this time, that the citizens of Durham began to grumble about how Richard was conducting his empire. Instead of spending some of the profits from his companies to better the city, he was holding onto every single dollar, and refusing to do what was best for the community. The rails of the old trolley line continued to damage the wooden carriage wheels that stumbled down the streets, while unsightly telephone wiring littered the main roads of Durham. No matter the pressure he received from the local government and newspaper, Richard refused to remove the rails and hang the wires. Because of his refusal to do what was best for the city, Durham's roads remained unpaved and potholes made driving difficult.

In contrast to his lack of empathy for the Durham citizens, Richard had provided well for both Lucy's and Thomas' children. He paid for the education of each child who wanted to pursue higher education, and provided opportunities for them to travel with him overseas to Europe, Asia, Africa and India. Richard's nieces and nephews were given strict instructions on who they could date, and he made sure they were introduced to prominent suitors all across the state of North Carolina.

Richard began to give his nephews more business responsibilities and took them with him as he visited the Rose Brothers in Gainsborough, England. They were clearly being groomed to carry on his business empire, particularly Richard's most cherished accomplishment, Wright Machinery Company.

In 1914, Richard Jr. was attending Virginia Military Institute, while Thomas Jr. was being trained to take over the family business. Lucy had begun seeing a lawyer by the name of Sidney Chambers, and Nannie Bet was engaged to a prominent businessman from Franklinville, Virginia. In the same year, Lila married a doctor from Weldon, North Carolina. In her wedding announcement, the Roanoke News reported, *"Ms. Wright had greater advantage in travel than any other young woman in North Carolina."*

World War I had begun in Europe following the assassination of Archduke Franz Ferdinand, heir to the Austro-Hungarian Empire, by a Serbian nationalist. Even though the war was thousands of miles away, Richard's experience from his time in Europe caused him to become more concerned about its potential effects than his business associates were. Richard thoroughly read the newspaper from cover to cover every morning, searching for clues of how the war might personally impact his business and family.

At the time, Woodrow Wilson was president and took a neutral stand, partially due to being distracted by the depression he was suffering at the loss of his wife. All of this changed on May 7, 1915, when Germany torpedoed the Lusitania, a British ocean liner off the coast of Ireland. When Wilson received word of the loss of one hundred twenty-eight Americans, his stance changed from neutral to engaged. Not long afterward, when Wilson was told about the bombing of an Italian ship with twenty-seven Americans on board, he knew that the United States had to act.

In April 1917, Congress broke ties with Germany and Wilson declared war. In June, the first deployment was ordered. Even though the United States deployed troops for less than two years, 116,516 American lives were lost, with more than half of these due to an influenza outbreak. Thankfully, neither of Richard's nephews were deployed before the war ended in November 1918.

With the war over, and the servicemen headed home, a far more deadly battle was consuming the attention of Durham residents. Veterans carrying the Spanish Flu were infecting entire cities. All public events, including church services and any public gatherings, were strictly prohibited. Even so, over four thousand Durham residents contracted the virus.

When the soldiers came home, they didn't just bring a deadly disease with them. They also brought home a new way of thinking. For the first time in history, black soldiers had been given equal footing with white soldiers. During the war, they had experienced what it felt like to be given respect, and wanted this treatment to continue when they arrived on American soil.

When the soldiers returned to Durham, many demanded fair treatment and pay. But the South was not willing to let go of their biases so quickly. Three years earlier, an organization had been formed in Atlanta that spread throughout the South like wildfire. White men, who feared riots and change, covered themselves with white garments and hoods, instilling fear among the South's black population.

As much as the members of the Ku Klux Klan in Durham wanted to provoke fear among black men, they also desired the white population to view them in a positive light. To accomplish this, they often presented gifts to organizations and individuals. Whenever such gifts were presented, it was their custom to draw as much attention to it as possible.

One Sunday, Richard and his family attended Trinity Methodist Church for the eleven o'clock service. The traditional church service always began with a song from the hymnal, followed by readings from the New and Old Testaments and, after the recitation of the Lord's Prayer, the minister would begin his fifteen-minute message. In all the time Richard had attended the church, he had never known of a single disruption to the predictable routine of Trinity's time of worship.

Richard always sat in the third pew from the front with Nannie beside him. The rest of the pew space was occupied by Bettie and her grown children. Every Sunday, the pew would hold at least four members of the Wright family. On this particular Sunday, everyone seemed to be paying attention to the pastor as he was getting ready to bring the message to a close. Then, a murmuring sound from the back of the church caused Richard to turn his head around. He turned to Nannie and, with an annoyed tone in his voice, stated, "What are these people doing here?"

As Nannie was getting ready to respond, the group spotted Richard and walked straight up to him. None of the men in the white hoods and masks spoke. They just handed Richard an envelope, turned around, and walked out.

By this time, people had started talking among themselves, and it was clear that the service would not continue until Richard disclosed what was in the envelope. He was used to being in the spotlight, but found this situation irritating. After unfolding the paper and looking at it closely, Richard stood up and faced the congregation. "I want to begin by stating that I have never solicited any support from the Klan."

Richard paused to allow the murmuring to stop and to ensure the attention of the parishioners. Once he had everyone's attention, he spoke. "Ladies and gentlemen, it is a check for $300 toward the construction of a home for orphans here in Durham."

After speaking, he motioned for his family to rise and follow him down the aisle, past the murmurs, and into the parking lot, where his car stood out like a sore thumb. People followed the family, shaking their heads, and wondering about this man who had done so much, but also so little, for the city of Durham.

Richard had tried to stay as far away from politics as he could get. He didn't appreciate being singled out by an organization that he wanted no association with. Word had spread about the gift he received from the Klan and how he must be linked to these masked men. Whenever he was approached, Richard would either ignore the accusations or, in a very calm voice, state that he had nothing to do with the Klan.

The people of Durham and the local law enforcement agencies turned a blind eye to the attacks made on the black community. But, in 1920, the lynching of an innocent man caused law enforcement and *The Herald*, the local newspaper, to reflect on their practices.

In early July, Edward Roach, a Durham laborer for the Nello Teer Construction Company, was working in Person County, where he was constructing a road. He had fallen ill and told his boss that he needed to go home. While walking to the Mount Tirzah train station, he was apprehended by the Person County Sheriff's Department. He pleaded with the sheriff to speak to Nello Teer, who could vouch for his whereabouts, but his request was denied.

When word spread that a suspect had been apprehended for the assault on a white woman, the Klan immediately made their way to the sheriff's office. With little resistance, The Klan took Edward out and lynched him in front of a black church, three miles from Roxboro. Later, *The Herald* reported: *"The lynching party performed its task quietly and in a well-organized manner."*

When Nello Teer read the newspaper article, and the positive reaction from the readers, he was furious. He knew the truth and was not going to keep quiet. He wrote to the newspaper and declared the lynching was a "ghastly mistake". Even with prominent businessmen like Nello Teer screaming for justice, the lynchings continued.

Richard was aware of the racial tensions in Durham, but rarely got involved in political or social matters. He was too focused on developing methods to make money and expand the Interstate Telephone and Telegraph Company, as well as The Wright Machinery Company. And, when he wasn't working business transactions, he was busy escorting his nieces and nephews around the world.

Richard particularly enjoyed spending time with Cora, one of his youngest nieces. He found her intelligent and pleasant to be around. Even though he didn't have time for silliness, he found Cora's wit to be insightful, which was a change from the businessmen he spent time with. She was an independent woman with a strong sense of self-esteem. Cora, now twenty-one, had never brought a man home to introduce to the family and didn't seem interested in dating the young men Richard had introduced her to.

Lucy, Cora's older sister, had begun courting Sidney Chambers, a local attorney. He was an intelligent man with lots of ambition. He was also pleasant to be around and could make everyone in the room feel special. But, as much as Lucy's suitor engaged in conversations with her sisters, it was clear that Sidney was smitten with Lucy. So, when Richard noticed how Cora's disposition changed when she was around Sidney, he became concerned that she might get hurt.

| 25 |

Aaron (1919)

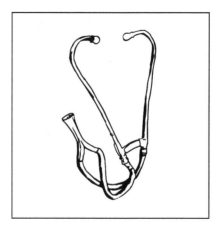

Aaron stopped, took in a deep breath, and placed his hand on the door handle. His palms felt damp from perspiration and his heart beat so hard that he contemplated leaving. Considering his nervous state, he wondered if he could approach his dying friend without shedding the tears that welled up in his eyes.

As a physician, Aaron had witnessed his share of death and the feel of its grip as it took hold of the many patients he had treated. In most cases, he shielded his emotions as he witnessed their passing, but this time was different. This was his lifelong friend and business partner who now lay suspended between the physical and spiritual world.

Aaron turned the handle and opened the door to find white cotton drapes fluttering in the breeze. A beam of sunshine crossed the room and landed on the bed where John Merrick lay. For a moment, Aaron wondered if his friend had already passed, but when he saw the rising and lowering of his chest and heard the gurgling sound of his breathing, he knew his time had not yet come.

Aaron tapped on the open door, making a loud enough noise to waken someone from a deep slumber. After the third tap, John turned his head and opened his eyes. A smile formed across his face as he looked up. "Aaron Moore, come in."

Aaron tightened his hold on the worn medical bag that he had used for years and walked over to the bed. He placed his hand on John's arm, feeling his warm flesh. "I don't want to disturb your rest, but I wanted to come by and check on you."

John made a wheezing sound and, with a quiet voice, responded. "I'm always glad to see you, even if you are calling as a physician."

"No, John, I'm not just calling as a physician, but also as a friend."

Aaron took a stethoscope out of his bag and placed the diaphragm on John's chest, listening to his heart and lungs. After a moment, he placed the stethoscope back into his bag and positioned a chair so he could face his friend. "Can I get you something? Water, or some soup?"

"No, not now." John tried to turn his body to become more comfortable, but was too weak. Aaron noticed his friend's efforts and assisted him by placing a pillow behind his back, allowing him to sit up. After a moment of letting the pain settle down, John spoke. "I was just having a dream about the days when we were starting our insurance company. Do you remember when we met with John Avery, C.C., and my son, Edward, in the back room of your office?"

"How could I ever forget? We were all young and determined. You were in pursuit of creating a successful business and I was wanting to meet the needs of the many families living here in Hayti. It's hard to believe that it almost didn't happen. I was particularly disappointed when our first group of investors pulled out, but once that first policy was paid and people started to understand that we were men of our word, we were overwhelmed with business."

John looked up at the ceiling with a grin on his face. "I can't believe we've become a million dollar company. I'm so glad I was able to attend the twentieth-year celebration at White Rock Baptist Church. It truly moved me when everyone started singing *"Praise God from Whom All Blessings Flow"* as I stumbled down the aisle. John paused a moment, creating a peaceful silence. After a few minutes, he spoke in a quiet voice. "To be honest, I was so moved by the sound of the voices, I almost collapsed before I got to the podium."

Aaron remembered the scene of his good friend hobbling down the aisle with his daughter holding him up. "I can't imagine the pain you've been experiencing since your foot was amputated."

John started to laugh, which puzzled Aaron. "What are you laughing at?"

"I never would've considered how painful it's been for Richard Wright for all the years he's been walking with a peg leg. After having my foot amputated, I can now understand why he can be so ornery."

Aaron smiled. "He surely is that."

John appeared at peace as he continued to reminisce. "But, even so, Richard treated us just like his white customers when we needed electricity for our businesses on Parrish Street. And we can't forget other men like the Dukes, Julian Carr, and John Sprunt Hill; men who were willing to give us advice on how to pursue our business ventures."

"You're so right. And even though George Watts didn't want blacks practicing medicine at Watts Hospital, it didn't stop us from our dream of building a hospital to serve the people of Hayti."

"So true. I'll never forget how you turned that situation around."

Aaron smiled at his friend. "And now Lincoln Hospital is thriving, along with a successful nursing school."

"It sure has been a good life. I never thought when I arrived here in Durham, just opening up my first barbershop, that I'd have the privilege of being recognized by men like Booker T. Washington and W.E.B. Dubois." John stopped a moment to take a deep breath of air. Once he caught his breath, he continued. "And then there is you, Dr. Aaron McDuffie Moore from Columbus County, a world traveler and advocate for education for all children, and let's not forget the library you opened."

"I have to agree with you, John. It's been a difficult road, but one I wouldn't pass up for anything." Aaron began to cry and stopped speaking until he could clear his throat. "I feel so thankful for our friendship. What am I going to do without you?"

John turned his head and wiped a tear that had fallen down his cheek. "Aaron, can you do me a favor?"

"Sure, anything."

"I'm ready to go meet my savior, but I need to know you'll make sure Martha and the kids will be taken care of. This Spanish influenza scares me. If they get sick, promise me you'll do everything you can to help them."

"John, I promise I'll do everything in my power to make sure everyone stays well."

"Aaron, I love you like a brother."

"And I love you as well."

Aaron felt at peace as John closed his eyes. A light breeze stirred in the room as the sun dropped below the horizon. Aaron knew this would probably be the last time he and John would speak, and wanted to treasure every moment he had left with his friend.

Moments later, John's breathing became labored as he struggled for air. Aaron knew he should call for Martha and their children, but didn't want to admit it was time. After squeezing John's arm one last time, he stood up and walked out the door.

John Merrick died on August 6, 1919, and his funeral was held at his beloved church, St. Joseph AME. People from all walks of life and races attended. It was a celebration that John would've appreciated.

In 1943, the S.S. John Merrick, the only Liberty ship built during World War II named after a black man, was commissioned in Wilmington, North Carolina.

After years of struggling from heart disease, Aaron McDuffie Moore died on Sunday, April 29, 1923, surrounded by friends and family. Two days later, his life was celebrated at White Rock Baptist Church. Over two thousand people attended his service, including several prominent white citizens, such as Julian Carr, and Durham's former mayor, M.E. Newsome. From eleven o'clock, when the coffin was rolled into the church, until the coffin was closed at 2:00 p.m., thousands of men, women, and children paid their respects to this beloved man, who had sacrificed so much for the community he loved.

The relationship between these two men has stood the test of time, and will continue to do so, recognized by the naming of Merrick Moore Elementary School in Durham.

| 26 |

Cora (1919)

Tears slipped down Cora's cheek and onto her pillow. What was she thinking? There was no way that Sidney's eyes would ever dance in the way they did whenever her sister Lucy entered the room. Why would she even think that a man like Sidney would ever care for her? Lucy was much more sophisticated, and the five years between them gave her a maturity that was well suited for an attorney's wife.

Cora gazed at her reflection in the mirror, wondering why she had never been able to pull a man's heart strings. Male suitors always complimented her on her curly brown hair and petite figure, but that was where the compliments seemed to end. As she leaned into the mirror, peering at her round face, with the ordinary hazel eyes and thin lips, she only wanted to be someone else.

Cora turned away from the mirror and walked across the room to the wardrobe that contained her dresses. She was just about to unbutton her dress, when she heard a soft knock on the door. "Who is it?" she asked, with a rude tone that she immediately regretted.

"It's me, Lucy. Cora, can I come in?"

"I'm not feeling well," Cora lied.

"Cora, please let me in. I need to talk with you. It's important."

"Don't you have a guest waiting in the parlor?"

"Sidney can wait. It's you that I'm concerned about."

"Okay, you can come in."

Cora tried to brush the tears from her cheeks before Lucy could detect her sadness. Lucy walked across the wood floor, sat down on the full-size bed, and patted the space beside her. Cora hesitated, wanting to hold on to the anger that welled in her chest, but didn't have the willpower to be mad at her sister.

As the two women sat in silence, memories popped into Cora's mind of the times when Lucy had tried to protect her from the hurts and heartaches their family had endured over the years. She could remember how Lucy had wrapped her arms around her as their mother told the children of their father's death. She also remembered when Uncle Richard had reprimanded them for wearing inappropriate dresses, and how Lucy had shielded her as he went on and on about how disgraceful they appeared. Cora sighed and allowed the tears to fall. "Lucy, I'm so sorry. I shouldn't have assumed that Sidney would want me. It's clear when he looks at you, that he's madly in love."

"Cora, you know how much you mean to me. I know there are a few years between us, but I've always felt a bond with you and I don't want to do anything that would cause you pain."

"Oh, Lucy. I want you to be happy. I'm feeling a little pity for myself. Just witnessing Nannie Bet's beautiful wedding to John Clark, and now thinking how life will be here at Bonnie Brae without you, is causing me to be full of doubt."

Lucy placed her arm around her sister and allowed Cora to continue. "This house is so different from our home on Dillard Street and I feel like it might swallow me up. I'll also miss how you've always been there to buffer Uncle Richard's harsh words and Aunt Nannie's demands. People on the outside don't understand what life is like for us. Lucy, I'm afraid of what my future will be like without you."

"Cora, I'm not going far. Sidney has a beautiful home only a couple of minutes away by car. I promise we'll spend time together. Anyway, Mary Ruth needs you now, more than ever."

About that time, Mary Ruth, Cora's younger sister, poked her head inside the door. "What are you two doing? Uncle Richard and Sidney are asking for you, and Nannie is working with the kitchen staff to keep the meal warm. She's fit to be tied."

Lucy motioned for Mary Ruth to join them on the bed. "Now, sisters, no matter what happens between me and Sidney, I'll always love you. We have come through some very rough times and it has only made us stronger. Are we okay, Cora?"

"Yes."

"Good. Now, let's go down and see who can get Uncle Richard to turn that frown of his into a smile."

As the three girls walked out of the room and down the staircase, Cora thought about what Lucy had said. She was right. Mary Ruth did need her. But little did the women know, how much.

| 27 |

Cora (1919)

As Cora stood in front of the church and watched her sister walk down the aisle, she smiled to herself. After her conversation with Lucy, she rethought her priorities and promised herself that she would never come between her sister and the man she loved. Cora glanced over at Sidney and held back a giggle. He looked like a young boy in love for the very first time. His brow glistened with sweat and his hands were shaking. He kept looking toward Lucy, then back at his best man. It was almost comical.

Lucy was stunning in her silk wedding dress, designed and created in Brussels, Belgium. The cream-colored dress lay perfectly upon her body and the veil, made with beautifully embroidered silk, was stunning. A string of pearls circled her neck and a bouquet of pink and cream roses adorned her waist.

Lucy held her head high and beamed, as she took the last few steps toward the altar. Once Uncle Richard left her side and hobbled over to his place, a hush spread throughout the church. Cora looked down at the front pew and watched her mother dab at her eyes. In that moment, she was flooded with emotion. She looked to her left and saw Mary Ruth tearing up and, without hesitation, she squeezed her sister's hand. Both sisters smiled and then turned their attention to the pastor as he pronounced Sidney and Lucy, husband and wife.

The wedding reception was held at Bonnie Brae. The spacious foyer was decorated with beautiful flowers and candelabras for the wedding. A corner of the room was roped off for a small quartet and a dance floor had been constructed for the occasion. An entire army of wait staff was hired to tend to the impressive guest list. Businessmen, attorneys, and well-known physicians from all over North Carolina were in attendance.

This occasion was marked as one of the most prestigious events in Durham's history within the highly affluent social circles. Rarely, did anyone receive an invitation from Richard Wright, particularly at his expense. So, when word got out that Richard was going to host the reception at his home, everyone who was invited felt honored to be included.

Champagne flowed and cigarette smoke filled the space. The wait staff, in formal wear, wound their way through the crowd, making sure no one had an empty glass or clean plate. Laughter was heard above the soft music and, by all appearances, everyone seemed to be enjoying themselves.

When Lucy and Sidney arrived, there was a thunder of applause, as they walked through the crowd. A platform, with a table designated for the young couple, had been set up on a side wall. The wedding director parted the crowd so that the bride and groom could make their way to the platform and take their seats.

After they were seated, Uncle Richard rose and surveyed the crowd. Cora and Mary Ruth looked on from the corner of the room in anticipation of what their uncle would say. After a moment of silence, the older man spoke. "Ladies and gentlemen, I would like to welcome you to my home and this festive occasion. I would personally like to congratulate Lucy and Sidney on their marriage. I have watched Lucy grow up and become a woman who we're all proud of. As for Sidney, his reputation as a successful attorney speaks for itself. I want to be the first to welcome Sidney to our family. Let us all raise our glasses to Mr. and Mrs. Sidney Chambers."

"To Mr. and Mrs. Sidney Chambers," the guests responded, as they lifted their glasses.

Cora looked around the room, scanning for her siblings. Nannie Bet and her husband, John, were sitting alongside Lila and her husband, Sterling, near the front of the room. Her brother, Richard Jr., was looking on with a young woman by his side. But it was her brother, Thomas Jr., who she was concerned about. He was standing up against a back wall with a cigarette in his hand. It was clear by the way he stared at his uncle that he wanted to speak up. Ever since Uncle Richard had banned Thomas' girlfriend from coming to their home, he had been enraged.

A few weeks prior to the wedding, Cora had overheard a conversation between the two men and saw Thomas Jr. leave the house, slamming the door on the way out. She couldn't go to sleep that night and went downstairs to wait for her brother's return. When she finally heard the door open, she sighed with relief. Thomas Jr. tried to walk past the room without being noticed, but Cora called out, "Thomas, are you okay?"

"Cora, go to bed. I don't want to talk right now."

"Thomas, please come in for just a moment. I want to share something with you."

Thomas Jr. walked into the beautifully decorated room, with all of its expensive imported furniture, and sat down in a wingback chair across from his sister. Cora placed her book on the couch and looked over at her brother. "Thomas, I don't know what you are feeling right now. As you know, I've never had a serious suitor and, other than being infatuated with several boys from school, I've never experienced how it feels to be in love."

"Well, you're right about that. You don't know how I'm feeling. It just makes me so mad that Uncle Richard feels like he controls who we can fall in love with. Elizabeth is a nice girl. Her father is a hard worker, but just because he isn't a successful man with lots of money, Uncle Richard told me that I'll have to leave his house if I keep seeing her."

"Thomas, I'm so sorry. He has always had such high expectations for all of us. But you know, as well as I do, that if it wasn't for his generosity, we'd be homeless. When Daddy died, we could have been abandoned. I can't imagine what Mother would have done. Uncle Richard can be so closed-minded, but he did make sure we knew that this was our home for as long as we wanted."

"Yes, but now being here is causing me to lose the one woman I love. If I knew I could make a good living without Uncle Richard's support, I'd be gone. But I know better, and that's what is making me so angry."

"Thomas, I believe you will find a woman who Uncle Richard will accept. Anyway, I can't imagine what my life would be like without you here."

"Oh, Cora. You've always helped me to see things logically. Thank you for being the little sister that you are."

Later that evening, as the couple was getting ready to cut the cake, Cora scanned the crowd and didn't see Thomas Jr. anywhere.

Lucy was laughing as Sidney placed a large piece of cake in her mouth. Friends of the young couple were headed in the direction of the cake table, but there was no sign of Thomas Jr. Cora made her way through the crowd and out the back door that led to a covered porch. She spotted her brother's silhouette and walked over to where he was standing alone, smoking a cigarette. "Hello, big brother. I thought I'd find you out here."

"How are you doing, Cora?"

"What do you mean?"

"Well, I know I've been lost in my own self-pity, but I can recall, months back, the way you looked at Sidney. I know that look and have been wondering how you were feeling?"

"That's very nice of you to think about me. To be honest, I'm doing okay. I love Lucy, and I made a decision that my feelings for Sidney weren't as important as my relationship with her. So, yes, my heart hurts a little, but I'm getting adjusted to the fact that they are meant to be together."

"Cora, you're a smart and thoughtful young woman, and I hope you'll find a man who makes you as happy as Sidney makes Lucy. Now, would you like to go in and dance with your brother?"

"Only if you promise not to step on my feet."

"Very funny."

| 28 |

Cora (1919)

When Uncle Richard proposed a trip abroad, Cora didn't feel the desire to travel like she usually did. In the past, before the Great War, she had yearned for the time on sea, surrounded by nothing but the lapping of waves and the watery horizons. But, since the end of the war, the thought of the innocent lost lives, floating in the cold waters off the coast of Liverpool, sent chills up and down her spine.

So, when Uncle Richard told her of the trip he had planned for the two of them, Cora didn't feel the same zeal she had possessed in prior years. But, no matter her fears or doubts of the journey's safety, she packed her bags with newly bought gowns from

Baldwin's and shoes from Gilmer's. She smiled to herself, thinking about the shopping trip she'd gone on the previous day with her sister, Lucy.

"Cora, you must be getting excited about your trip across the ocean. I've heard that the Megantic refitted its first-class berths since the end of the war. And, even as bland as Uncle Richard can be, you'll have the opportunity to dine with the captain and, hopefully, spend your time dancing in the large ballroom."

"Lucy, I guess I do have reasons to be excited."

"I wish I could be going with you, but Sidney and I are just getting into the rhythm of married life."

"I hope you're enjoying yourself."

"I never thought I would love someone so much. He's so kind and considerate of my needs. As busy as he is, he always finds time to give me his undivided attention."

"Lucy, I couldn't be happier for you."

"Now, as for you, we need to pick out a couple of voile dresses. They truly accent your cute figure."

"If you say so."

The following day, Cora and Uncle Richard boarded the Norfolk Southern Railroad to travel north to New York, where they were to board their ship. Uncle Richard had brought his briefcase and spent the hours looking over briefs and making notes. Cora read through a book she had recently purchased, but found it boring and was having difficulty staying awake.

When they finally pulled into the New York train station, a car was waiting outside of the terminal to take them to the port. Cora was apprehensive about this trip, but once she saw the Megantic, and how large it was, she began to get excited. After going through customs, they were ushered to two berths, right next to each other.

"Cora, I've work to do, but will be ready to escort you to dinner at six o'clock sharp."

"Yes, sir. I'll be ready."

Cora walked into her room which had a twin bed, a desk, and a small bathroom. She went over to the porthole and peered out. There were throngs of people transporting the luggage onto the boat. Cora stared through the dusty window at the flocks of people waving from the pier. After a few minutes, she noticed how stuffy the room was and began to perspire.

Cora tried to lie down and fall asleep, but the lack of air circulation made her feel faint. She rose, opened the door, and walked down a narrow corridor that led to an outside door. As she pulled the door inward, a burst of air blew against the heavy door, causing her to lose her footing. Once her feet were securely planted, she turned the handle and pulled at the door, only to find a young man holding on to a bag.

"Can I help you with the door?" he asked.

"Yes, if you can hold it open, I would greatly appreciate it."

"Of course."

The man held the door and allowed Cora to walk through the opening onto the outside deck.

"Thank you for your assistance. I wasn't aware how heavy these doors can be."

"You are so right about that."

"Have a good day."

"You as well."

Cora walked onto the deck and made her way to the stern of the boat, where the motor was beginning to churn the water. She stood looking out over the harbor as the large ship headed toward open waters. Several couples were standing near her, embracing as they waved to the people who walked along the shore. Cora felt out of place and turned to return to her room. But, just as she turned, the stranger appeared at her side.

"Hello. I love this part of the voyage. Don't you?"

"I guess I do," Cora said, as she gazed back toward the shore.

"I hope you don't think I'm too intrusive but, when I saw you out here alone, I felt drawn to speak. By the way, my name is James Rawlings."

"Hello, Mr. Rawlings. My name is Cora Wright."

"So, why is such an attractive young woman sailing on this ship alone?"

"Oh, I'm not alone. My uncle is escorting me on this trip."

Cora's curly hair began to blow into her face, so she turned to allow the wind to push it behind her. James rotated his body around so that Cora was by his side. "So, Ms. Wright, have you ever been on a ship before?"

"Oh, yes. Many times. All before the war. I used to love being out in the ocean with nothing but water on all sides. But now, with the number of ships torpedoed near Liverpool, I have to admit that I'm a little anxious."

"I've had to travel a lot since the end of the war and, I must say, that after the first voyage, I've been feeling more relaxed."

Cora felt some mixed emotions about this young man and his pursuit of her. She had only dated once or twice since Sidney and Lucy were married. As bizarre as the feelings were, she almost felt like she was betraying Sidney.

James looked at her with a smile on his face and an eagerness to keep the conversation going.

"Did you know that the ships Laurentic and Megantic were built by the same company?"

"No, I didn't."

"The Laurentic was bombed by German mines in 1917. Thankfully, the ship we are standing on came through the war unscathed. On December 11, 1918, it was returned to civilian service."

"Are you trying to make me feel better or worse?"

"I don't know. I just thought it was interesting how this ship survived the war, and I believe it will get us to our destination safely."

Cora smiled at James and asked, "So, where is your destination?"

"Several countries in Europe. You see, I'm one of those cigarette salesmen. I work for a company in North Carolina called Liggett and Myers."

"Is that right?"

"It is. Do you know anything about the tobacco industry?"

"More than you will ever know. By the way, do you have a cigarette?"

James pulled out a pack of cigarettes from his coat pocket. As Cora spotted the package that had been made by the machines that her Uncle Richard had sold to Liggett and Myers, she begun to giggle.

"What's so funny?"

"Nothing," Cora stated before inhaling the mild tobacco and exhaling it out over the water.

"I believe there is a lot about you that I would like to get to know."

"I'm not too complicated. Now, my uncle is an entirely different story. Speaking of my uncle, I need to leave. He doesn't tolerate tardiness of any kind. James, it was nice to meet you. Maybe we can see each other again."

Cora snuffed her cigarette out and placed it in a tray that was permanently fixed to the deck. She turned and waved to James and made her way back to her room, where she washed up and dressed. She looked at her reflection in the mirror and hoped Uncle Richard would find her dress and makeup presentable.

At six o'clock, Uncle Richard knocked on the door to Cora's room. She checked herself in the mirror and applied one more layer of lipstick onto her lips. She pinched her cheeks to enhance the color and then grabbed her small purse and wrap. When Cora opened the door, Uncle Richard was leaning on his cane dressed in a formal tuxedo.

"Cora, you look very pretty."

"Well, thank you."

"I have made reservations for us to sit with the captain tonight. I believe there will be others in the tobacco business joining us."

"Should I expect to hear you speaking about business or is this night for pleasure?"

"Now, Cora, you know that every social interaction has a purpose beyond pleasure. I believe every conversation can lead to a way to enhance my business."

"Uncle Richard, can't you just enjoy yourself without thinking about the bottom line?"

"Cora, you should know me well enough to understand that my business aspirations are what bring me pleasure."

Cora shook her head. She knew that her uncle would never change and it wasn't worth getting upset over. He had made a decision when his wife, Mamie, died, to never pursue another woman; if pursuing business connections brought him pleasure, so be it. Cora clasped her arm around her uncle's and walked down the narrow corridor.

As they approached the entrance to the dining room, Cora looked out over the beautiful table settings, delicate flower arrangements, and abundant food. Instead of relishing in the setting, she felt a sense of guilt, as she thought about the growing homeless population in and around Durham. She considered taking a stand against such overindulgence, but knew it would not go over well with her uncle. This was not the time or place to bring up her concerns about such social matters, so she decided to play the part of grateful niece and be on her best behavior.

After providing their names, Cora and her uncle were escorted to a table in the center of the room. Several couples had already been seated and the captain was busy introducing himself to various guests and giving them his undivided attention.

After Cora was seated, she took a sip of water, while her uncle began a conversation with the man on his left. She was accustomed to his indulgent discussions about his latest business interests. This time, the conversation was based on electricity and how it could change the world. Cora was pleased to have a woman about her age sit down beside her. The woman seemed a little timid to speak, which Cora found refreshing. "Hello, my name is Cora."

"My name is Katherine."

"Is this your first voyage across the Atlantic?"

"Yes. How could you tell?"

"I've been coming with my uncle for many years. I can usually tell when it's the first time sailing for someone. It can seem very intimidating to be in the middle of the ocean for days. I can promise you that it gets easier."

"Thank you for reassuring me. My husband thinks I'm acting foolish but I've heard horrible stories of shipwrecks and ships being bombed."

"I must admit I was a little nervous about this trip. I sailed on many occasions before the war, but this time is different for me as well."

At that moment, Cora heard someone laughing at a table behind her and turned her head to see James sitting between two attractive women. She felt a pang of jealousy, then told herself that it was silly to think that way about someone she had only briefly met. Cora turned back to Katherine and could tell she had missed a part of the conversation. "I'm sorry, I was distracted. What were you asking?"

"I was asking about the types of entertainment this ship has to offer."

"Every day there are readings in the library and you can find a game of Bridge if that is something you enjoy. Usually, in the evening, the ship provides music or a short play. I particularly enjoy the music."

Before Katherine had a chance to respond, James walked up and tapped Cora on the shoulder.

"Hello. I thought I might find you at the captain's table."

"Hello. James, this is Katherine."

"Hello, Katherine. I hope you are enjoying your trip."

"Yes, I am."

"Cora, may I have a moment of your time?"

"Yes."

James reached down, took Cora's hand, and led her across the room to a couch that was tucked up against a wall. As she sat down, she could see her uncle staring in their direction. Cora wasn't sure if he would approve of James but, for now, she was enjoying the attention this attractive man was giving her.

"James, I'm not sure about this. My uncle is very opinionated about the people he wants me to interact with."

"Are you saying that you don't think he would approve of me?"

"I really don't know, but I believe it would be best to walk back over to the table and for you to properly introduce yourself."

"If you think it will make a difference, let's go."

James turned and walked with confidence back toward the captain's table. As Cora rose, she smiled at this young man's demeanor and hoped that he could handle the grilling she knew would greet him. James stood a couple steps away, as Uncle Richard finished a conversation he was having with the captain. Once Uncle Richard turned to face the two young people, a scowl appeared on his face.

"Mr. Wright, I'm glad to meet you. I met Cora this afternoon on the deck. I would like to ask if she can spend some time with me on this voyage."

"Who are you, young man?"

"My name is James Rawlings. I'm presently employed with Liggett and Myers. My destination is Europe where I plan to work with several clients who are instrumental in the sale of our brand. Mr. Wright, do you know much about the tobacco business?"

Cora snickered as she watched her uncle gaze up at James. If only James had any idea of who he was speaking to. Uncle Richard didn't seem impressed by this young man and she knew this situation wasn't going to improve unless she interjected something in James' defense.

"Uncle Richard, James shared with me about the success he has been experiencing as a salesman. He reminds me a lot of you as a young salesman for the W. Duke, Sons and Company. I think it would be a great idea for us to sit down and allow James to share his business goals and objectives with you."

"Now, Cora, if you put it that way, I guess I should give this young man an opportunity to convince me he can meet the standards I expect from all of my nieces' suitors."

"Thank you, Uncle Richard."

"Take a seat, young man. Tell me about you and your family."

"Well, sir, I was born in Chapel Hill, North Carolina, and was attending the university when President Wilson declared war in 1917. I enlisted into the Army and was stationed in Great Britain. While I was there, I came to love the countryside and people of Europe. At that time, I promised myself that I would find a career where I could revisit the country I fell in love with.

When the war was over in November 1918, I came home to North Carolina where I finished my degree in business."

"So, what do you do now?" Uncle Richard asked, as he sat back in his chair, giving James his full attention.

"I've always been intrigued with the tobacco industry. My father owned a store in Chapel Hill, where I learned how to be an effective salesman. I was particularly interested in observing what brands of cigarettes did well, while others not so much. I paid close attention to the industry, and must admit, I was pleased when the American Tobacco Company was dissolved. When Liggett and Myers was given a portion of the divided company in 1911, I knew then that I wanted to work for that company."

"And what is your current position?"

"Sir, I'm one of the main sales reps for the company in Europe. I spend a great deal of time traveling back and forth across the Atlantic."

Cora began to smile as she heard James speak about his life. Given Uncle Richard's pursuit of success through the tobacco industry, she believed he would find James a suitable suitor. "Uncle Richard, are you going to grill James all night long?"

"No, but I do have some advice for you."

James leaned in, and with a sincere interest in his eyes, said, "Please, I would like to hear it."

"Cora can tell you that I've had to work hard to obtain the success that I've achieved. Over the years I've realized that, to become a great success, one must select a business for which one has a natural talent and taste, and master it until he loves it above all other pastimes or amusements."

James was silent for a moment and then responded, "Thank you for the advice. I do love what I do."

Uncle Richard looked right at James and asked, "How much time do you spend sailing back and forth across the Atlantic?"

"At least six months out of the year."

Uncle Richard turned toward Cora and spoke in a flat voice, "Cora, you're a grown woman who can make your own decisions. If you want to associate with this young man while on this sailing, I'll not stand in your way. But, I wouldn't recommend it."

Without another word, Uncle Richard turned away from James and Cora and began speaking to the person sitting beside him.

| 29 |

Richard (1922)

Richard handed his coat and hat to the butler and entered the foyer of Benjamin Duke's home. He looked around the room before stepping in, wanting to assess who to avoid and who he wanted to engage with. Even after so many years, the loss of his leg below the knee continued to cause him pain and discomfort. Every time Richard entered a room, it was important to have a destination in mind before moving forward.

Richard personally didn't like social gatherings, and how pretentious everyone could be. He didn't like wasting his time with small talk and became irritated when people wanted to share trivial information with him. He preferred working and spending his time on matters that he felt were important to his success. So, when he walked into this particular gathering, Richard already had a poor attitude.

Richard looked around the spacious room, spotted Buck, and noted how he had aged in the last couple of years. He no longer carried himself as the man who was so determined to monopolize the tobacco industry back in the late 1800s. Richard couldn't keep the grin off his face as he thought back to when Teddy Roosevelt and the U.S. Supreme court ordered the American Tobacco Company to be carved up, leaving Buck and his siblings without a share in the business.

As Richard gazed around the room, his eyes focused on Buck and his wife, Nanaline. He had never been able to get over how Buck had lied to him about his business agreement with the Bonsack Machine Company. He was tempted to walk out, then Benjamin walked up and shook his hand. "It was so nice of you to come tonight."

Richard knew he had to be cordial, even if he didn't feel like it. "Thank you for the invitation."

"It's been a long time since we've all been together. Even though we live in the same city, our paths rarely cross."

"Benjamin, I was thinking the same thing. I was sorry to hear last month about the death of your former partner, George Watts. He truly was a good man and did so much for the city."

"You're right about that. I can't imagine what Durham would be like today without the hospital he sponsored. And, because of George, the Presbyterians have a beautiful church on Main Street where they can worship."

Richard adjusted his cane and leaned back against a chair. "Speaking of good men, I always respected your father and how hard he worked. He was a forward thinker and, like me, didn't sit on an idea, but cultivated it. I also respected how he, a single father, raised such an ambitious group of men."

"My father loved his family, no matter the mistakes we made. And we know my deceased brother, Brodie, made plenty of them. He just couldn't stop drinking and, even after being institutionalized, it took only three years for him to return to the bottle. His drinking played a key role in his bad business decisions. I can't imagine how successful he would've been if he had just stayed away from the bottle."

Richard chimed in. "I have no tolerance for people who drink too much. If Thomas had stayed sober, I believe he would still be alive today. But I don't want to get into that now. How is Erwin Mills doing?"

"Thank goodness, the mills are very successful," Benjamin noted.

Richard looked over at Buck. "How did you get your brother to come to Durham? He must have plenty to keep him busy in New York City."

"When the judgment against the American Tobacco Company came down, he was beside himself. I believe that was the first time he realized that all his money couldn't change the result of the antitrust suit against our company. Over time he turned his focus to the building of the Southern Power Company. I'm glad to see he's finally pulling back from working so hard and is actually doing some traveling."

"So, let's get to the point. Why did you invite me here tonight?"

"Richard, you've always been one to be direct. I would say that I just wanted to see you, but we both know that wouldn't be the truth. There's someone who wants to speak with you and I thought a social gathering would be a perfect setting for the two of you to meet."

"I'm not sure if I want to be placed in this situation."

"Richard, it isn't that big a deal. Judge Wilbert Young wishes to have a conversation with you and I thought I would bring the two of you together."

Benjamin turned and walked to the center of the room. "Ladies and gentlemen, dinner is now being served in the formal dining room. There are name cards to help direct you to your seats."

Most of the men snuffed out their cigars or cigarettes and walked into the adjacent room, accompanied by their wives. Richard shrugged as he watched his contemporaries guide their spouses to their seats and pull out their chairs for them. He considered all this attention paid to another person a waste of effort.

Once Richard found his seat, he placed his cane against the wall and sat down. He reached over, took a sip from his water glass, and scanned the room for people he might want to speak with. A younger man, dressed in an inexpensive suit, sat down beside him. Richard became annoyed at Benjamin for placing him beside someone who clearly was of no interest to him. The man smiled. "Hello, Mr. Wright, my name is Judge Wilbert Young. I'm so pleased to have this opportunity to speak with you."

Richard pulled at his pocket watch and looked at the short hand pointing to the seven. He didn't care about being rude, and entertained the idea of scooting his chair back to get up and leave, but thought better of it. His stomach was grumbling and the thought of missing out on a good meal kept him seated. "So, young man, what was it that you wanted to discuss?"

Just as the judge was about to speak, the sound of a fork clinking against a glass stopped all of the conversations around the table. "Ladies and gentlemen, I'm so glad that you could join Sarah and me for this wonderful occasion. As you look around the room, you will notice some older faces of people for whom I have great respect. You will also note some others, who are now becoming influential to the city of Durham."

Richard looked at the men around the table and noticed that Julian Carr was seated at the other end. He recognized John Sprunt Hill, George Watts' son-in-law, and thought about how he had become a successful banker here in Durham. Several of Benjamin's children were also present, along with other family members. Everyone appeared to be familiar, except the man sitting next to him, which caused him to become irritated. *Why would Benjamin seat him next to a complete stranger when there were so many others whom he found worth his time?*

Benjamin continued to address his guests. "After George's death last month, I decided to have a gathering of the men who I would call the founding fathers of Durham. I believe, even though we have had our differences, we have one common interest, and that is our love for our city. No one knows how long we will be around, and I thought it would be beneficial to this next generation to hear from the men who, I believe, made Durham into what it is today. So, after we have enjoyed our meal, I would like for each of these men to share a memory or accomplishment they have made to make our city great."

Richard was happy to note that the judge had turned his head away to begin conversing with the woman on his right. The couple to Richard's left was also engrossed in conversation, which allowed him to enjoy his dinner without having to partake in the inconsequential exchange of words. But, once the dessert dishes had been removed from the table and the cups filled with coffee, Benjamin rose once more. "I'd like for my brother, Buck, to share an event or experience with us."

Buck rose and placed his napkin on the table. Richard thought he was looking right at him for a moment before opening his mouth. "Now, everyone sitting here knows some of the highs and lows of my career. You've been told how ambitious I was, and how my dream of monopolizing the tobacco business came to fruition. But, thankfully, our family had diversified before it was all taken away. I'm grateful to my brother, Brodie, for his willingness to move to Durham back in 1869, and for his foresight in setting the foundation for our success in the textile business. Let us all raise our glasses in remembrance of my brother."

Everyone seated at the table followed Buck's example and raised their glass to a man who had made an impression on all of them. "I'd also like to thank William T. Blackwell for the bull that rubbed me the wrong way for years. That damn bull provoked me to do everything in my power to get ahead of my competitors. Let's raise our glasses to William, God bless his soul. We all know he had a good heart, maybe too good. It's hard to believe he has been gone for over two decades."

As glasses were raised, snickers could be heard around the room. Buck continued. "At this time, I'd like to hear from Julian Carr." He pointed at the man, and said, "And I don't want to hear about your allegiance to the University of North Carolina. We're in Durham, the home of the only college of any importance, Trinity College."

Julian Carr rose from his chair and grinned. "I'd like to begin by saying that, since I gave up my land for Trinity College to be built in Durham, I'd have to agree. We both desire to bring educated men to Durham and since 1891, Trinity College has done just that. It's incredible to think about how far we have come since those first days, back in the 1870s, when we were all trying to sell our own tobacco. And Buck, I love knowing how much that bull got under your skin. Just the thought of the train pulling through Durham, making a sound like a bull, makes me smile."

Buck shouted above the laughter. "Okay, Julian, enough about that obnoxious bull. Tell us about what you've been doing since you sold your interest in the William T. Blackwell Company and how it was later swallowed up by the American Tobacco Company."

"I'm not sure I see it that way, but since moving away from the tobacco business, I've been active in the textile business, as well as pursuing lots of other ventures." Julian took a sip of water and looked back at Benjamin. "Once again, you got ahead of the game, and were able to invest the necessary capital into several up and coming industries, electricity being at the top of the list. I hate to admit it, but you've done a fine job providing electricity to the city of Durham through your company, Southern Power."

Benjamin interjected, "I believe we all have benefited from our pursuits in this fine city. Richard, you and Julian are doing an excellent job providing telephone service through the Interstate Telephone and Telegraph Company, but we all would appreciate it if you did something with the telephone lines that litter Durham's main streets."

Julian looked back at Benjamin and waved his cigar in the air. "We'll talk about that later. In closing, I'd like to tell everyone here that I'm most pleased with how we've helped our citizens through our generous gifts to the many religious and educational institutions, not only here in Durham, but throughout the state."

Benjamin rose from his chair. "Thank you, Julian, for sharing. Now, I'd like to hear from a man whom we have rarely seen in recent years. Richard Wright, we're all glad to see you here tonight and would love to hear how you have contributed to the good of our city."

Richard paused to think about what he had done for the city that had been his home since 1877. Gathering his thoughts, he rose and glanced down at the familiar faces staring up at him. After clearing his throat, he began. "As most of you know, I've spent a great deal of my adult life traveling around the world. It's hard to keep up with the number of times I've boarded a ship to cross the Atlantic or Pacific Ocean. But, as far as I've gone, I'm always drawn back to this city that took me in over four decades ago. Now, unlike some of you, who have given so much to Trinity College, I've given money to Louisburg College in memory of my sister, Pattie Julia. She was a gifted poet and I made sure one of the buildings was named after her. Not many of you know this, but when she was living in Franklin County, she would travel to Louisburg each day. It was a long drive by horse and buggy, and I wanted to make sure other women could, not only attend Louisburg College, but stay in a dormitory. I could also list the different businesses I've been instrumental in creating here in Durham, but I don't want to bore you. It's hard to pinpoint what my greatest achievement is due to the sheer number of them."

Richard paused, and then continued, "But enough about me. Benjamin, what would you like to contribute to this conversation?"

Richard sat back down and watched Benjamin rise to his feet. "When I was a young man, I didn't have time to dream. My family was too busy manufacturing tobacco and traveling across the country. When Brodie came to Durham and built a larger space for manufacturing tobacco, I never knew it would lead us to where we are today. Ever since then, our family hasn't stopped to count our blessings. From the tobacco industry to the textile mills, we have only looked forward. Tonight, I wanted to stop and count our blessings with the men who have contributed to making our city one of the best places in the country to live. Let's raise our glasses."

After the clinking of glasses, Benjamin continued, "Trinity College means a great deal to our family. Higher education is becoming more important for the betterment of our city and our country. Our family believes that this college will be a school that young people from all over the country, and world, will want to attend. We want to let you know that we will be donating a sizable amount toward its future."

Everyone seated around the table applauded. Benjamin continued. "We know that there have been times when our ambition has caused disagreements between some of us here."

Julian, Buck, and several others began to laugh. "But now, as we reach the last few years of our lives, I hope that we can reflect on all the good we have collectively accomplished. Thank you for coming. I hope each of us will be inspired to share the blessings we have received for the betterment of our city. In the meantime, let us raise our glasses to our city and its future."

Richard raised his glass along with the others and then placed it down on the table in front of him. He was ready to leave. It had been a long day and all he wanted to do was get home and to his bed. He reached for his cane and was scooting his chair back when Judge Young addressed him. "Mr. Wright, can I have a minute of your time?"

"Please, make it short. I have an early morning meeting and a long drive home."

"Yes. I'm not sure if you know me or my position in the court system. I listen to court cases dealing with neglected children in Durham. Recently, since the end of the war and the influenza outbreak, we have been inundated with more children than I care to count. These children have nowhere to go. Many are sent to orphanages or are living on the streets. I would like your assistance in building a refuge for them. This home would be temporary for these children until a permanent placement can be found. I would like for you to consider donating $10,000 and the land for this cause."

"Young man, this is a lot to ask."

"All I'm asking is that you think about it. We would, of course, name it after you. Think about your legacy and the impact it would have on Durham."

Richard had no intention of entertaining this idea. He wasn't much of a philanthropist and didn't like giving away money to projects that couldn't provide a return. "Judge Young, I'm not sure where you got the idea that I would help you with this project."

"Mr. Wright, I know that you have assisted your brother's children since their father's death. I also know about your donation to

Louisburg College. All I'm asking is for you to consider the impact such a home would have on our city. Please feel free to contact me at any time to discuss this further."

Richard pushed his chair back and grabbed his cane. As he rose, he looked at the young man and said, "I will consider it. Now, if you will excuse me, I need to go."

| 30 |

Cora (1919-1923)

Cora did spend time with James during the voyage across the Atlantic, but then never saw him again. Knowing how her uncle felt weighed heavily on her mind during every interaction she had with the young man. She enjoyed James' company and, particularly, enjoyed the nights they danced to the music played by the small orchestra. Once the ship docked in Liverpool, they embraced and James brushed his lips across her forehead. "Cora, you've been a joy to be with."

"I feel the same way."

"I guess this is goodbye."

"Yes, James. As much as I'd like to see you again, I think it's best to end it here. I'll never forget this voyage across the Atlantic and the man who made it so memorable."

"If you ever change your mind, please don't hesitate to call me."

"Thank you again, but as you know, I can't."

James took his bag and walked down the corridor while Cora stood and watched him disappear among the throngs of people on the dock. It made her sad to let this man go, but in her heart of hearts, she knew he wasn't her soulmate and it was best to end it now.

When Cora returned to Durham, she felt lonely and without a purpose. Lucy was happily married and spent less time at Bonnie Brae. Without her dear sister to share her days with, she poured herself into the rigorous schedule she had known since childhood. There were always tasks that her Aunt Nannie wanted her to complete, along with reading books and practicing the piano. Cora also loved taking care of her horse, and the hours she spent riding among the hundreds of acres that surrounded the property.

One of Cora's favorite pastimes had always consisted of engaging in conversations with her Uncle Richard, particularly after his arrival home from his travels across the ocean, or when he was on the verge of a new business venture. Over time, Cora realized if she asked just the right question and took a posture of intrigue, he would open up. And once he did, she would sit back and soak in his stories of exotic places with strange languages and cultures, or hear about an incredible business undertaking that appeared impossible to accomplish.

During the months after her return from Europe, Uncle Richard made it a point to invite her to ride horses with him around the estate. Often, when reading outside on the porch, he would call for her to change into her riding clothes and meet him at the stables. Cora had come to understand the importance of remaining silent as the older man led the way across the hilly pastures and into the forests that lined the property. This posture of silence suited her well.

It was on these rides that Cora was honored with some of this man's secrets; secrets no one else knew. For some unknown reason, Uncle Richard trusted his young niece and believed that, no matter what was spoken, it would remain between the two of them. So, on this particular ride in 1922, Cora was the first to hear Uncle Richard's thoughts about the judge who had tried to persuade him to donate generously toward the refuge for neglected children.

As they took their horses from a trot to a canter, Uncle Richard began to shout out his anger toward the man who had caused him to feel guilty. "I don't appreciate anyone trying to make me take on a responsibility that isn't mine to have. I've given to Louisburg College and created the Lakewood Amusement Park for the common person. Why should I have to give toward the cause of taking care of neglected children? Does this man know my background and think that, because I was an orphan, I'd be willing to help other orphans? I didn't take from anyone, even when I was on my own. I worked hard and did everything in my power to make a living. Why can't these neglected children do the same?"

Cora wasn't sure what to think about the words she was hearing. She had recently started volunteering with Ms. Mattie Southgate Jones, a prominent woman in Durham, who was known for her desire to help those in need. Cora had personally met several young children who were living on the streets without any resources to take care of themselves. As she heard her uncle rant on about his point of view, she wanted to speak up, but knew this was not the time. Instead, she decided to remain silent and wait for the right moment to broach the subject. "Uncle Richard, it's such a beautiful day. I'm sorry you're so upset. Let's enjoy our ride. I'm sure the situation will be resolved in due time. For now, I'd love for you to share with me about your most recent trip to Gainsborough, England. I want to know about the new products your company has created packaging for."

Uncle Richard appeared happy to have Cora change the subject. After he began sharing about his company, and how successful it was, his mood changed. Instead of anger, he took on a lighter attitude for the remainder of their ride.

Two nights later, Lucy and Sidney came over for dinner. Aunt Nannie and her mother, Bettie, were excited about entertaining the young couple and had the cook make a special dinner of shrimp and steaks. Cora enjoyed being around her sister and new husband. She loved watching them as they interacted with each other. Cora found Sidney's stories about his career as a lawyer entertaining and informative.

Ever since Lucy married Sidney and moved out, the house just didn't seem the same. Cora and Mary Ruth were the only girls left at home. Richard Jr. and Thomas Jr. occupied rooms, but were hardly ever present due to the demands that Uncle Richard placed on them. So, when Lucy visited, Cora was always happy to see her. This evening was no exception. After bathing and dressing for dinner, she entered the parlor and played the piano to pass the time.

Cora had become entranced in her music and didn't hear the door open when Lucy and Sidney entered. As she played, she became preoccupied with thoughts about the conversation with her uncle. Feelings of sadness overtook her as she thought about the children she had seen on the streets of Durham. In that moment, Lucy wrapped her arms around Cora's shoulders, causing her to slam her hands down on the keys.

Her first instinct was to pull back but, after realizing it was Lucy, she reached over and hugged her. "Lucy, I'm sorry. I was lost in my thoughts."

"Cora, I'm sorry if I startled you. What were you thinking about?"

"Yesterday, I was helping Ms. Jones and a little boy came up to me. The smell of him made me gasp and I felt so ashamed. As he looked up at me, I was overwhelmed by the beautiful eyes tucked back into his filthy face. All I could think about was how I don't deserve this life we've been given."

At that moment, Richard Jr. and Sidney walked into the room.

"What are you two women talking about? You look so serious."

"Oh, Sidney." Lucy said. "Cora was telling me about a little boy she saw yesterday in the streets and how sad it made her."

"I know what you mean," Sidney said. "I've also seen homeless children huddled against buildings in downtown Durham. On occasion, I've given them food or a couple of coins."

Cora looked down at the floor. "I wish I knew the solution to this ever-growing problem."

Her mother, Bettie, peeked into the room and saw the young adults gathered around the piano. "Your Uncle Richard is waiting for you in the dining room."

Cora and Lucy walked in and made their way to their seats. Richard Jr. and Sidney followed. "Last night, I visited the Piedmont Club and found it most entertaining," Richard Jr. began. "Judge Sykes shared his vision for the club and how he's planning another ball in the coming months."

"Speaking of judges," Uncle Richard chimed in. "Sidney, what do you know about Judge Wilbert Young?"

Cora sat down and waited for Sidney's response. She was glad that the topic had been raised and she wasn't the one to do it.

"Judge Young has a good reputation among the attorneys. He seems to care deeply for the underprivileged and is always trying to recruit people of influence to help."

"Well, last night, he tried to recruit me."

Aunt Nannie was seated to her brother's right and spoke up, "What do you mean?"

Cora noted how Uncle Richard was gazing around the room and wondered what he would say next.

"Last night, I attended a dinner at Benjamin Duke's house. He intentionally sat me next to Judge Young. At the end of the dinner, the judge had the audacity to ask me to give money and land toward a refuge for neglected children."

"I think that's a wonderful idea!" exclaimed Aunt Nannie. "Richard, I know you've been wondering how your legacy could live on after your death. A home for neglected children bearing your name would be a perfect way to do just that."

"You know I don't care about assigning my money to places that don't make me a return."

"But, Uncle Richard, what better return than your name living on in the hearts of all the children you provide a refuge for," Lucy stated.

"If I was to give my money and land to this project, I'd like to see Durham at least match it."

Sidney said, "Richard, I can look into it. I'll be glad to speak to Judge Young on your behalf. I must agree with the women at this table. I think it would help your image as well as the many children who find themselves out on the streets of Durham."

"Uncle Richard," Cora said. "You are such a giving man. I was just thinking about how blessed we've all been due to your generosity. I believe, with a little assistance, these children could grow up to be prominent members of society."

"Well, I guess I'm outnumbered on this. Richard Jr., do you have anything to add to this discussion?"

"No. I think they've said it all."

There was no further discussion of the refuge that night, but Cora believed her uncle would act in his own time. She had found it best to let him develop his own conclusions when he was making a decision, particularly one like the refuge.

Over time, Richard did decide to donate toward the home. After many discussions with the judge and a committee from the city, Uncle Richard wrote a check for the amount of $10,000 to build the refuge on several acres in northern Durham. Judge Young was able to convince the city of Durham to match the amount. After construction began, it was clear that the $20,000 was not enough to finish the structure or maintain the facility. After several conversations with his sister and nieces, Uncle Richard reluctantly provided an additional $50,000 as an endowment for the refuge.

Cora and Aunt Nannie often visited the building site to oversee the construction. Even though women weren't usually welcome to provide input into such projects, it became clear that the two women had strong opinions that weren't going to be ignored. Cora was a little disappointed by Uncle Richard's apathetic stance toward the construction of the refuge. But, even if he personally didn't care about the project, she was happy to know something was being done to help the children living on the streets of Durham.

Cora had hoped he would have some of the same zeal that he had possessed when Bonnie Brae was built back in 1916. She would never forget how excited her uncle was as the walls and roof went up over his summer home. He loved working on every aspect of the plans. She remembered how he wanted the nine thousand square foot home to be a summer retreat from Durham's heat but, after its completion, he quickly changed his mind. After the house was furnished with expensive pieces from his trips overseas, he decided to move out of his home on Dillard Street and have Bonnie Brae as his permanent residence.

Once Cora had moved into her room with the full-size bed and large wardrobe, she felt exceedingly grateful toward her uncle. Many nights, when she would look around her spacious room with imported furniture and beautiful wallpaper, she couldn't help but think of the children living out on the streets. As much as she enjoyed her room, a sense of guilt would often consume her, which served as a fuel to fight for the children who would make the refuge their home.

| 31 |

Richard (1924)

Richard had begun to struggle with his health. But no matter the ailment, he was resolute in his routine to keep working for as long as he could. He continued to go to the office for a couple hours a day to keep his finger on the pulse of his business dealings. His drive to become more profitable than the Dukes had subsided due to their massive fortune. It irritated him how the Dukes had monopolized the American Tobacco Company and bought out all the smaller tobacco companies, including the William T. Blackwell Company.

Richard couldn't argue that the Dukes were smart and knew when it was time to diversify their investments. In the 1890s, Benjamin Duke and George Watts invested $85,000 to open a textile manufacturing company. They hired William Erwin to manage the textile mill. Mr. Erwin believed in the project and invested $40,000 of his own money. When the American Tobacco Company had been dissolved due to the anti-trust legislation in 1911, the Duke fortune far surpassed Richard's personal wealth.

When word reached Richard that Buck had signed the documents for the endowment toward the building of Duke University, he had mixed feelings. Richard knew that the development of a university would bring more affluent men from all over the world to Durham. But when he read the words that Buck spoke upon signing the papers, he became angry. Buck had been a thorn in Richard's side for as long as he had lived, but Richard still had great respect for his driven spirit and determination to succeed.

Upon reading Buck's words, Richard felt a sense of betrayal. When Buck was asked about the massive amount of money providing luxury to so many people, Buck had responded, *"There will be no luxury. Nothing makes people so unhappy as luxury. Satisfied ambition is an awful thing."*

Richard would never agree with this statement. His ambition had never been satisfied, and the luxury he was surrounded by brought him the only happiness he had experienced since the death of Mamie.

The only satisfaction Richard felt was when Buck died less than a year after penning those words. This made Buck's brother, Benjamin Newton Duke, Richard's only other living contemporary. When Richard heard of Buck's death, he stated to the newspapers, *"They might have earned more and built bigger, but I'm determined to outlive them all!"*

With the deaths of so many of his contemporaries, Richard came to the decision that it was time to write his will. One night, he sat down with two of his closest friends, J. Martin Umstead and

R.P. Rogers, to draft his last will and testament. He had spent quite a bit of time contemplating how his estate would be divided up. For hours he had sat in front of his typewriter, planning stipulations that his family would have to meet in order to receive their inheritance. In death, as in life, he expected them to act in accordance to the standards he had set in place.

He handed both men the one typewritten paper, and waited for them to read through it and sign the document. J. Martin knew his friend didn't want comments, only affirmation of the words printed on the page. R.P. looked up after he was given the page to proof. "So, from what I gather here, you'd like your sister, Nannie, to receive all of your property of every kind. Well, that's understandable. Your sister has been devoted to you for as long as I can remember."

"When I lost Mamie, so many years ago, I wasn't sure what I'd do. When Nannie came to live with me, she forfeited love and marriage to be the woman of my home. Over the years, as I've watched her devotion to my wellbeing, I made a decision that she would be provided for."

Richard looked at his friends and could tell that J. Martin had something to say. "What's on your mind? I can tell you have a question about something in the will."

J. Martin hesitated a moment and then asked, "Why are you so adamant about the estate keeping your property for thirty years before selling it?"

"I thought you'd raise this question. I worked my entire life acquiring property around Durham. Even though I'll be dead, I just want to make sure that people will still remember me and my legacy. And I believe this can happen if the property stays intact."

R.P. sat very still, gazing down at the document. Richard could tell he had something to say. "So, R.P., I can tell you are thinking about something. Go ahead. Let me hear it."

"Why are you stipulating that your nieces and nephews will lose their inheritance if they marry a divorcee?

Richard looked directly at his friend and, with a stern voice, stated, "I don't want any of my family members tarnishing my good name. I can't accept a marriage between one of my nieces or nephews with a divorcee. It's my money and I will do with it what I want!"

Richard looked over at J. Martin. "I can tell you have another question. Go ahead and ask."

"Well, it looks like everyone will receive $1,000 per year including all of your nieces and nephews, except Mrs. E.L. Miller. Why are you giving her $2,000?"

"My niece, Elizabeth, has always been special to me. In the 1890s she moved up to New York, at my expense, of course. It was at the time when I'd been advised by Theo Allen to become a resident of New York, so I could continue my suit against the Dukes. Those years of visits by Elizabeth and her friends brought such joy to me. Anyway, she's been ill, and she and her husband have had a difficult time with paying their medical bills, and I want to assist her."

"That's very commendable of you," J. Martin said. "I don't see any charitable contributions. I thought you might be giving some of your money to Louisburg College. I know you've given to their endowment in the past."

"I just don't feel the need to give the college any more money. It is true that Louisburg College has done well with my financial backing but, upon my death, the backing will cease. I don't think you know this but, when my mother died, I promised her that I'd take care of my family, and that's what I intend to do."

R.P. then piped up and said, "Well, Richard, you're in relatively good health and, hopefully, you'll be around for several more years. If you want to make any changes to your will, just let me know and I'll be glad to witness any revision you would like to make."

"I doubt I'll reconsider but, if I do want to make a revision, I'll let you know."

| 32 |

Cora (1924)

Now that Lucy, Lila, and Nannie Bet were married, and living away from Bonnie Brae, Cora fell into a routine that kept her mind occupied. Each day, she would rise for breakfast with the family members who weren't traveling or busy with business responsibilities. After listening to her mother and Aunt Nannie discuss the tasks that needed to be accomplished around the large house, Cora would drive out to the Wright Refuge building site, followed by volunteering with Ms. Southgate Jones. Once these obligations had been met, she would make her way to Lucy's home. Typically, the two women would enjoy a cup of tea and cookies, and discuss decorating ideas or just local gossip. Cora loved these afternoons with her sister and the light-hearted nature of their time together.

One summer day in late June, Cora made her usual stop at Lucy's house. She took hold of the large brass knocker and tapped the wooden door. When no one answered, she glanced into a window, seeing no sign of life. Cora knocked once more and waited. She was about to turn and walk back to her car, when Lucy opened the door with a handkerchief in her hand. "I'm sorry, Cora. I'm not feeling well."

"You scared me. What's wrong?"

"Come in."

Lucy sat down across from Cora and placed her head down between her legs. Cora looked over at her sister and, with concern in her voice, asked, "What can I do for you?"

"Nothing. I haven't felt well all day. It must've been something I ate."

"Are you sure?"

"No."

Lucy got up and raced back to the bathroom where she became violently sick. Cora followed her, finding a wash cloth and placing it on her sister's forehead. "Could you be pregnant?"

"I've thought about that."

After a while, Lucy got up and made her way to the parlor where she lay down on a couch. "I will make an appointment with my doctor. Hopefully, he'll have some suggestions to help me feel better."

The next day, Lucy went to the doctor's office and was told the good news. After that, Cora came over every chance she could and became her sister's companion during the day while Sidney worked. Cora accompanied Lucy to many of her doctor's appointments. At one such appointment, Lucy's doctor shared his concerns about the stress the pregnancy was having on her heart.

Lucy was so excited about having a baby and refused to consider the impact that the pregnancy could be having on her health. In the following weeks, she spent most of her time in bed, too exhausted to do the simplest of tasks. As time went by, Cora noticed that Lucy was becoming weaker, hardly able to raise her head up. She became gravely concerned when Lucy refused even a sip of broth or a bite of a cracker.

One day, Cora came into her sister's room and witnessed Sidney leaning down over Lucy. It was clear from Sidney's facial expression that he was very concerned. "Lucy, your sister is here. Are you going to be okay? I can change my appointments if you think I need to."

Lucy opened her eyes long enough to make eye contact with her husband. In a voice that Cora could barely hear, she mumbled, "Sidney, I'll be okay. Go to work. I know you're needed there. Cora is here."

Cora walked over and tapped her brother-in-law on the shoulder. "Sidney, I'll be right here. I promise I'll call you if there are any major changes."

Sidney grabbed his briefcase from a nearby chair and then faced Cora. "Please call me if there are any changes. I'm not feeling good about her condition. She's gotten weaker and weaker. The phone number for the doctor is on her bedside table. Please call me and him if you feel the need."

Cora looked at Sidney and, with confidence in her ability to take care of her sister, responded, "I promise I'll call both you and the doctor. Now go to work."

Once Sidney left, Cora sat in a nearby chair and watched her sister sleep. Every once in a while, she tried to get Lucy to take a sip of water or chicken broth, but as the day went on, Lucy couldn't keep her mouth open long enough to take it in. As the day slipped into night, Lucy's condition seemed to only worsen. Her breathing was labored and Cora reached over and shook her sister. "Lucy, are you alright?"

Lucy barely opened her eyes and looked at Cora. "Help me."

A cold chill arose in the pit of Cora's stomach. "I need to get you to the hospital."

Lucy only nodded and, with all the energy she could muster, she sat up. Cora, with the help of two servants, carried her sister down the stairs and into the car. Before leaving, Cora went over to the telephone and picked up the receiver. "Mary, this is Cora Wright. Can you please get Sidney Chambers on the line?"

"Of course."

"Please let him know it's extremely important."

As Cora waited for Sidney to pick up the phone, she became increasingly anxious about Lucy and was tempted to hang up the phone. Just as she took the receiver away from her ear, Sidney came on the line. "Hello, this is Sidney."

"Sidney, something's wrong with Lucy. I'm taking her over to Watts Hospital. Please meet us there."

"Oh no! What's happening?"

"I don't have time to explain. Just please get to the hospital as soon as you can."

Cora ran out to the driveway and climbed into the driver's seat. After squeezing her sister's hand, she turned off of the circle driveway and headed toward the hospital. The roads had suffered from the cold temperatures and there were more potholes than she could count. As Cora was watching the road, several snowflakes floated down from the dark sky and bounced on the windshield before melting. At any other time, the snowflakes would have brought joy, but not now.

The snow picked up, which made it difficult for Cora to see, and the dirt-packed roads turned into mud. She gripped the wheel with both hands and felt the perspiration on her palms. As Cora made a sharp turn, the car veered into a deep mud puddle. Cora was ready to cry, but knew she had to get her sister to the hospital as soon as possible. She remembered a time when her Uncle Richard had become stuck in a hole and how he had stopped the car and placed it in reverse. Cora took some deep breaths and, after placing the vehicle in reverse and tapping on the accelerator, the car lunged backward and onto solid ground.

Cora looked over at Lucy, who was now slumped against the passenger door, and knew she didn't have much time. She raised her voice and shouted out, "Lucy, now you hold on. We're almost there."

Cora refused to consider the worst scenario and made herself remember how Lucy had recovered from other health conditions. She had to believe that, once she got Lucy to the hospital, the doctors would be able to treat her. But, deep down, Cora knew her sister was extremely ill. It was the look on Lucy's face that scared her the most. Her beautiful mouth was turned downward and her skin tone had turned an ashen color.

Finally, Cora could see the lights of the hospital. She turned the car sharply up the driveway. Before reaching the main entrance, tears began to form in her eyes. Lucy looked so helpless and her breathing had become more of a gasping noise. "Lucy, we're here. Please be okay. I love you so much. Please be okay."

Sidney, along with two hospital attendants, opened the car door and whisked Lucy out of the passenger seat and onto a gurney. By this time, the tears wouldn't stop. Cora parked the car and placed her head onto the steering wheel long enough to get her wits about her. She grabbed her bag from the back seat, and trudged through the mud puddles, snow falling all around her. Cora approached the open hospital doors and sighed. Her heart was beating so hard she had to stop and catch her breath. As she arrived at the nurses' station, she saw two nurses talking near the back wall. "Please, tell me where they took my sister."

"Ma'am, I'm unable to give you that information. Mr. Chambers can provide more information when he returns. Now, please find a seat and, if I hear anything, I'll let you know."

Cora found a chair against a back wall and began to shake. All she could think about was how much she loved her sister and how she couldn't imagine life without her. Lucy had always been there for her and the thought of losing her was almost too much to bear. Several minutes later, the doors of the hospital opened up and her mother, Bettie, and Aunt Nannie walked toward her. Her mother looked so scared and practically screamed, "Cora, what happened? Where have they taken Lucy?"

"Mom, I wish I knew. When I drove up, Sidney and the attendants took Lucy back and I haven't heard anything."

Aunt Nannie approached the nurses' station with authority and looked down at the nurse who appeared to be instantly frightened by this older woman. "We need to know what has happened to Lucy Chambers."

Just as Aunt Nannie was taking her fist and hitting the desk, Sidney walked through the swinging door that separated them from Lucy. The three women stood frozen as they saw Sidney's expression. His shoulders were slumped and it was clear he'd been crying.

In an unusually calm voice, Bettie asked Sidney the question that no one wanted the answer to. "Sidney, what has happened?"

"Bettie, Nannie, Cora, please come sit down. As we all know, Lucy has had a heart condition for a long time. When we discussed getting pregnant, she refused to listen to the doctors about the possibility of complications. Well, apparently her heart couldn't handle the needs of the baby."

By this time, Sidney was so upset he couldn't go on.

Cora spoke up, "Sidney, is Lucy going to be okay?"

"I'm sorry. If only she hadn't wanted this baby so much. She's gone. She died just a few minutes ago."

The women huddled together, sobbing in disbelief. "Sidney, are you sure?" Aunt Nannie asked.

"Yes, I'm so sorry. She struggled for her last breath, but she wanted me to tell all of you how much she loved you."

Cora looked over at her mother and saw the grief that she could hardly bear. Her mother had experienced so much death in her life and was not ready to let her daughter go. Cora got up and walked over to her mother, took her in her arms and, for what seemed like an eternity, allowed her mother to sob until there was no more energy left in her body.

The next afternoon, friends and acquaintances met the family at the funeral home to pay their condolences. Each time the door opened, a person dressed in black would enter and head straight over to the open coffin. Many of them teared up and shook their heads in disbelief. Cora was mesmerized by the parade of people going through the motions of grief. Her own sense of sorrow was so great that she thought it might swallow her up. But she, like all of her family members, played her part with as much dignity as she could muster.

After a couple of hours, Cora's feet began to hurt and she made her way to a chair where she could see Sidney. She couldn't fathom how tired he must be. As she watched the crowd, Cora noted how pretentious everyone appeared. People stumbled over their words and no one could look her brother-in-law in the eye. Even Uncle Richard seemed lost in how to approach the situation. The old man shook Sidney's hand and then hobbled over next to Cora and sat down. He didn't even acknowledge her, which was fine. She was in no mood to talk with anyone, particularly this man who never showed his emotions.

Finally, in the late evening, the family left in Uncle Richard's Model T and drove back to Bonnie Brae. Cora walked into the large house and ran upstairs to the safety of her room. Immediately, she began to cry and hugged her pillow. *"Why Lord? Lucy was such a good person. She loved Sidney so much and would've been such a wonderful mother. Why did you take her from us?"*

After hours of sobbing and questioning God, sleep finally came and Cora slipped into a fitful slumber. Near morning, Cora dreamt of her childhood on Dillard Street. Lucy, Nannie Bet, and Mary Ruth were playing tag, and Cora was running around the house, with someone chasing her. She slipped and fell on the ground and, as she looked up, Lucy was laughing, her long auburn hair brushing up against Cora's face. And with a sweet voice, Lucy stated, "Cora, it's your turn."

Immediately, Cora opened her eyes and looked around the room. She tried to close her eyes and slip back into the dream but, as hard as she tried, reality made it impossible. Cora repeated the words to herself several times, swearing to never forget the image of her sister standing over her.

That afternoon, a funeral service was held at Trinity Methodist Church, followed by a graveside memorial at Maplewood Cemetery. Just over a decade had passed since Uncle Richard had the large mausoleum built in the old section of the cemetery. Cora wasn't sure how she felt about the day Uncle Richard's wife, Mamie, had been exhumed along with their four-year-old daughter. Her uncle had also been adamant about moving her father's body, along with his sister, Pattie Julia, to this cement tomb. She didn't want to think about her three-year-old sister, Francis Julia, and the remains of her burned body being placed inside. The only relative who almost brought a smile to her face was her Aunt Elizabeth, the woman who'd ruffled Uncle Richard's feathers when she'd tried to marry at the age of 70.

The large family crowded around the massive mausoleum. As the pastor spoke of eternal life and about Lucy now being with the Lord, Cora noticed how the doors into the rotunda were open. She thought about the family members who were already laid inside.

Mary Ruth came up beside her after the service concluded and took her hand. "Cora, what are you thinking about?"

"I know it sounds morbid, but I can't help but think how we all will end up in this building laid in columns for eternity."

"I never thought about that," Mary Ruth said. "I kind of like knowing we'll all be together in death."

"I wonder what the generations that follow us will think about, as they look inside these walls and see our names printed so neatly on our personal vaults?"

Mary Ruth took her handkerchief and dabbed at her cheeks. "I don't know. I just hope they'll remember Lucy as the kind woman that she was, and how loved she was by her husband."

"Me, too," Cora said, as she walked over to the black hearse and climbed inside.

| 33 |

Richard (1924)

Richard picked up his leg and placed it on a pillow. He tried to get comfortable in bed, but no matter what position he took, he was wracked with pain. He often spoke to himself as a way to convince his body to get up and go back to work. *No matter how bad I feel, I must move past this sickness and get my work done. There is too much to do and my nephews are not ready to take on all the responsibilities I have acquired.*

For some unknown reason, Richard's lingering illness began when Lucy died. Just seeing her being placed in the mausoleum was hard to move beyond. Too many women he knew had died during their pregnancy or childbirth. What should've been a time of celebration and new life became a time of suffering and grief.

He picked up the small bell beside his bed and rang it. When no one showed up, he picked it up once more and swished it above his head. He was becoming angrier by the minute, and was going to reprimand his sister when she came through the door. After several minutes had passed, the door opened and Nannie rushed into the room. He noticed how old and feeble she appeared. "I'm sorry, Richard. I was in the kitchen discussing tonight's dinner with the cook."

"Nannie, you know how much pain I'm in. Please try and stay closer by."

"I don't understand why you don't want one of the staff to come in and help you."

"We've discussed this before. I don't like to appear weak to anyone, particularly one of my servants."

"Yes, but as you get weaker, I'm having to carry more of your weight."

"Well, I don't plan on being in this bed for much longer. I'm feeling a little better and I have meetings to get back to."

"Richard, you know your nephews can cover for you."

"Richard Jr. has been busy conducting my main business accounts, and Thomas hasn't been as productive since he and that girl from East Durham broke up. Anyway, I need Richard Jr. in Baltimore and Thomas has responsibilities at the office. Now help me get up and to the bathroom. I'm determined to make it to dinner tonight."

Richard spent the whole day sitting in a chair near a window. He had his lunch brought to him and only had one visitor. In the afternoon, Nannie helped him dress in his formal attire to prepare for dinner.

Later that evening, Richard wheeled his chair into the dining room and placed himself at the head of the table. He looked over at Richard Jr. holding the hand of his new woman friend. She was a petite woman with curly, strawberry-blond hair. When Richard Jr. had brought Helen home for the first time, he wasn't sure if he liked her. Richard had to admit he did like her confidence, but also thought she was a little too assertive for his taste. The one thing that continued to rub him the wrong way was the fact her father was the minister at First Presbyterian Church. Richard had always attended Trinity Methodist Church and didn't appreciate it when Richard Jr. began attending the Presbyterian Church that George Watts had built in 1871. Their family had always been members of the Methodist Church and he didn't like his nephew's decision to attend a different church. He looked at Helen and asked, "Hello, Helen. How have you been?"

"Very well, sir. I'm glad to see you up and around. Richard Jr. has kept me updated on your improvement."

"Is that so?"

"Yes, sir."

Richard turned his attention away from Helen and looked over at Cora. "Now, Cora, what have you been doing lately?"

Cora was picking at her food. She still hadn't been able to shake the grief from her sister's death. "I'm trying to stay busy. I went over and helped at the refuge today. Most of the children are well-behaved and grateful to be fed and sleeping in a bed. It has really helped me to take my mind off of Lucy."

"I'm glad to hear it. Has anyone seen Sidney lately?"

Bettie looked up from her plate and answered, "He came over to the house yesterday to bring over some of Lucy's belongings. He told me he felt awkward keeping them and thought someone could make good use of her clothes and jewelry."

Richard looked at this woman who had lived under his roof for close to three decades. He knew Bettie had been a good mother, and friend to his sister, but he couldn't get past the thought of what a weak person she was. As he looked back at Helen, he believed that this woman was more like him; someone who was determined to get whatever she set her mind to.

Richard looked at his nephew and asked, "Richard Jr., is there any news you would like to share?"

"I heard that Julian Carr is sick. After he presented the portrait of Bartlett Durham to the city, he went up to Washington D.C. to get his tonsils taken out. Word is that his throat hasn't healed well. He left this morning for Chicago to see his daughter."

"I'm sorry to hear that. He's one man I have a great deal of respect for. Can you please send him a telegram tomorrow telling him my thoughts are with him?"

"Yes, sir. I also wanted to fill you in on the news about Trinity College. Apparently, President Few has been negotiating with Buck Duke about an endowment for the college to become a full-fledged university. Buck has been working on the agreement from his home in New Jersey."

"That's very interesting. Keep me informed as the talks progress. I do believe a university will bring more educated people to Durham. And the more educated our citizens are, the more affluent our city will become."

Richard finished the rest of his meal in silence. He was growing extremely tired but didn't want his family to witness his physical struggle. He hated men who were weak and was determined to be strong until his death. As he took the last bite of his dessert, he turned to his sister, Nannie. "I'm ready to return to my room."

"Yes, of course," Nannie said, as she stood and walked over to assist her brother.

"Richard Jr., please keep me informed about Julian Carr. Goodnight, everyone."

Two days later, news arrived that Julian Carr had died from pneumonia. A week later, Richard forced himself up and, with the help of his sister, was able to attend the funeral of his friend and business partner. As they made their way through the procession, Richard was overcome by the sight of multiple businesses that had draped their storefronts with black.

While the car moved slowly down Main Street, Richard noted the number of people from all socioeconomic backgrounds standing in reverence for his business partner and friend. This was, by far, the largest funeral service in the city's history. People were openly sad about the death of this man, who had given so generously to the people of the city he loved so much.

| 34 |

Helen (1924-1926)

As the last child left, Helen picked up her books and turned toward the door. She was filled with a sense of elation as she walked out of the classroom and into the spring sunshine. For the last nine months, she had lived in Lynchburg, Virginia, teaching young children in a poverty-stricken community. Given her wealthy upbringing, it had been difficult for her to understand the mentality of people who couldn't make a decent living.

Helen would never have chosen to teach in Lynchburg, but her father had insisted. After finishing her education at Vanderbilt University, her father informed her that he had found a place for her to teach. Being a Presbyterian minister, her father had spoken to a colleague in Lynchburg, who shared their need for a teacher. Given her father's strong desire to help the poor, he believed this was the right place for Helen to begin her teaching career.

When her father told Helen of the teaching assignment, she was devastated. She'd had her sights set on teaching at a private school in Durham, where she could continue to enjoy the company of her friends. Helen finally consented when her father told her that it would only be for one school year. Then, she could move back home if she didn't want to return.

Now that her term of duty had been served, and she was headed home, Helen began to smile at the thought of the parties she would attend. Several days earlier, she had received a letter from her sister, Mary. The letter spoke of her engagement party and how she was excited about Helen returning home in time to attend her bridal gala. The letter also mentioned a young man who would be attending the party, who came from a wealthy family in Durham.

Upon returning to the residence hall where she had lived during her time in Lynchburg, Helen packed her few belongings into a suitcase and made her way to the railroad station. Once she boarded the train and settled into her seat, she began to daydream of her sister's gala and the young man she would be introduced to. Thoughts of whirling around the dance floor in the arms of a wealthy man brought a smile to her face. But, as she looked down at her plain dress, she realized she didn't own an appropriate party dress for such an occasion. Frustration began to build inside of her and, by the time the train pulled into the Durham train station, she was livid.

Once Helen saw her father waiting on the platform, a plan on how to obtain the perfect dress began to form. She had always been able to persuade her father to purchase items that he considered frivolous. So, with a pretentious smile on her face, she made her way down the aisle and through the door. "Daddy, it's so good to see you!"

"Helen." Her father paused and glanced at her from head to toe. "Look at my girl. You're all grown up. I'm so glad to have you home." He gave her a quick hug and then released her. "Your mother and Mary have worked hard all day in the kitchen, fussing over the preparations for your first dinner back at home."

After getting into the car, he continued to speak his mind. "It appears you could use a couple of good meals. The main reason I was concerned about sending you to Lynchburg was your weight. Now, you have to promise me that you'll try and to put on a couple of pounds this summer."

"Oh, Daddy, I'm fine. You don't have to worry about me. I love Mom's cooking and I'm sure there will be tasty appetizers at the parties I will be attending. Enough about that, now tell me what has been going on in Durham since my last visit."

Helen sat back in her father's new car, closed her eyes, and listened intently to stories about family events and church members. The way her father put together words and phrases always soothed her. Helen had always looked up to her father and enjoyed listening to him preach. She had wonderful memories of her father standing high above his congregation, with his long robe swaying back and forth, bellowing out stories about Jesus.

Over the course of her childhood, Helen's family had moved from smaller churches in rural areas to larger congregations. Each church had been special but, when Helen entered the sanctuary of First Presbyterian Church in Durham, she felt right at home. The beautiful stained glass windows were incredible to look at and the pipe organ created a sound she had never experienced before. In that moment, Helen knew this church was where she would ultimately say her marriage vows.

The car pulled into the driveway and Helen jumped out, running barefoot across the front yard before her father could pull the key out of the ignition. She rushed through the front door calling out, "Mary, where are you?"

Immediately, Mary ran out of the kitchen and into the foyer, where the two young women embraced. "Oh, Helen, it's so good to see you. Mother and I just finished making dinner. Come sit down and share with all of us how you've been doing."

Helen's mother walked out of the kitchen and ran up to her daughter. The two women briefly embraced. "I'm so glad you're home. I can't wait to hear all about your time in Lynchburg."

"There isn't much to say. I'm just glad to be home with my family and be able to eat your wonderful food."

"Oh, Helen. That's very sweet of you. Let's sit down to dinner and catch up." Helen's father sat down at the head of the table and held out his hands for everyone to take hold of. "Dear Father, we want to thank you for bringing our daughter home safely. Help Mary be the wife to Tom that you have called her to be, and let us strive to put the needs of others before our own. Bless this food and my wonderful family. Amen."

Minutes later, Helen looked down at her empty plate and realized how famished she was. As she looked around and saw all the happy faces, she knew this was the time to approach the dress topic. "Mary, I can't wait to see the dress you'll be wearing to your party."

"Helen, I'd love to show it to you. Mother and I purchased the dress at one of the new stores on Main Street. They had a wonderful selection of dresses and accessories."

"Oh, Mary. I'm so happy for you. I can't wait to see you in such a beautiful dress, dancing with Tom."

"Helen, we need to find you a dress. Mother, don't you agree?"

"Now, Mary, I'm sure that Helen has a dress in her wardrobe that'll work just fine."

Helen was tempted to open her mouth and say something, but instead she bit her lip to keep from allowing words to blurt out. It was best to let Mary fight this battle for her. And, sure enough, her sweet sister came to her defense. "Mother, Helen only has an appropriate wardrobe for teaching or attending church. There's a young man who I want to introduce her to and he comes from a wealthy family. I can't imagine him giving Helen a second glance with the dresses she has to choose from. Please, Mother. It'll be so much fun to take her shopping and fit her into one of the new dresses we saw on display at Tilly's Department Store."

"Well, if your father will agree, we can go shopping in the morning."

"It appears that I have been overruled. Helen, go and pick out a dress, but remember you're the daughter of a minister and, as beautiful as the dress is, it needs to be modest."

Helen rose from her chair and went over to her dad. "Thank you. I promise I'll only make you proud of me."

Helen then went over to her sister and squeezed her hand, mouthing the words, "Thank you."

Helen was able to find a lovely dress that was discreet, yet accentuated her curves and highlighted her strawberry-blonde hair and her unusual orange-colored eyes. Her mother lent her some pearls and a pair of shoes that fit perfectly. As she looked at herself in the full-length mirror, she smiled at her reflection. *Helen Scanlon, you're going to meet the man of your dreams tonight. And then, you're going to live happily ever after in a large mansion, travel the world, and have servants taking care of all of your needs.*

There was a knock on the door. "Yes?"

"It's Mary. Can I come in?"

"Of course."

Mary walked in and gasped with delight. "Helen, you look beautiful!"

"Mary, you look lovely as well. Come on. I can't wait to meet this young man you've been telling me about. Oh, and I'm excited about your engagement to Tom."

"Oh, Helen. You know, if you weren't my sister, I would be jealous of how beautiful you look. But, I love you too much."

"I love you, too. Now, come on, let's go."

The gala was held at the Teer Home, located in North Durham. The beautiful home had a spacious back yard, decorated with candles and flower arrangements. A string quartet was playing from a gazebo situated in the far corner of the yard. A wooden dance floor had been built for the event, with chairs and tables scattered around the perimeter.

Helen and Mary entered the large plantation-style house and were escorted toward the back and onto a veranda decorated with flowers and dimly lit candles. Immediately, a cluster of young women, wearing beautiful spring dresses, closed in around them. Mary introduced several of the women to Helen, then left them in search of her fiancé, Tom. Helen tried to pay attention to the small talk and gossip, but was just too excited about meeting the man who Mary had mentioned in her letters.

Helen scanned the crowd, trying to spot the young man, but didn't see anyone fitting Mary's description. The sun sank slowly below the tree line leaving a beautiful, orange-colored sky. As Helen stood watching the skyline, she heard a male voice in the distance. She glanced in the direction of the voice and, at that moment, their eyes locked. She could feel the bright pink blush as it crept across her cheeks, then turned and walked toward the opposite end of the yard.

Helen was confused by how she was feeling. She knew she wanted to meet this young man, but didn't want to set herself up to be hurt. So, she decided to walk away to wait and see if he would seek her out. As she looked into the woods that bordered the yard, she spotted a doe and her fawn grazing on some plants. In awe of what she was experiencing, she didn't notice the young man approaching. "Are you Helen?"

The young man came up beside her and looked toward the deer. Helen kept her head still, not daring to look. Her heart was pounding and her hands began to moisten. With a soft voice she barely recognized, Helen responded, "Yes. And may I ask your name?"

"Richard, but people call me Richard Jr. I'm not really a junior, but my uncle refers to me in this manner because he raised me.

"Oh. So, may I ask why your uncle raised you?"

"You see, my dad died when I was seven. I barely remember him. My Uncle Richard took all of us into his home on Dillard Street."

"So, how many are in your family?"

"Well, there are seven children, five sisters, one brother, and myself. My sister, Lucy, recently passed away so there are just six of us now. My oldest sisters, Lila and Nannie Bet, have been married for quite some time and have their own families. So that leaves four adult children at home and my mother, Bettie. Oh, and did I mention my Aunt Nannie? She has lived with Uncle Richard since his wife died."

"Your uncle must have a big home to house so many people."

"Oh, he does. If you look across the street, you can see it."

Richard Jr. pointed his finger and directed Helen's eyes toward the large, white mansion set back from the road.

"You live in Bonnie Brae?"

"Yes. Why?"

"I've always wanted to see what it looks like on the inside. My family often drives out to Quail Roost and, when we pass Bonnie Brae, I always try to envision what it looks like. It's one of the most spectacular houses I've ever seen."

"Well, my uncle would be glad to hear that. He takes a lot of pride in that house. It's funny, to me it's just a house. But to him, it's a monument to all of his accomplishments."

"When my family moved to Durham, my father spoke about how your uncle had started the refuge for neglected children. My father is the minister of First Presbyterian Church. He's always been one for getting Mary and I to work with the underprivileged. I did go out to the refuge once, but then I moved to Virginia to teach school."

"How did you like teaching?"

"To be honest, I found it depressing. I wanted to teach in Durham, but my father was adamant about my first year being dedicated to working with needy children."

"So, what are you going to do now that you're back in Durham?"

"I'd like to find a position in a private school. I'll look into it after Mary's wedding. For now, I want to enjoy this time with my sister. So, what do you do?"

Richard Jr. began to laugh.

"What's funny about that question?"

"The question should be more like 'what do you not do'? You see, ever since I was in my early teens, my uncle has been prepping my brother, Thomas, and me to take over his business. His main enterprise is in Gainsborough, England. He discovered the cigarette packaging machine back in the late 1800s when he was selling the Bonsack machine in Europe. Anyway, he's a very driven man and wants my brother and me to be prepared to continue his various business ventures. So, I have a lot of responsibilities."

"Have you ever gone with him to England?"

"Many times. There is one trip I'll never forget. Back in December 1921, he and I went to England on the S.S. Baltic. Before you start envisioning a smooth sail across the ocean, think again. I was exhausted, both mentally and physically. Whenever we traveled together, he had me carry his suitcases everywhere we went. I could understand how difficult it was for him to navigate around a ship with his peg leg, but it was no easy feat to carry the bags. The Atlantic was brutal and I felt nauseated for most of the trip. I'd prefer to stay right here in America, but traveling is a large part of keeping the business moving."

"Wow. I like a family that pushes one another to reach their potential."

"You would get along well with my sisters. All of them want to get involved with a business."

"Really? They sound interesting."

"They are. We are all very close. I guess it has a lot to do with how we were raised by our uncle."

For a moment, neither had anything to say. Helen wanted to fill the space with something; anything to keep this man close by. She could hear the music from the band and observed the couples moving onto the dance floor. It looked like he was about to leave, but then he turned to her and looked right into her orange-colored eyes.

"You have beautiful eyes."

"Well, thank you."

"I have to say I have never met a young woman who seems so certain of herself."

Helen wasn't sure what to say. She did have a lot of self-confidence about most things, but being around this man caused her to feel a little intimidated. She was thinking about walking away when he asked, "Helen, would you like to dance? I promise I won't step on your toes."

"I'll hold you to that promise."

For the rest of the evening, Richard Jr. and Helen were either dancing or engaged in deep conversation. When the party ended,

Richard Jr. walked Helen over to her sister, Mary. "Helen, I'll call you once I return from England."

"I look forward to it."

A sense of sadness swept over her at the thought of having to wait so long for his return. Helen had never met someone who captured her interest so quickly, but she didn't want to appear vulnerable. So, she merely smiled at Richard Jr., then turned and walked away with her sister, hoping that he was watching her every move.

Sure enough, Richard Jr. called Helen when he returned and set up a time to visit her at her home. Over the next couple of months, Helen saw Richard Jr. when he was home from Europe or free from his business obligations. Many times, she would tell herself that the relationship was just too difficult but, once Richard Jr. was sitting next to her in her parent's parlor or they were dining at Bonnie Brae, Helen knew she was meant to be with Richard Jr. for the rest of her life.

Helen couldn't help but daydream about the luxuries that could be hers once she and Richard Jr. were married. She had fallen in love with this man and the lifestyle he could offer. Whenever he went away, she would spend hours writing him letters that described in detail the love that she had for him. When she didn't receive a timely response from Richard Jr., she pouted to everyone around her.

In November 1925, Richard Jr. brought home a beautiful three-carat diamond ring, took to one knee and asked Helen to be his wife. The wedding was planned for January 1926, at First Presbyterian Church. For weeks following the engagement, Helen and Richard Jr. were showered with gifts and parties.

The evening of the wedding was magical. Everything was just as Helen had imagined. No expense was spared for their wedding. Newspapers from all over the state included articles about the wedding ceremony, and how beautiful Helen appeared in her exquisite gown. But as Helen walked down the aisle, with friends and family looking on, she was oblivious to the remarks about how stunning she looked. All she cared about was the man who was standing at the altar waiting for her.

| 35 |

Richard (1926)

In the spring of 1926, Richard Jr. and Helen rode a train up to New York City for a business meeting. Richard knew that Helen would take advantage of the trip to purchase multiple items from all of the department stores and boutiques to add to her growing wardrobe. He knew that she hadn't had a large assortment of dresses before marrying his nephew. Her father had done well as a minister, but his income couldn't compare to the amount of money she had access to as Richard Jr.'s wife. Now that Helen was married to Richard Jr., she was constantly purchasing new clothes and accessories which suited her. Richard liked how Helen's look was becoming more aristocratic and, if it cost his nephew money to create this image, it was fine with him.

The night the couple returned from New York, Richard Jr. came over to dinner without Helen. He appeared to be in deep thought and didn't add to the conversation. Richard looked at his nephew and asked, "Where's Helen?"

"She doesn't feel well and I thought it best to let her rest. We were meaning to tell you something, but we just haven't found the right time."

Richard put down his fork and looked at his nephew. "Tell us what?"

Richard Jr. hesitated a moment before responding. "Helen is pregnant."

Nannie stood up and went over to her nephew, reached down, and gave him a hug. "This is wonderful news!" When Richard Jr. didn't return her embrace, Nannie pulled back and looked at him. "Is everything alright?"

Richard Jr. clearly seemed upset and hesitated a moment before responding. "When we were in New York, Helen went out to do some shopping while I was in a meeting. She told me that the store she entered had one of those revolving doors. When she stepped inside, she tripped and the door slammed up against her stomach. It took a moment before the people entering and exiting could tell that something was wrong. So, she got pretty banged up."

Nannie looked at Richard Jr. with a concerned expression. "Is she okay? Has she seen a doctor?"

"We did have a doctor come up to the hotel room and check her over. At that point, everything appeared well, but once we were headed home, she began to have cramps."

Bettie looked at her son and asked, "Why aren't you with her?"

"I was going to stay home tonight, but she told me to come here. She was insistent."

Nannie got up from her chair and looked over at Bettie. "Come on, Bettie, we're going over to check on Helen."

Richard Jr. followed the two older women out the door, leaving Richard sitting by himself. Later that night, Nannie and Bettie returned with the news that no one wanted to hear. Helen had lost the baby boy and was recovering at the hospital with Richard Jr. by her side.

A few months after the miscarriage, Richard Jr. left to go to Baltimore for business. Before leaving, Richard had called him into his office to discuss the tasks that would need to be addressed. "Richard Jr., I need you to determine that the Wright's Automatic Machinery Company plant in Baltimore is being as productive as I believe it should be. I'm counting on you to make sure the management knows we have our eyes on them."

"Yes, sir. I'll try not to disappoint you." Richard Jr. looked tired and wasn't giving him the attention he was used to getting from his nephew.

Richard could tell that his nephew wasn't acting like his usual self and appeared apathetic, but he was too concerned about the business to care about Richard Jr.'s mental health. "You know that I believe you are the right person for this job. I thought I could count on your brother, but he doesn't appear to have the insight that you do. He seems preoccupied with spending money on Claudia and going out and entertaining our clients. You're the one who has the skill set to oversee the different plants."

Richard Jr. hesitated a moment and, with a monotone voice, responded, "Thank you for believing in me. I'll try my best."

"That's what I want to hear. Don't worry about Helen. She'll be fine. You told me yourself that she's moving back home with her parents while you're away. Now, go and represent our company in a manner that will make me proud."

Several days later, Richard received a telegram from Richard Jr. stating that he'd had a panic attack and was going to admit himself into the hospital. Richard knew that he needed to share this information with his family, particularly Helen.

That afternoon, Richard requested that Helen come over for dinner. He had also included Sidney in the invitation, given his closeness to the family. When he rolled his wheelchair into the dining room, he noticed Thomas Jr. whispering something to Claudia. Lila and Nannie Bet were chuckling about a story Lila was sharing. Both women had moved away years ago and were visiting for an event at the new country club in Durham. Sidney sat next to Cora, which Richard was happy to see. He was hoping that something would occur between the two of them and, by the looks of it, it was.

Helen sat on the other side of Claudia, who was immersed in a deep conversation with Bettie. Richard was disturbed by how secretive they appeared and was certain the conversation had to do with Richard Jr.

As the dinner drew to a close, Richard addressed the group gathered at the table. "Family, I wanted to have dinner together to share some news with you. It's important that this news stay within the boundaries of this room."

Everyone looked at each other with curiosity. "I received a telegram from Richard Jr. He's checked himself into Mercy Hospital in Baltimore. I believe he's been under a lot of stress and needed to receive some help."

Helen looked at Richard. "I don't understand. He told me he was okay to travel."

"I'm sure he is. For now, he wanted to let us know that he is receiving some medical attention and will contact us when he's ready."

Helen bowed her head down and began to pick at the food that was left on her plate. Cora looked over at her sister-in-law and asked, "How are you?"

"I'm okay. I've been staying with my mother and father. It's so lonely at our house. I miss Richard Jr. and also the baby."

"I'm so sorry, Helen."

"Thanks."

Richard wanted to put an end to the conversation and spoke in a loud voice. "I believe it's time for a good cigar and, Cora, I would very much like to hear you play the piano."

As he moved his wheelchair away from the table, he thought about Richard Jr.'s condition and didn't want to believe that his nephew was so weak that he needed medical assistance to get through the stress he was experiencing. His nephews didn't have any understanding of the obstacles he himself had overcome, and the pressure he had endured for so many years. If Richard had anything to do with it, he wouldn't tolerate any excuses of weakness by any of his family members. Frustrated by his thoughts, Richard let out a loud sigh.

As a conditioned response, everyone sitting at the table stood and strolled into the parlor. The men continued through the room and into the library. Richard followed, stopping beside his favored wingback chair. He then locked the wheelchair and began to lift his body up, balancing on his peg leg. Sidney walked over to help him, but Richard motioned him away. Once he had transferred himself into the chair, he took several cigars out of a box and offered one to Thomas Jr. and Sidney. Each man took a match, lit their cigar, and blew small clouds of smoke into the air. As the men smoked and discussed business, the sound of the piano could be heard from the adjacent room.

Richard glanced through the open doors and saw Cora's back, as she sat on the piano bench. The other women were circled around the piano, singing songs as the black and white keys moved up and down.

Listening to the music, Richard thought back to when he had first met Mamie, the only woman who had ever captured his heart. He tried to push the thoughts from his head, but as Cora continued to play, he was transported back to that moment in time that had changed everything.

"Richard."

Sidney was looking at Richard.

"I'm sorry, what were you asking?"

"I was going to ask if I could have your permission to take Cora to a social event."

"I don't see anything wrong with that. Lucy has been gone for over two years now and you should be moving on with your life. And, personally, I like having you around. So, if Cora would like to spend time with you, I'll be glad to give you my blessing."

Sidney began to smile and answered, "Thank you."

| 36 |

Helen (1927)

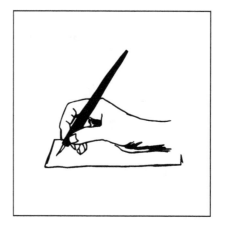

Helen sat at her desk, with her pen in hand, trying to begin a letter that was almost too difficult to write. She wasn't sure how long she could continue to pretend to be okay. The loneliness was almost too much for her to bear. Thankfully, her mother and father were gracious enough to allow her to return to her childhood room, while she waited for the return of her husband.

No one understood the grief she felt from the loss of their son. This child would have made everything perfect. He would have carried on the Wright name and lineage that everyone had so hoped for. A precious boy now lay buried in a grave; one that was set outside the mausoleum under the direction of the man who ruled over everyone in his family.

As she placed her hand on her belly, she was filled with such mixed emotions. If she had known Richard Jr. would be separated from her for so long, she would have tried to hold off on another pregnancy. But, with her husband in Mercy Hospital in Baltimore, for reasons she was still unsure about, all Helen could do was place pen to paper and try to connect with the man she loved so much.

Sunday, 10 AM

Well, good morning, my dear little boy. How are you today? I hope you had a good rest last night. I surely did. It was so cool and delightful on the sleeping porch and I slept like a log, to make up for the previous night. I arose about 8:30, read the newspaper and had a good breakfast. Mother has gone to Sunday school and church. But I shall not go, as it is warm, and I do not want to risk fainting again.

I have just cut some of mother's lovely flowers to take out to the dear little grave. I shall mail this as I go by the P.O. Today, I am thinking of the two souls I love better than anything in the world. One is in this world and the other little one is in a better world.

It is quiet and nice here and I shall be very comfortable and as happy as is possible, with you away. I had a nice spoil at Bonnie Brae last evening. The children are so dear. Lila will go home Monday, but Nannie Bet will stay on a week longer.

The "mother heart" of your mother is distressed that you are having such a long stay there. She is constantly thinking of you and wanting you to come home. But, I told her I thought you were not unhappy, as there is now an end in sight.

She said, "I don't think either Richard or Aunt Nannie have the slightest idea what the love of a husband and wife can be. I don't blame Richard Jr. for staying at Mercy Hospital. But if he can't come home soon, if I were you, I would go be with him."

No, your mother has not forgotten those long years of the devoted look of one man and one woman.

Such an understanding heart.

My own sweetheart, I'm missing you so. But during these days, I shall try to think only of the few weeks hence, when we shall be in our own little home together.

With a constant and devoted love—
Helen

As Helen placed her pen down, she was suddenly overcome by the heat that had filtered into her room. She walked into the foyer where she discovered a cool breeze and the ticking of the grandfather clock. As the clock struck twelve, she walked back to the kitchen where Pearl, the family's help, was making Sunday lunch.

"Mrs. Wright, why don't you sit down and I will pour you a glass of lemonade."

"Thank you, Pearl."

Helen sipped her lemonade without saying a word. Once the glass was empty, she turned to Pearl and asked, "Pearl, have you ever been in love?"

"Why, yes. My husband Lester and I have been in love for over forty years. You know, we have never been away from each other that entire time. Mrs. Wright, I hope I'm not being too forward, but it's just not natural for a husband to be away from his wife, while she is in a motherly way."

"I know. I'm hoping Richard Jr. will be home soon. I want him to speak up to his uncle and tell him that he needs to stop traveling and stay in Durham. All of these unrealistic expectations and the excessive traveling are causing him harm."

"Well, I hope Mr. Wright does return soon. I know how much you want him to be home when you deliver this baby."

"Thank you, Pearl. It's nice being here with Mother and Father, but I can't wait to be together with my husband in our home."

| 37 |

Cora (1927)

The thirty candles on the cake stood for each year of her life. That life that had been filled with adventures across both the Atlantic and Pacific Oceans, beautiful clothes, and elaborate parties. But it also stood for years of hoping for the love of a man; someone with a compassionate soul and a caring heart. As Cora gazed down at all the candles, she wondered if this would this be the year that she would fall in love and finally be able to have a family of her own.

Cora took a deep breath and smiled at the familiar faces sitting around the table. As always, she first turned toward Uncle Richard and proclaimed for all to hear, "I want to thank you for your generosity over the years. The trips we have taken overseas have been more than any young woman could ever dream of. I respect you so much and am forever grateful for your generosity. You inspire me to be the best I can be."

The old man nodded his head and looked up to see the affirmation from all the guests sitting around the table. Guests and family members raised their glasses toward the old man who looked ghastly pale. Uncle Richard, in turn, raised his glass to Cora. "You're quite welcome. You've grown into a wonderful woman whom I'm very proud of."

"Thank you, Uncle Richard."

Cora then looked over at her mother, paused a moment and, with tears in her eyes, spoke, "Mother, I want to tell you how much I love you and how grateful I am for our relationship. I can't imagine raising seven children, particularly ones that have so much drive and determination. You've always been willing to put our desires above your own."

Thomas Jr. chimed in, "Amen to that!"

Cora brushed away a tear and turned to her Aunt Nannie. "I want to also thank you for always giving so much and being willing to direct this ship, even when the waters have been rough. I love you." Then Cora turned to all of her siblings and friends and declared, "I love all of you as well. Okay, that's enough of that."

Once the candles had been lit, Cora leaned down, and blew as hard as she could. Half the candles were still blazing, which made everyone laugh. Cora inhaled, tried once more, but still left several candles burning. "Let me help you with that."

Cora turned around and saw Sidney standing above her. "Sure. Give it a try."

Sidney blew out the rest of the candles and then turned to face Cora. "I hope you have a wonderful year. And, by the way, you're looking very beautiful tonight."

"Well, thank you, Mr. Chambers."

"You're quite welcome, Miss Wright."

People began to stare at the two of them, which caused Cora to feel a little uncomfortable. She turned and faced Richard Jr. and Helen. "Helen, how are you feeling? I know you've got to be excited about the arrival of your baby."

"I am. We've already picked out a name for him."

"Oh, so you think it is going to be a boy."

"It surely must be. We're going to name him Richard."

Richard Jr. looked at Helen. "Now, Helen. If it's a girl, we're going to love her just as much as if it's a little boy."

It was clear from her expression that she didn't want to discuss it any longer. Cora watched as Helen turned away from her and started having a discussion with Mary Ruth.

Cora looked over at her sister-in-law and sighed. She felt bad for her brother, who seemed to be dominated by this petite woman with the curly, blonde hair and orange-colored eyes. Since they'd been married, Helen had dictated what they did and where they lived. It was sad to think how Richard Jr. was now ruled by both Uncle Richard and this woman.

"Cora, what are you plans for the coming year?" Thomas Jr. called out.

"Just the usual stuff. I have several benefits planned, as well as a couple of trips. And, by the looks of it, I will probably be doing some baby-sitting."

Claudia, Thomas Jr.'s wife, chimed in, "I'm going to remember that."

"I'll be glad to help out. Anyway, I want to thank everyone for coming tonight. Now, enjoy this delicious cake and piping hot coffee."

Throughout the rest of the evening, Cora made an effort to speak to each of her guests. She was able to pull her brother, Richard Jr., aside and speak to him. "Richard, I know you have had a rough year. I just want you to know that if you want someone to talk to, please don't hesitate."

"Cora, you don't have to worry about me. I'm doing much better. Uncle Richard finally agreed to let me work here in Durham until after the baby is born. I know Helen can come across as strongly opinionated, but I do love her. By the way, I noticed how Sidney spoke to you. Is there something going on between the two of you?"

"I really don't know. Before he and Lucy were married, I was infatuated with him. When it became clear that he loved Lucy, I trained my heart to lessen my feelings for him. I just don't want to get hurt again."

"I can understand that, but things are different now. It's been close to three years since Lucy passed away. And, anyway, Sidney seems truly smitten with you."

"Is that right, big brother?"

Richard Jr. gave Cora a hug, then walked over and placed Helen's mink stole around her shoulders. Helen said something under her breath and made her way out the door.

Later, after all of her family had retired and the guests had left, Cora went into the parlor and sat down on one of the love seats that Uncle Richard had purchased in China. The cotton material was rose-colored, framed with cherry wood. She always liked the way it felt while reading a good book or entertaining friends. She took off her shoes and was laying her head back, taking in a deep breath, when she was startled by a voice coming from the library.

"So, Miss Wright, did you have a good birthday?"

Cora looked up and spotted Sidney sitting diagonally from her in the dimly lit library. He had his legs crossed and was smoking a cigar. The smoke drifted into the parlor and Cora inhaled the sweet aroma, keeping her head relaxed against the soft material. "I did, Mr. Chambers."

Sidney, pressed his cigar into the ashtray and walked over to Cora. He took a seat beside her and remained quiet for a few seconds. Cora raised her head and looked at this man, wondering about his intentions. Thinking the worst, she blurted out, "Sidney, what do you want?"

"What do you mean?"

"I can't be a replacement for Lucy. I know you loved her. When I watched you at the altar, I could tell that every molecule in your body desired only her. And then, when she got pregnant, I witnessed a man who took care of every one of her needs. But when she died, I could tell a part of you died with her."

"Cora, you're so right. I did love Lucy with all my heart. I'll never deny that. When she died, I didn't know if I wanted to go on. I could totally relate to your uncle's pain when his wife, Mamie, died. But, unlike him, I made a decision that I wasn't going to swallow up all of my emotions and become bitter. For several months, all I wanted to do was work, and hoped that if I worked hard enough and became engrossed in my cases, I might forget the pain. But my feelings of loss only deepened."

"So, what has changed?"

"It's hard to say. The day I brought Lucy's clothes and jewelry over, I realized that I missed this family. So, that's when I started coming over for an occasional meal. Over time, as I watched you interact with your Uncle Richard and comfort your mother, I became drawn to you. I just liked being in your presence and felt a certain peace that I haven't had since the death of your sister. I haven't said anything because I wasn't entirely sure of how to define my emotions."

"Sidney, I'm sure you know that, in the months prior to your engagement, I was under the illusion that you might want to be with me. I was so infatuated with you and your charming demeanor, that I wouldn't allow myself to consider that you were visiting Lucy and falling in love with her. A piece of my heart was broken. But, as time went by, I witnessed how happy you and Lucy were, and I pulled my feelings back."

"Cora, I'm glad we have had this conversation."

Sidney reached over and took Cora's hand in his. For a moment, all he did was brush her fingers with his other hand. "Cora, would it be okay if we spent some time alone together? I'd really like to spend time with you, away from your family."

"I think I'd like to do that."

"Okay. I'll call you."

Before releasing her hand, Sidney brought it to his lips and lightly kissed it. He then rose, grabbed his coat, and walked out the door. Cora was suddenly overcome with a feeling deep inside her, making her want to go after him. But, with every ounce of self-control she could muster, she sat still, listening, as the grandfather clock in the foyer ticked off the final seconds of her thirtieth year.

| 38 |

Helen (1927)

Helen woke with a strange sensation in her lower back. She wasn't sure, at first, if she should be concerned and waited to see if anything more would happen. The temperature had dropped during the night and she was so comfortable lying underneath the warm comforter. Just as she was going to roll over and try to go back to sleep, she felt a deeper pain.

"Richard, wake up."

"What, are you okay?"

"I'm not sure. I'm feeling pain in my lower back and it seems to be getting worse."

"Well, I guess we should get up and head to the hospital."

"Oh, Richard, I'm scared."

"Helen, everything is going to be okay. You've been so cautious during this pregnancy. I believe this baby will be healthy and beautiful, just like you."

"No, Richard, this baby is going to be a boy."

"Helen, you can't be so sure. Please don't pin all your hopes on it being a boy. It can be a girl, and we will love it just as much."

Helen felt another pain and didn't want to continue arguing with Richard. She rose and pulled a garment over her large stomach, thinking how grateful she would be to get back into her regular clothes. Ever since the death of their stillborn baby, Helen was adamant about traveling to Richmond for this delivery. She had heard from friends that the medical facilities were far superior to Watts Hospital. Uncle Richard and her mother-in-law, Bettie, agreed that it was best for them to make the trip.

Helen didn't like the way she was feeling. She had always been in control of her circumstances. She had a knack for getting her way in almost every situation and didn't like the uncertainty of this experience. She was scared that something might go wrong and she would be left with another humiliating disappointment.

Helen only remembered the ride to the hospital and how she was whisked up to labor and delivery. Once the nurses had checked her vital signs, everything went quickly. She was given some medicine that made her groggy and, in the haze, she was told the news. She had had a baby girl.

Once the drugs had worn off, she noticed Richard sitting in a chair beside her bed. "Oh, Helen, we have a healthy baby girl."

Tears began to fall down Helen's cheeks. "I want to be happy, but all I wanted was a boy. Just like the boy we had."

"Oh, Helen, you have to stop punishing yourself. It just wasn't meant to be. But now, we have a healthy little girl. Please, be happy."

Richard went out to the nurses' station and asked for someone to bring their baby into the room. After a couple of minutes, a nurse rolled a bassinet through the door and placed it next to Helen. She sat up and looked down into the brown eyes of the chubby baby that was supposed to be hers. Her first instinct was to declare that they had made a mistake. They must have made an error. This couldn't be her baby. She had wanted a boy and, if she couldn't have a boy, at least she could've had a cute, petite blonde with orange or blue eyes.

"Helen, do you want to hold her?"

"Not particularly."

"Oh, Helen. Once you hold her, she'll grow on you. Look at her. She wants her mother."

"Richard, why don't you take her and feed her. I'm not feeling well."

"Helen, this is our daughter. Please, try and put your feelings aside and hold her."

Helen looked at the baby, turned over and closed her eyes. Maybe, if she went to sleep and woke up again, it would be a boy. But, no matter how much she wanted the baby to be a boy, it just wasn't.

After several nurses spoke to her about the importance of bonding with her infant, Helen took her baby in her arms and placed the bottle in her mouth. After the bottle was empty, Helen handed the baby back to the nurse and went back to sleep. No matter what Richard or the nurses said, Helen refused to try and bond with her baby.

When the hospital discharged Helen and the baby, Helen climbed into the front seat looking straight ahead with no regard for her baby. Richard placed the bassinet in the backseat and the little family drove home. Once they crossed the North Carolina state line, Richard asked in a nervous voice, "So, what do you think we should name her?"

"I really don't care. You can name her whatever you want."

"Well, I was thinking we could name her after you and your mother. Her name could be Helen Turissa, but we'll call her Turissa. What do you think?"

"If that's what you want to do."

For the remainder of the car ride, no words were spoken. Once they arrived home, Richard hired a nurse to take care of the baby. For days after their return, Helen spent her time in bed with the door shut. Helen knew Richard was concerned about her, but it wasn't enough to motivate her to get up. She only wanted to sleep and had no desire to take care of her baby.

After a week of tending to the baby and the house, Richard returned to work. Every night, he would come home to the nurse sitting in the nursery while Helen slept. Richard made it a habit to lift his baby girl out of the bassinet and place her on the bed beside Helen. But no matter how hard he tried to form a bond between them, Helen refused to feel for the little girl.

During the weeks following Turissa's birth, Helen became bitter toward Richard. She just wanted to be left alone. She didn't know how to get her husband to understand the disappointment she felt, and attempting to force her to love this baby wasn't helping at all.

One day, Helen rose from her bed, put on her makeup, and slipped on a pretty dress that brought out the orange in her eyes. She walked into the dining room where Richard was having breakfast. When he saw her, he placed his cup of coffee down and stared at her transformation.

"Well, Helen, it's so nice to see you up and around."

Helen turned to the servant and said, "Doris, can you please bring me some scrambled eggs, bacon, and toast?"

"Yes. Right away."

Helen turned her attention to her husband and his puzzled expression. "What, Richard?"

"I'm curious about what motivated you to rise."

Helen folded her napkin and looked up. "Do you know what would make me happy?"

"No, I don't think I do."

"Well, I have an idea."

"Okay. I'm listening."

"Well, you know how much I love Bonnie Brae."

"Yes, but you have made it clear that you don't want to live there." At this point, Richard had placed his newspaper down and looked straight at Helen.

"I'd like to have our own home built, similar to Bonnie Brae. Not quite as big. It doesn't need to be that large, but one that makes a statement."

"So, you're suggesting that I have a large house built for you?"

"Yes. Do you remember when we went to Charlottesville, Virginia?"

"Yes."

"Well, I just loved the style of the Mount Vernon mansion."

"Helen, what are you suggesting?"

"When we were at one of our last parties, I had a conversation with George Watts Carr. Well, he told me that, when we were ready, he would be glad to draw up some plans for us."

By this time, Helen knew she had Richard Jr.'s attention. "I'm not sure it would be a good idea. You're still recovering from Turissa's birth."

"This is exactly what I need to feel better. Please, Richard. Please consider it."

"Well, I'll need to speak with Uncle Richard about the finances. Are you sure you want to undertake such a large project?"

Helen got up from her chair, leaned over her husband, and gave him a kiss on his forehead. "Oh, Richard, this is exactly what I need. And I promise you that I'll be a more attentive mother."

"Well, if you promise to spend time with our daughter, then I'll speak with Uncle Richard."

"Oh, I promise. I love you. I can't wait to get started."

Helen felt a sense of elation that she hadn't felt in a long time. If she couldn't have the boy she wanted, at least she could have a house that would be the envy of all her friends.

| 39 |

Cora (1927-1928)

Sidney did call Cora and the two spent as much time together as his busy schedule allowed. One Saturday night, they went to Hope Valley Country Club with her sister, Mary Ruth, and their mutual friend, Hubert Teer. Cora noticed her sister's demeanor and how happy she appeared. When Mary Ruth returned to the table, Cora took hold of her sister's hand and gave it a squeeze. "Do you remember when we were Lucy's bridesmaids?"

"Of course, I do. It seems so long ago."

"Sometimes, it feels like yesterday. Mary Ruth, do you think it's okay for me to be with Sidney?"

"Does he make you happy?"

"Yes. He's always concerned about how I'm feeling. I've never been with someone who truly cares about my feelings in the way he does."

"Then, I think Lucy would be happy to know that you're with Sidney. She loved both of you so much. I can't help but believe she's up in heaven rooting the two of you on."

"You really think she would be okay with the two of us being together?"

Mary Ruth took Cora's hands and looked right at her. "Cora, I know that all of our family couldn't be happier for you. Mother and Aunt Nannie love Sidney and want you two to be together. And you know how Uncle Richard feels about him. He's already made it through the inspection process."

Both girls laughed and hugged. Mary Ruth gave Cora a serious look. "Really, you've waited so long for happiness and I believe all the stars are lined up for you to finally have all your dreams come true."

"Oh, thank you, Mary Ruth. And by the looks of it, it appears that you and Hubert are enjoying each other's company."

Mary Ruth hesitated, and Cora could tell that there was something she wanted to say.

Cora said, "Mary Ruth, I feel that you want to tell me something but are concerned about how I would accept it."

"It's not how you would accept it, but how others might."

"I don't care what anyone thinks. I just want you to be happy and, if Hubert makes you happy, that's what matters to me."

"Sister, I love you and only want what is best for you. Please share with me what is on your mind."

Mary Ruth lowered her head and paused. Cora was just about to interrupt the silence when Mary Ruth spoke. "Hubert was drafted into the war. He was educated and was immediately placed into the higher ranks. Since he was from the South, he was believed to be better suited to lead the colored troops. He was assigned to the 371st Infantry and was sent to France, where he joined other French and American troops."

Mary Ruth took a sip of water and continued. "On September 29, 1918, around 11:00 a.m. he was shot in the back. Even though he was losing blood and in extreme pain, he wouldn't leave his men. Several times, he was told to get medical assistance, but he refused until around 4:00 p.m., when he had to be taken away."

Cora looked over at Hubert, standing with Sidney, and laughing about something Sidney had said. "Mary Ruth, you must be very proud of him."

"I am. Even today, he receives letters from all over the country from the men in his unit. Hubert speaks of many of these men like he is talking about his own flesh and blood. Just thinking about his willingness to die for them is very attractive to me. It's so funny how we lived across the street from one another but, it wasn't until we joined Hope Valley and traveled across town, that we actually became a couple. Hubert is so special."

The two men returned and simultaneously enlisted the two sisters to join them on the dance floor. Cora felt so comfortable in Sidney's arms. He never pushed himself on her and gave her plenty of space. As they danced across the floor, Sidney looked down at Cora and asked, "Are you happy?"

"More than you'll ever know. I feel so blessed to be with you. It makes me even happier to see Mary Ruth and Hubert together. They seem like the perfect couple."

"I find it just as funny to think how I've known you for so long and have just realized what an incredible woman you are. Cora, please believe me when I tell you that I'm falling in love with you, for who you are."

Cora's breath almost caught in her throat. "Sidney, thank you."

That night, when she was sitting in front of her mirror, Cora played Sidney's words over and over again in her mind. Should she have told him that she felt the same? As she took her brush and ran it through her hair, she pushed away the insecurities that wanted to rob her of this moment. No, she had time to tell Sidney how she felt and believed the time would be sooner, rather than later.

The following morning at church, Sidney slipped in beside her. This was the first time that he had intentionally made his way past other family members to sit next to her. She knew that the eyes of the congregation would be on them as they rose, and sat down, with the rhythm of the service. Once the benediction was pronounced, and the people started exiting the church, Cora leaned over toward Sidney. "Would you like to come over for Sunday dinner?"

"You know I would."

"Good. Can I catch a ride with you?"

"I would be glad to have your company."

Cora and Sidney found it so easy to be together. Sidney enjoyed telling Cora about his past and how he loved making Durham his home. She shared about her volunteer work at the Wright Refuge and the stories of the children she met there.

When they arrived at Bonnie Brae, other family members were pulling into the large circle drive. Richard Jr. and Helen pulled in beside them in their new Model A. Cora looked over and noticed that their baby wasn't in the car. She also noticed that Helen appeared happier than usual. Cora was overcome with anger toward this woman who had everything she had ever wanted, and took it all for granted.

"Helen, where's your baby?"

"She's at home with the nanny. I didn't think people would want to be bothered by an infant at church and dinner. Everybody is better off this way."

"Please bring her the next time we have dinner together. I'll be glad to hold her if she becomes fussy. She's family. And all of us Wrights put our family members first above all else."

Helen didn't respond to Cora's words. She turned around in a huff and walked into the foyer. She began speaking to Bettie about the nice dress she was wearing and complimenting her on her hair. Cora could clearly see that she was trying to build an alliance with her mother-in-law.

About that time, Sidney came up beside Cora and asked, "What's wrong? I can tell you're upset."

"Sidney, it makes me so angry to know that my niece is being treated so poorly. I would do anything to have a baby one day and would never leave her with a nanny, when she needs to be here with her family."

"Oh, Cora. Please don't let her upset you. I must admit I was thinking the same thing when they drove up. You have such a big heart and I hope, one day, you'll have your own child to lavish your love on. Now, let's go in and enjoy our time with the rest of your family."

Claudia and Thomas Jr. arrived shortly afterward. As they entered the house, they were laughing at something that was clearly an inside joke. Hubert had driven separately and met Mary Ruth at the front door. As the young couple walked into the parlor, Uncle Richard seemed to be giving Hubert the once-over. Everyone noticed how the old man was interrogating him, and couldn't help but smirk at the ritual that they had all come to know. After he finished asking Hubert the usual questions, Richard turned his attention to the family sitting in front of him.

Cora noticed that Uncle Richard looked particularly frail as he sat in his wheelchair. His hands were shaking, and he didn't sit up as straight as he usually did. She then turned her attention to her siblings and smiled. She felt a strong bond with each of them.

Outsiders would never understand what it was like being raised by such a driven man. All they saw was the big house and expensive cars in the driveway. No one on the outside of their world could ever realize how these things came at such a high cost.

Cora looked over at her mother and noticed that she was deep in conversation with Helen. Her mother loved her grandchildren, which was obvious whenever Lila or Nannie Bet visited. Even though Aunt Nannie or Uncle Richard reprimanded her, Bettie would get down on the floor to play with each one of her grandchildren. Hopefully, her words would have an impact on Helen.

Uncle Richard's frail voice interrupted her thoughts.

"I would like to tell everyone something before we go in for dinner."

Even though his voice was hard to hear, it still commanded everyone's attention. "I wanted to let all of you know that Nannie and I will be leaving for Craig Springs in early December. Over the years, I have discovered that the warm springs there help my ailments. Now, I know this might be an inconvenience, but I will be conducting business from there."

Everyone looked at each other, silently questioning whether this was a good move for Uncle Richard. The trip itself would take a lot out of him but, as usual, no one was willing to challenge his judgment. "Richard Jr. and Thomas, we will speak of the details later. But, for now, I wanted to let you know so you can start preparing."

The two men looked stunned, but remained silent. Cora knew they had a lot of questions about how to run the many businesses without Uncle Richard being in Durham. "Now, you boys don't need to worry. I'll keep the correspondences going back and forth. Since I'm going to be leaving soon, is there anyone else who would like to share any upcoming events that might involve all of us?"

Everyone looked at each other, wondering if there was some information that someone had kept from their siblings. Then Sidney raised his voice. "Mr. Wright, can I speak with you in private?"

"Of course. I believe dinner is ready. So why don't the rest of you head into the dining room and leave Sidney and I."

Cora couldn't imagine what Sidney had to speak to Uncle Richard about. She felt awkward about going to the dining room without him. It seemed like a secret was being told that might concern her and she didn't like it one bit.

After a brief moment, when Sidney and Richard joined the rest of the family, it was clear that neither was going to discuss it. Helen was seated across from her and Sidney. Richard Jr. and Sidney started talking about a common friend and Cora noticed that everyone else was already engaged in conversation.

Cora saw Helen looking right at her. "Did you hear that Richard Jr. and I are building a house? George Watts Carr is designing it for us. When it's completed, we're going to have the most extravagant parties. I can't wait for everyone here to see it."

"No. I didn't know anything about it. You must be very happy to have a healthy baby and now be in the midst of building a new home. I'm happy for you."

Cora looked down at her plate and noticed the food that she hadn't eaten. She began to pick at it and tried to keep her head down, so she wouldn't have to continue the conversation with Helen. No wonder she was so happy?

As dinner was ending, and it appeared that people were getting ready to leave, Sidney pulled at Cora's hand. "Cora, would you please sit down for a moment?"

"Sidney, is everything okay?"

"When your uncle said he was leaving Durham, I had to ask him."

"What?" Cora looked at Sidney with a quizzical expression.

"I had to ask him if I could have your hand in marriage."

Cora was shocked. For a moment, she sat back and tried to find the words she needed to answer him.

"Cora, I'm sorry if I presumed you loved me like I love you. I just know that we don't have time on our side. I'm sorry, if I did something wrong. I just love you and want you to be my wife."

Tears began to glisten in Cora's eyes. "Oh, Sidney, I do love you. I've just become resigned to the fact that maybe this would never happen. I'd love to marry you."

Sidney reached for Cora and the two hugged each other. He gently kissed her on the cheek and said, "I can't believe you said yes. I'm so thankful. I do love you with all my heart."

Mary Ruth was the first to reach over and give Cora a hug. "I'm so happy for you. It's funny how fairy tales do come true. Maybe later than we think, but they actually can happen.

| 40 |

Richard (1928)

As the last of the items were being packed into the back of the car, Richard transferred from his wheelchair to the seat beside Nannie. His pain had kept him up the night before, coupled with an irritation caused by the outcome of a conversation he had had with his nephew. Earlier yesterday, he had summoned Richard Jr. to come by the house to discuss a topic he had raised several times before, but never resolved.

"Richard Jr., come inside and take a seat."

"Uncle Richard, are you sure you are up for this trip?"

"I am. You should come up and visit while I'm there. I know if you spent some time in the springs, you would find it refreshing."

"Well, with a new baby, and a wife who wants to entertain all the time, I'm not sure if I can get away."

"Speaking of your wife, I want to talk to you about something."

"Yes."

"As you know, I've always wanted you to inherit Bonnie Brae. All I need you to do is live here until your aunt and mother are deceased. "

"I had every intention of doing just that until I married Helen. You know how she is. Ever since we've been married, she's been insistent about having her own home. She cares for Nannie and mother, but doesn't understand why we would want to live in a house with so many people under the same roof."

Richard wasn't happy with Helen's domination of Richard Jr., and the way that she pulled him away from his family. He was particularly disturbed by how she appeared inconvenienced by her new baby.

"So, the other day at Sunday dinner, I overheard Helen telling Cora about a new house that you are planning to build."

"I was going to discuss this with you, but haven't had a chance. Helen has it set in her mind to build a house that is similar in style to the Mount Vernon house in Charlottesville. She pursued George Watts Carr, the popular architect, to draw up some plans, before she approached me. I would've tried to curtail the project, but she has been very persistent. Anyway, it's the first thing that has made her happy since the loss of our son."

Uncle Richard moved around in his chair and tapped his foot on the floor. He looked at his nephew and wondered how to broach the next topic. "Richard Jr., do you know that I've always thought of you as my son?"

"Yes."

"You know I didn't have to bring all of your family into my home when your parents moved to Durham. But I did. And do you know why?"

"No."

"Because, when my mother died, I made her a promise that I was hoping would be honored for generations. I promised her that I would take care of our family, no matter the price."

"Sir, what does this have to do with me?"

"When we had dinner together last Sunday, Helen left her baby at home. I can see why you want to build your own house, but I don't understand why Helen doesn't seem to want to bond with her own baby. This greatly concerns me. Richard Jr., I won't be around much longer and feel the need to share something that I've never shared with anyone else."

Richard Jr. held his head down and had a difficult time looking at his aging uncle. He was also concerned about the way Helen had been neglecting their baby, but didn't know how to approach her.

When I lost Mamie, I thought my world was over. The grief was so great that I couldn't think straight. All I wanted to do was get away. And that's what I did. I not only left New York, I left the country. And, when I left, I also turned my back on my little girl."

Richard paused for a minute before continuing. The only sound came from the ticking of the grandfather clock that stood in the foyer. Both men were filled with their own personal regret, but particularly the elderly man who slumped in his chair. "Richard Jr., please don't repeat my actions. If I could go back, I would've spent more time with my daughter. Initially, when I heard that she had died, I was somewhat relieved. But, as the years have passed and I have watched all of you grow into upstanding men and women, I can't help but believe that, if I had loved her, she might be with us today. Love is so important to the development of a child. And if your wife doesn't have it in her to love this little girl, then I expect you to take it upon yourself to make sure your daughter feels loved."

Richard Jr. felt the tears well in his eyes. At first, all he could do was nod his head, then, after a moment, he cleared his throat. "Yes, Uncle Richard, I'll do my best."

"Now, while I'm gone, I expect you to make sure to check on everyone. Please set aside a budget for Cora's wedding. I want her to feel just as special as all of her sisters have in the past. I'll try and be back in time for the event but, if I'm not, I want you to take my place, and give her away. Also, keep an eye on Hubert. I know he comes from good blood and his family has done well. If there's any news about a proposal, please let me know. And, Richard Jr., please try and develop some backbone when it comes to your wife. She needs to know that you're in charge."

"Yes, sir. I'll do my best."

| 41 |

Helen (1928)

Earlier in the evening, Helen had sent the nanny to her quarters and made her way into the nursery. She glanced around the room, brushing away a tear as she looked into the crib at her baby girl. She had taken such pride in this room as she prepared for the delivery of her son. A theme of blue, from the quilts to the small stuffed toys, reminded Helen of what this baby was not, a boy.

Helen was consumed with thoughts about how people reacted when they first saw Turissa. No one had even pretended to compliment her appearance. And why should they? She was chubby and had a plain face that held no hint of beauty. No matter how many times she looked at her baby, there was nothing about the infant that provoked feelings of love.

As Helen was leaving the room, the smell of a dirty nappy overtook her. She was about to call the nanny, when she noticed her husband leaning up against the door frame. "Well, well, I was hoping to find you attending to our child."

"Well, I had nothing better to do tonight and thought I would give the nanny a little break. Can you please hand me a clean diaper?"

Richard Jr. reached over, pulled out a clean cloth, and handed it to Helen. He then looked down at his daughter.

"Helen, look at those fat cheeks. Aren't they cute?"

"Richard, I personally don't see anything cute about her. I know I should have feelings for her, but I don't.

"Helen, please keep trying. She needs her mother."

"Well, she needs her father as well." And with that, she placed the baby in Richard's arms and turned to leave.

Richard Jr. began talking to his baby and cuddling her close to his chest. "Helen, can you please go and get me a bottle?"

"Sure, I'll be back in a moment."

Helen walked to the kitchen, taking her time as she warmed the milk and filled the bottle. She could hear Turissa crying, but even the loud noise of a hungry baby didn't urge her to go any faster. She told herself that the baby needed to learn patience, and blocked the noise out with a loud hum. When she finally walked back into the nursery, Turissa was crying so hard that it was hard for Richard Jr. to prod the bottle into her mouth. Finally, after a little coaxing, Turissa took the bottle and melted into Richard Jr.'s chest.

Over the next couple of weeks, Helen was consumed with the creation of the architectural plans for her new house. Every time she had an idea about a room or a design choice, she would spend hours on the phone with George Watts Carr, or one of his associates.

When she wasn't studying the house plans, she was going out to lunch or shopping with her friends. If one of them mentioned her baby, Helen would change the topic and bring up something about the new house or boast about Richard Jr.'s new business ventures. Helen did all she could to pretend that the little baby didn't exist.

In early February, when Helen was getting ready for Cora's bridal shower, she began to feel queasy. At first, she thought it must be related to last night's dinner but, as the feelings persisted, she wondered if she could be pregnant. After eating some dry toast and taking a wet washcloth to her head, she dressed and headed out the door.

The bridal shower was being held at Hope Valley Country Club in a dining room that overlooked the golf course. When Helen arrived, everyone was seated and the lunch had already been served. One of Cora's childhood friends was sharing a memory that was particularly funny to Cora and other family members. When Helen walked into the room, everyone glanced in her direction and then back to the speaker. Mary Ruth waved her over to the empty seat beside her. "I'm sorry I'm so late. I didn't feel well this morning."

"That's okay. You haven't missed much. Do you want lunch?"

"I better not."

Helen didn't like not being at her best when she was at social gatherings. She already knew that Cora was unhappy with her and didn't want to alienate Richard Jr.'s other siblings.

Once the gifts had been opened and people were beginning to mingle, Claudia, Thomas Jr.'s wife, approached her. "You don't look too good."

"I don't feel so great, either."

"Look, Helen, I wanted to speak with you."

"Oh, you, too?"

"What do you mean?"

"Well, it seems like everyone is unhappy with Richard Jr. and me for not being willing to live at Bonnie Brae."

"Oh. Well, to be honest, I'm happy with your decision."

"Why?"

"Ever since Thomas and I were married, we have felt at home at Bonnie Brae. I know Uncle Richard can be difficult at times, and Nannie can also act the part of a dictator but, even so, I love being there."

"Really?"

Claudia laughed. "Yes, really."

"Well, you have no idea how relieved I am to hear this. I'm so excited about our new house. Now, that I know you and Thomas are okay with living at Bonnie Brae, I believe I can share our plans with others."

For the rest of the shower, Helen interacted with mutual friends and tried to steer clear of a conversation with Cora. When she had just finished speaking with someone whose husband worked with Richard Jr., she looked around to see that everyone was gone. The last of the gifts were being taken out to Cora's car as Helen walked out.

"Helen, can I speak with you?"

Helen turned around and saw Cora in the hallway. "Yes."

"I just want to apologize to you."

"What for?"

"I was harsh with you at Sunday dinner. It wasn't my place to say anything to you about your baby. I guess my feelings about wanting a baby came out toward you. That wasn't right. I do hope we can be good friends. You know how much I love my brother."

"Yes, I'm aware of how much you care for your siblings."

"Anyway, I want you to feel welcome in our family."

"Thank you, Cora. I'm sorry, but I have to get to the bathroom right away."

"Are you okay?"

"Yes. Now, go along."

Helen rushed into the bathroom and made it just in time, before getting sick. As she took one of the napkins beside the sink and wiped her face, she thought about the conversation she had had with Cora. A smile came to her face. She really did have it all. A wealthy husband, a baby and another one on the way. And a beautiful mansion being built just for them.

| 42 |

Cora (1928)

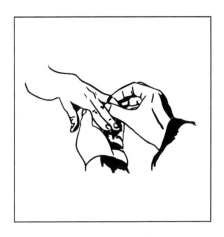

Cora looked in the mirror and began to cry. She thought this day would never come. For over a decade, she had witnessed one sibling after another walk down the aisle and state their vows, first Lila, and then Nannie Bet, followed by Lucy, Thomas Jr., and Richard Jr. All happily married. And now, it was her turn. If only she could have a sense of peace about what she was getting ready to do. Feelings of betrayal kept slipping into her consciousness. One moment she was ecstatic, and then the next consumed with guilt.

Mary Ruth came up behind her and grasped her shoulders. "Now, Cora, we have discussed this before. Lucy would be so happy to know that you're going to become Sidney's wife. She would be so sad to think you are feeling guilty, particularly on a day that should be the happiest day of your life. Now, brush those tears away and let's see a smile."

"I know you're right. Thank you, Mary Ruth, for always being there for me."

Nannie Bet and Lila walked in the door. "What are your two doing?" Lila asked.

"Cora is feeling a little sad about Lucy."

Nannie Bet looked at Cora and began to tear up. "Oh, Cora. This is your day and I know she would be so happy if she was here. Look, we Wright girls stick together. And I know Lucy is right here in spirit, wishing you only happiness."

All the women embraced, and then held hands, as they walked to the back of the church to wait for the wedding director to give them their signal to begin. Richard Jr. looked at Cora and then squeezed her hand. "You are absolutely beautiful. Sidney is the luckiest man in the world to have you as his wife."

"You really think so?"

"I do. Now let's get this show on the road."

At that moment, the doors opened and each of the bridesmaids were escorted down the aisle. Then, Cora and Richard Jr. walked slowly down the aisle as their guests looked on. Cora's heart was beating so loud that she thought Richard Jr. must be able to hear it. But as nervous as she was, she kept her eyes focused on the man she had loved for so long; the man who was finally going to be her husband.

Once Cora and Richard Jr. approached the altar, she made a rehearsed detour over to Uncle Richard, and kissed him on the cheek. Cora noticed the brief smile on his face. "I love you, Uncle Richard."

"Enough about that. Now go on," he said, as he hushed her away.

Cora returned to her position in front of Sidney and looked him right in the eyes. And, as the music was ending, she heard a voice in her mind that she could swear was real. It was whispery and sounded just like Lucy. "I love you, little sister. Be happy. You deserve it."

Cora quickly looked around, realizing the voice must be in her mind. She smiled up at Sidney as he squeezed her hand. Tears welled up in his eyes as they shared their vows. Once the pastor announced them as man and wife, Sidney leaned down, took her face in his hands, and, oh so gently, kissed her.

Later, during the reception, Mary Ruth came up to Cora with a puzzled look on her face. "Oh, Cora, that was the most incredible wedding I've ever witnessed."

"What do you mean?"

"It was so special how Sidney kissed you at the end, but that wasn't it. At the beginning, when the music was just ending, I had a strong sensation that's hard to explain."

"Like Lucy was present?"

"Yes. I thought you'd think I was crazy. But it was like she was standing right next to me. Just like you did when she was married."

"Oh, Mary Ruth. I heard her. She was telling me she loved me and to be happy."

"Well, I know people will think we're crazy."

"No one needs to know. It'll always be our cherished secret."

Mary Ruth looked at her sister with such devotion. "We'll always have this piece of Lucy with us. Just you and me. And, by the way, you look radiant."

"I can't stop smiling. I'm so happy."

"What are you two women talking about?" Sidney asked, as he slipped his arm around Cora's slim waist.

"Nothing much. Just how happy I am to be Mrs. Sidney Chambers."

"That does have a nice ring to it. Now, come on, the wedding director is calling for us to cut the cake."

"Oh, you need to be prepared for a good smothering of cake," Cora said, with a mischievous tone.

"Is that right?"

"It is. So, I hope you like chocolate cake with white icing."

"It's my favorite."

There were many things that Cora wouldn't remember about that night, but she would never forget the few moments she spent with Uncle Richard. Soon after arriving at the reception, she found her uncle and sat down beside him. People knew better than to interrupt their conversation, given the respect others had for this man.

"Cora, you've grown into a dignified woman. I'm very proud of you. Don't tell the others, but I've always felt something special for you."

"Well, thank you, Uncle Richard."

"When you were standing up there in front of the church, I thought, for a moment, that I would've wanted my daughter, May, to have turned out like you."

Cora paused a moment while trying to clear her voice. "I know May would've made a beautiful bride, just like her mother."

Cora heard Uncle Richard gasp softly, and wondered if she had said something wrong. But then he reached over and squeezed her hand. "You're so right. Her mother was a beautiful bride and I loved her so much."

"I know you did."

After several moments, with all the people at bay, Cora gave Uncle Richard a brief hug, rose, and disappeared back into the crowd, leaving the old man with thoughts of the past and wishes of what could've been.

| 43 |

Richard (1928)

A few days after the wedding, Richard scheduled a meeting with his nephews to go over plans on how to proceed with the Wright Machinery Company and several real estate projects they were presently involved with. Even though his nephews wanted to bring the documents to him, Richard insisted that they meet downtown.

As Richard was dropped off by his driver, he looked up at the building that had brought him such pride. Wright's Corner was almost fifty years old, and displayed some wear, but was still sound in structure. Richard couldn't help but reminisce back to 1888 when the building first opened, and was the largest building in Durham at the time.

His mood changed as he turned around and caught sight of the Washington Duke Hotel and all its glory. The sixteen stories loomed over the center of Durham with the most contemporary architecture of the present day. "Damn those Dukes!" he yelled out loud.

People turned in his direction to watch the old man hobble into the doorway. Richard's agitation grew as he walked through Stein's Clothing Store to the back, where his office was located. He would've chosen a more upscale business to occupy his front store space, but they all seemed to have gravitated toward the Washington Duke Hotel. "Well, at least they pay their rent on time," he thought, as he walked through the clothes racks, back to the office he and his nephews occupied.

Richard opened the door to find Richard Jr. huddled over Thomas Jr.'s shoulder. Smoke filled the air from the cigarettes that had already been consumed. Thomas Jr. looked up from the document and addressed his uncle. "Good Morning."

"What's good about it? That hotel is blocking our view of the rest of the city. We're having trouble getting people to rent our space because they all want to be closer to that hotel."

"Uncle Richard, all of the office space in this building is occupied. We're bringing in a sizable income from our rental property. We also have plenty of other income flow from other sources."

"That all may be true, but it doesn't make me feel any better. Anyway, let's get down to business."

Richard sat down in a large leather-bound chair and leaned his cane against the wall. His nephews took their positions in chairs facing Richard. "As I stated the other night, I'm going back to Craig Springs. I'm not sure how long I'll be there. In case I don't return, I want to make sure all of my business affairs are in order."

"Uncle Richard, here are the ledgers that you might want to look at." Richard Jr. placed the large books in front of his uncle, sat back, and waited for him to review their work.

After a few minutes of batting information back and forth, Richard closed the books and looked at his two nephews. "Now, if something were to happen to me, you know that you two will be the executors of my estate. I have clearly stated this in my will, and believe it is for the best."

"Yes, sir. We understand our roles."

"You shouldn't have any objections to this, except from my sister, Lucy. Just recently, I have heard from her son, Mack Ball. It appears he feels the need to be involved in the distribution of my assets. I'm not surprised. His family feels slighted by what I have given to all of you."

The two men didn't say anything. They had met their cousin on several occasions, and knew that he had gone to the University of North Carolina on their uncle's dime. They also knew that Richard had provided for two of Mack's sisters and helped out their mother when her husband died.

"Look, if something happens to me, please strive to keep my will intact. I know you don't agree with my directive to keep my property as part of the estate for a period of thirty years, but that's what I want. Do you understand?"

Richard Jr. was the first to respond. "Yes, sir."

The rest of the morning was spent going over details pertaining to the Wright Machinery Company. Once Richard felt he had covered all the information, he asked for Thomas Jr. to escort him back to his car. When they were on the sidewalk, he faced his nephew. "Thomas, I want to thank you for being willing to stay at Bonnie Brae. It means a great deal to me that you and Claudia want to make it your home."

"Uncle Richard, you are quite welcome. I hope Claudia and I can appreciate it as much as you have."

"I'm sure you will."

Richard slid into the backseat of his car and motioned for the driver to leave. As the car moved away from the curb, he watched the building slip from his sight. Once they turned onto Roxboro Road and drove toward home, Richard was overtaken by a strong belief that he would never see his building again.

| 44 |

Helen (1928)

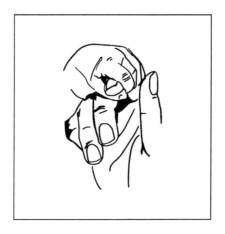

During the past couple of weeks, Helen had been having a difficult time finding a comfortable sleeping position. Upon realizing she wouldn't be able to go back to sleep, she lay awake, waiting for the first glimpses of sunlight to creep into her bedroom.

Helen couldn't shake off the feelings of discontent as she rested beside Richard Jr. She just couldn't believe she had become pregnant so soon after Turissa's birth. She had just started to fit into her dresses, when she had to start taking a notch out of the belt that typically wrapped around her slim waist. After staying in her preferred wardrobe for as long as possible, she returned to the dresses she had worn at the end of her last pregnancy.

Helen noticed Richard Jr. opening his eyes and turning to face her. "Good morning, Richard."

"Well, good morning to you. How are you feeling this morning?"

"I feel like a cow. I don't remember getting this big with my other two pregnancies."

"Well, I find the look very becoming."

"You would. So, what are you doing today?"

"I'm going into the office for most of the day. Thomas and I are finalizing all of the details surrounding the building of the new Wright Machinery Company. I think it's going to be a long day. Why don't you go over to Bonnie Brae for dinner?"

"Richard, have you have forgotten all the details that I need to address regarding our new house? I'm meeting an interior decorator at the house to pick out paint colors and wallpaper. I also have a doctor's appointment."

Richard Jr. rose from bed and headed to the bathroom. Helen could hear Turissa crying down the hall and hoped the nanny would attend to her needs. Her baby was now close to nine months old and was still as unattractive as ever.

Helen rolled over, hoping to go back to sleep, when she heard a knock on the bedroom door. The nanny had been told countless times never to interrupt them and, thinking the worst of her, Helen responded with a harsh voice, "Yes. What do you want?"

"Mrs. Wright, there's a phone call for Mr. Wright. It's from his brother. He told me that it was important."

Helen grabbed her bathrobe and went over to the bathroom door. "Richard, Thomas is on the phone."

Richard Jr. walked out of the bathroom, wiping his face as he went. He walked down the hall and picked up the phone. "Yes, Thomas, what's wrong?"

After a pause, Richard Jr. stated, in an alarming voice, "I'll be right over and we can discuss what we need to do from there."

Once he hung up the phone, Helen asked, "What's wrong?"

Richard Jr. headed back to the bedroom and walked into the closet. "Uncle Richard is very sick. He was transported to the hospital in Roanoke, Virginia. Thomas and I are going to discuss the possibility of driving up to Roanoke to determine if he needs to be transported here to Watts Hospital."

"Richard, please remember that I'm going to have a baby any day now. And I'll need for you to drive me to the hospital. I want you to be present when our son is delivered into the world."

"Helen, how often do we need to discuss this? I'll be with you when you deliver the baby. But, again, you need to have your mind set on loving this baby, even if it's another girl."

Richard Jr. dressed and ran out of the house with a cup of coffee and a piece of toast. Helen couldn't understand why he jumped every time something happened with his uncle. Richard Jr. never responded to her needs in the way he did for his family members. Anyway, Uncle Richard had been sick for quite a while and was probably going to be just fine.

Late that afternoon, Helen packed up Turissa and made her way over to Bonnie Brae. Once she arrived, she took the baby out of the bassinet and placed the bagful of supplies over her shoulder. As she reached the door, Turissa was crying and Helen was becoming irritated. When she opened the door, everyone was in the parlor having a smoke.

"Hello."

Cora ran over and took Turissa out of Helen's arms. "Hello, Helen, and hello to you, sweet girl."

Turissa started giggling as Cora found a place on the floor to get down to play with the baby. Helen turned to Claudia and Mary Ruth. "Has anyone had any word on Uncle Richard?"

"Yes. Thomas and Richard Jr. are going to spend the night and then bring him to Watts Hospital in the morning. The doctors believe his kidneys aren't functioning and it's only a matter of time."

"I'm sorry about that."

Bettie walked up to Helen. "Can I speak to you in private?"

"Sure."

The two women walked into the library and sat down. "Helen, it looks like you don't have too much time before you deliver. I can remember when I was having children almost every other year. I believe those were the best years of my life. Thomas loved taking his hand and placing it on my belly to feel the baby move around. Even though I would get extremely large, I felt loved by my husband more than at any other time in our marriage."

Helen was getting a little anxious about what her mother-in-law wanted to speak to her about. She knew Bettie was very protective of her children and, even though they were all grown, it didn't change her motherly instinct to make sure they were happy.

"Helen, yesterday, Richard Jr. came by for lunch. We were discussing your new home and the arrival of the baby."

Helen wasn't sure where this conversation was going. She knew that Richard Jr. and his mother talked a lot, and wondered if they had spoken about her feelings toward Turissa.

"Anyway, Helen, we both know that Richard Jr. doesn't do well with a lot of stress. Right now, he has a lot on his plate regarding his uncle and the business."

"I understand."

"I'm sure you do. But I want to bring something to your attention. When Richard Jr. was a little boy, he was very close to his father. Thomas was also close to his father, but Richard Jr. had a special connection to him. So, when his father died, he took it very hard. Well, to make matters more complicated, Uncle Richard stepped in and immediately tried to replace his father. Well, this didn't go well at all. You see, his father gave him unconditional love in every way. But after his father died, Richard Jr. couldn't understand why he had to work so hard to receive acceptance from his uncle."

Helen was getting agitated by the length of time Bettie was taking to share her concerns. She tried to stay calm, but couldn't help but blurt out, "So, what does this have to do with me?"

Bettie continued, "You see, Richard Jr. loves you so much, and doesn't want to share anything with you that he thinks will upset you."

"So, what does he think will make me mad?"

"He's concerned about how you are treating Turissa."

Well, this wasn't news to Helen. She and Richard Jr. had conversed regularly about her lack of feelings toward Turissa. No matter how much people tried to convince her to change her feelings, she just couldn't turn them on and off like a faucet. Anyway, she knew this baby she was carrying was a boy. And, once he was born, all the attention would be placed on him.

Helen knew she had to be careful with her words. She didn't want to isolate herself from her mother-in-law but, then again, she wished she would mind her own business. "Bettie, I'll try harder. I have scheduled photographs to be taken of our family and I will even have one taken of just the two of us."

"Thank you, I truly appreciate your efforts. I love my granddaughter and want to make sure she feels loved by her father and mother. So, now, please tell me all about your new house."

"I can't wait for it to be finished. It isn't as large as Bonnie Brae, but it will meet our needs for entertaining and raising our family. It should be ready when the baby arrives. I do believe we'll be so happy there."

"Let me know if there is anything I can do to help you with your move."

"Thank you, Bettie."

Bettie turned away from Helen and loudly proclaimed. "I believe dinner is ready. Dorothy is cooking a pot roast that is one of my favorite dishes."

Helen pulled back and checked her face in one of the mirrors that lined the foyer. She took out her lipstick and placed a dab onto her lips. She moved her lips together and glanced back at her reflection to make sure she was presentable, enjoying the fact that she was causing everyone to wait for her.

Once Helen entered the dining room, she walked over to her chair and sat down. She was glad to see that Turissa wasn't present, but wanted to act concerned. "Where's Turissa?"

Cora responded, "Turissa was taken to the kitchen where she will be fed and watched over."

After Bettie said grace, conversations popped up, centering on events and times at Bonnie Brae. Helen felt excluded and wondered what everyone thought of her. It was clear that both Cora and Bettie had concerns about her parenting skills. The other members of the family also had their own opinions but, even so, Helen really didn't care. As she thought about her life, she knew she loved Richard Jr., but even more so, this life of luxury, and so, for that reason alone, she would make more of an effort with Turissa.

A week later, on the way to Richmond for the delivery of their second baby, Helen began to have contractions. Thankfully, they were only an hour away when the contractions began to come closer together. "Hurry, I don't know if we will make it to the hospital in time."

Helen looked up at Richard Jr., hoping for reassurance. "Honey, hang in there. We don't have much further to go."

"I'm not sure if I can keep going like this. Oh Richard Jr., I'm scared."

"I can see the hospital from here. Hold on just a couple minutes."

Richard Jr. pulled the car up to the main entrance, opened the door and ran inside. Helen could hear Richard Jr. screaming for help. Within moments, two attendants came out and placed Helen in a wheelchair. Helen grabbed the arm of Richard Jr. and pleaded, "Don't leave me."

"Honey, I'll be right inside. You'll be fine. I love you. Now go."

Everything went very quickly and, in only minutes, the baby was delivered and given to Helen to hold. When she looked down into the eyes of another daughter, something stirred inside her. Feelings welled up that brought Helen to tears. Even though this baby wasn't a boy, the baby girl was gorgeous in every way.

Richard Jr. walked into the room, and hesitantly went over to check out Helen's reaction to her new baby daughter. When he saw the smile on his wife's face, he walked over and gave her a kiss on the lips. Helen looked up into his eyes and smiled. "Oh, Richard. This is what I was missing with Turissa. Look at our baby. Isn't she beautiful?"

"She definitely is. What do you want to name her?"

"Since we named Turissa after my side of the family, I think we should name her Bettie after your mother."

"That would make Nannie very happy."

"I just can't get over how beautiful she is."

Helen became the mother to Bettie that she never was to Turissa. She showered her with attention and was always doting on her in public. Helen made a special effort to dress her up and was always talking about her to her friends. She rarely thought about how this favoritism could impact her older daughter. Even when Turissa looked up at her mother with a sad expression, she would call the nanny or one of the house staff to come get her. She rationalized her behavior by telling herself that her daughter wasn't being neglected.

Everything appeared to be coming together for Helen. The prestigious house that would be the envy of her friends and family, had recently been finished and was now being furnished. She had a baby who she was madly in love with and a husband she adored. Her only complaint was dealing with Turissa, and the constant nagging by Richard Jr.'s family to give her more attention.

| 45 |

Cora (1929)

Cora stood at the entrance of the Wright Refuge and watched the children walk into the dining hall for lunch. Each had been dropped off at the doors of the refuge by a parent or government official. When the doors closed behind them, their dreams had been shut out forever. As they filed past, she embraced the loneliness and hopelessness of each child. For some unknown reason, Cora could relate to the children and wanted to do something to relieve the grief that appeared on each face.

Cora walked into the large room and found an empty seat between two boys. One had his head down and wouldn't look up. The other appeared to be older than most of the children and only made snide remarks when asked a question.

"What is your name?" Cora asked.

"What's it to you?"

"Billy, be nice to Mrs. Chambers!" The director shouted from across the room.

"Billy Jones."

"Billy, it's nice to meet you."

"Yeah, right."

"Well, it is. My name is Cora Chambers. My uncle was the man who gave the money for this place to be built."

"Oh, so you must have a lot of money. How about you take me home with you?"

Cora was taken aback by Billy's question and didn't know how to respond. Billy began to laugh. "That's okay. I'll be out of here in a couple of years. My mother is trying to make enough money to take me home. If that doesn't work, I plan on getting a job and my own place."

"What kind of job are you thinking about getting?"

"I could get a newspaper route or work in a factory. The mills are hiring and, as soon as I am old enough to live on my own, I'm out of here."

"How old are you?"

"Fourteen."

"Well, you seem older than that to me."

"You grow up fast in a place like this."

"Do they treat you okay in here?"

"As well as to be expected. It doesn't really matter. I won't be here long."

"Billy, will it be okay if I come back and visit you?"

"If you want."

Later that evening, Cora and Sidney were having dinner and she just couldn't stop thinking about Billy. "Sidney, I went by the refuge today."

"How are things going over there?"

"Okay. I spent some time talking to a boy by the name of Billy. He seemed so angry. He told me that his mother had dropped him off there. He believes that she's going to come back and pick him up, but I spoke to the director and she told me that Billy's mother is an alcoholic and is in no state of mind to raise him."

"That's sad, Cora."

"I want to help him."

"What do you mean?"

"No, Sidney, I'm not thinking about bringing him home. But I'd like to see if he can read. Maybe, I could bring him some books and help him become prepared to do more than just work in a factory for the rest of his life."

"Cora, that sounds like a great idea. By the way, when is your next doctor's appointment?"

"I have one tomorrow. But I'm not going to raise my hopes. If I'm not meant to have a child, the least I can do is help a child who is already in this world."

Sidney put his fork down and reached over to take Cora's hand in his. "That's why I love you. You are the most generous person I've ever met."

"I'm not so sure about that. Anyway, I'm going by to see Helen after my appointment."

"Now, please be careful. You know how she can upset you."

"I will. I want to check on Turissa. I hoped Helen might be a better mother once she had a second child, but she seems to pretend that Turissa doesn't even exist. All she talks about is how beautiful and wonderful Bettie is. Anyway, I want to go and give Turissa some attention."

The next day, Cora sat in the chair that she had become all too acquainted with. As the door opened and Dr. London came in, she could tell that her condition hadn't changed. "Cora, it's so good to see you. How's Sidney?"

"He's doing well."

"That's good. Tell him I hope to see him on the golf course."

"I will. So, what can you tell me?"

"Cora, I really don't know what to tell you. Given your age, I believe you might have missed the window of opportunity to become pregnant. Now, I don't want you and Sidney to stop trying, but I wouldn't get your hopes too high about having a child."

The tears started to well up in Cora's eyes. She didn't want to cry, but she couldn't help it. All she ever wanted was to be a mother and now it appeared that it wasn't going to happen. Dr. London kept talking, but she didn't hear any of the words he was saying. Finally, he got up and opened the door for her to leave. Once she walked out of the office and got into her car, she placed her head down on the steering wheel and sobbed.

Cora didn't feel like going to see Helen, but told herself that she wasn't going for her, but for Turissa. As she drove into the circle driveway off of Knox Street, she was taken aback by the magnitude of the house that stood in front of her. Her first thought centered on how huge the house was for such a young couple. She had to admit that it was beautiful. The white exterior with black shutters gave it a stately feel. The circle driveway, hidden away from the road, provided lots of privacy. There was a rose garden to the side of the house surrounded by an immaculate green lawn. It was clear that Helen had worked closely with the architect and builders to create a house that would stand out above all others in Durham.

Cora opened her car door and walked up to the front porch. She had to take some deep breaths to compose herself. She was about to turn back, but knew she needed to be here. *Cora, you are here for Turissa. Don't let this petite woman with her beautiful baby and immense house intimidate you. You have a wonderful husband who loves you and don't you forget it!*

Seconds after Cora rang the doorbell, a butler opened the door. "Can I help you?"

"Yes, can you please let Mrs. Wright know that Cora Chambers is here to see her?"

"Please, step in. I'll let Mrs. Wright know you are here."

Cora gazed around the spacious foyer with the beautiful wallpaper and expensive paintings from Europe. Just as she was looking into the parlor at the imported furniture and grand piano, she saw Helen walking down the staircase with her baby in her arms. "Oh, Cora. I'm sorry. I forgot that you were stopping by."

"That's okay."

"Life has been so hectic. I'm planning an open house and inviting half the town. You and Sidney will get your invitation in the mail in a day or two. Anyway, Bettie has been a handful and Turissa has just started learning to walk."

Cora spoke up. "Where is Turissa? I'd love to see her."

Helen sighed and was clearly annoyed by the question. "I've just put her down for a nap."

"Oh. I really would like to see my niece. Can you have her come down for just a couple of minutes?"

"If I get her up now, she won't go back to sleep. I have things that I need to do. Anyway, you can hold Bettie." Helen extended the baby into Cora's arms. "Isn't she one of the most beautiful babies you've ever seen?"

"Yes, she is." Cora looked down at the baby and wanted to cry. The last thing she wanted was to be holding someone else's baby, when she knew she probably would never hold her own. "So how is Richard Jr.? I haven't seen him lately."

"He's doing great. He and Thomas are busy working out all the details for the Wright Machinery Company building. They have been stressed trying to work with Uncle Richard, given his health issues and all."

"Helen, you have a beautiful new home."

"Well, thank you. I'm pleased with how it all turned out. I can't wait to have people over. Richard Jr. imported a lot of the furniture and rugs from Europe and Asia."

Cora began to feel nauseated by the conversation. She didn't enjoy being around Helen with how focused she was on how things looked. She knew the conversation wasn't going to improve and felt like she was suffocating. "Helen, I need to leave now. I forgot I have an appointment that I scheduled." Cora handed the baby back to Helen and stood up.

"Oh, Cora, did I say something wrong?"

"No. I just need to get to my appointment."

Cora walked over to the door and, without another word, walked out, closing the door behind her. As she was getting into the car, her hands began to shake and tears fell freely down her cheeks.

| 46 |

Cora (1929)

When Cora reached her house and pulled into the driveway, she was a mess. Her eyes were swollen, and her cheeks red, from the tears that streamed down her face. She noticed Sidney's car in the driveway and hesitated for a moment before walking to the front door. When she opened the door, Sidney looked at her and then took her into his arms. "Oh, Cora, I guess you didn't get good news from the doctor."

"Oh, Sidney. It was a dreadful day. After leaving Dr. London's office, I drove over to Helen's house. All I wanted to do was spend some time with Turissa. But that woman wouldn't allow me to see my own niece. Then she practically thrust her baby into my arms! I'm so sorry, but she makes me so mad!"

Cora looked at Sidney and suddenly realized that he was home earlier than usual. "Sidney, why are you home?"

"I have some news. Your uncle is not doing well and the doctors have asked for the closest kin to come to Watts Hospital. They don't think he will make it through the night."

"Oh, Sidney. Can you please drive me? I'm just a mess and I don't know if I can go on my own."

"I'm here for you. Why don't you freshen up and I'll wait right here until you are ready to go."

"Sidney, I love you so much. You have no idea how much it means to me that you understand how I'm feeling."

Cora ran upstairs and gasped when she saw her reflection in the mirror. Just seeing herself made her want to break down, but she held back the tears as she washed her face and reapplied her makeup. After taking some deep breaths and trying to think positive thoughts, Cora composed herself and walked down the stairs to where Sidney was waiting.

Cora and Sidney rode the few blocks to the hospital in silence. The sun was beginning to set and she noticed the daffodils coming up, along with mounds of green grass. Spring would be here soon. It made her sad to think about how much Uncle Richard liked the spring time and how she missed the rides they had taken together through the open pastures. She wondered what life would be like without her uncle. He had been such a large part of her world. Even as sick as he had been recently, his presence still loomed over her.

After parking the car, Sidney took Cora's hand and walked her to the hospital entrance. They had been there many times in the past couple of months to visit Uncle Richard and knew exactly where to go. The halls were a pasty green with large windows between the wards. Their footsteps echoed as they continued down the long corridor. But it was the smell that haunted her the most. The unique smell brought back memories of when she had brought her sister, Lucy, into these walls, never to see her again. She tried to shut out that agonizing night and the hurt that followed. As they approached her uncle's room, she squeezed Sidney's hand and looked at him for reassurance.

The first person Cora saw was Aunt Nannie, who was sitting next to her brother's bed. She appeared very distressed, and rightfully so. Her aunt's brother was the one person who'd given her life purpose. They had shared life together for close to fifty years and stood by each other throughout the good and bad.

Richard Jr. and Thomas Jr. were in a corner of the room, speaking in quiet voices. It was clear from their serious demeanor that they were discussing something pertaining to business. Cora almost found it comical to think that her uncle would pass from this earth as he lived, in the midst of a business venture.

Cora walked over to her uncle and took his hand. As she brought it up to her face, he opened his eyes and tried to speak. At that moment, Cora leaned down and whispered, "Uncle Richard, I want to thank you for everything you did for our family. I know you loved us like your own. Even though you could be strict with us, I believe it was only because you wanted the best for us. And you were right. We're all happy and doing well, thanks to you."

Uncle Richard tried to speak, but his words were unintelligible. Aunt Nannie began to dab her eyes with her kerchief. "Cora, you know he loved you."

"I do. Uncle Richard, I'm so proud of being your niece. You have made my life richer in every way. I love you."

Uncle Richard looked up and Cora spotted one single tear slip from his eye. At that moment, Mary Ruth and their mother, Bettie, walked in the door. Cora sat at the end of the bed as Bettie spoke.

"Richard, can you believe we are all still together after so many years?"

Uncle Richard glanced around the room. Bettie took his hand and, with tears in her eyes, continued, "You know I was really mad at you for the way you treated Thomas? But I have to admit, you have made up for it by the way you took us all in and provided a lifestyle beyond my wildest dreams. We haven't always seen eye to eye on things, but I know that you are proud of how the children are now upstanding citizens, as well as good at business."

Everyone giggled at the thought of how Uncle Richard had molded them into the people they had become. Richard Jr. came over and looked down at his uncle, who he had been intimidated by for so long. "I want to thank you for the opportunities you've given me. I must admit that I didn't like carrying all your bags around Europe on those first business trips, but I'll always be thankful for the education you provided."

Thomas Jr. inserted, "And you'll be glad to know that you've outlived all of the founding fathers of this city. Benjamin Duke, the last of them, died in early January. So, you can be happy to know that no one can take that away from you."

Mary Ruth looked at her brother. "Thomas, that's not nice."

"Well, it's the truth," Thomas Jr. replied.

Nannie Bet and Lila appeared in the doorway. Lila made her way to the bed and leaned down to give her uncle a kiss on the cheek. "Uncle Richard, your wild niece is here."

Everyone laughed at the reference to the days before their father died and how rambunctious they all had been. Uncle Richard took in a deep breath and tried to smile. At that moment, his breathing became labored and he fell into a deep sleep. Aunt Nannie held tight to her brother's hand, as the rest of the family reminisced over the past.

Cora was in the middle of a conversation with Nannie Bet when everyone grew quiet. The end had come, in a manner that she knew her uncle would be happy with; surrounded by people who paid homage to him, in life and also in death.

| 47 |

Bettie (1929)

Bettie couldn't believe it. Richard was finally out of her life. For the last twenty-eight years, she had lived under the domination of this man, who had taught her children to believe that happiness came from wealth, but it had caused her such grief. Memories of the day Thomas died came to the forefront of her thoughts. Questions about what had happened still haunted her. On many occasions, she had tried to discuss the topic with Richard, but he always dismissed her questions.

Bettie reached for the black dress and pearls that were laid out for her. She placed the last hair pin, fastening her hat, and touched up her makeup. As she looked in the mirror and stared at the sixty-three-year-old woman who appeared, a sadness swept over her. She brushed away a tear and told herself to be grateful for what she did have. So many people would have given anything to have the things she possessed. But not Bettie. All she had wanted was the love of one man; a man who had been taken too early.

There was a knock on the door and a soft voice called out, "Mrs. Wright, the family is waiting for you. The service will start in only a couple of minutes. Is there anything I can do to help?"

"Thank you, but I'm ready."

Bettie smiled into the mirror and took a deep breath, before turning around and opening the door. While walking down the hallway, she could hear the voices of her children and their spouses. Everyone was present, even her grandchildren, who were playing in a room off the maid's quarters. She took a moment, as she descended the stairway that led to the foyer, thinking only of the days ahead.

Thankfully, Bettie was only attending, and not a participant in the planning and implementation of, the service. Nannie had worked out the details with Richard long before his death. Dr. J.W. Smith from Trinity Methodist Church, and the former pastor, Rev. W.W. Peele, would conduct the services. Dr. David Scanlon, Helen's father, had also insisted on participating. She had to laugh at the men in long gowns, fighting to have a place in the spotlight. Richard would be happy to know that he was the cause of such a stir among the reverends.

Bettie briefly walked among her children and their spouses, complimenting them as she went. When the family was instructed to take their seats, Bettie sat down in a chair between Nannie and Richard Jr. Bettie knew that Nannie was hurting over her brother's death and reached over, taking Nannie's hand in hers. She cared deeply for this woman, who she had shared life with over the past three decades.

The service began with a couple of hymns, after which a sermon was preached by all three pastors. Each man included lots of accolades about Richard, a man who had sat in their pews, but never cared much for religion. After close to two hours, a final hymn was sung and the crowd was dismissed to their cars, where they would follow the hearse to Maplewood Cemetery.

The funeral procession turned left out of the driveway onto Roxboro Road and drove slowly past the acres and acres of land Richard had purchased over the years. After a few miles, the cars passed the Wright Refuge, where all of the children stood silently in reverence to the man whose money had given them a home. Bettie was touched by the children's respect and began to cry. As she wiped her tears, she looked over at Nannie and Cora, who were also crying. The three women smiled through their tears, and would forever remember the sight of the homeless children standing in front of the white structure.

City officials had asked businesses to close for thirty minutes to honor this man who had made such a difference to the city of Durham. As the hearse made its way to Richard's final resting place, people lined the sidewalks outside of their businesses and homes. Some waved, but most stood silently in respect, as the cars rode by.

Once the funeral procession arrived at Maplewood Cemetery, Bettie exited the car and was seated under a large awning in front of the mausoleum. After the rest of the family had been seated, people wrapped around the edges of the chairs, striving to get close enough to hear each pastor's last words. Several newspaper reporters, along with spectators only interested in being a part of a newsworthy event, stood in the midst of the crowds.

The casket had been placed on a platform in front of the mausoleum for everyone to observe as the pastors said their final words. A few traditional hymns were sung, after which all of the family members laid a flower on top of the casket. Bettie walked up to the casket and placed her rose on top, noticing the void of emotion in her heart. As she walked back to her seat, Thomas Jr. walked up to her and gave her a hug. "Mom, I just wanted to tell you how much I appreciate you."

"Well, thank you, Thomas."

"I never could understand how you lived in the same house with this man who treated you so poorly. He never showed you any respect."

Bettie was taken aback by her son's words, particularly at this time. "Thomas, I did it for you and your siblings. As much as I grieved your father, I knew he would want for me to stay and raise you under his brother's roof. And now I have six incredible grown children and grandchildren to fill my heart."

Bettie and Thomas Jr. embraced, and after making sure his mother was okay, he walked over to his wife, Claudia, leaving Bettie to greet friends and others who she had only known from a distance. Before long, the crowds dispersed, leaving only the close members of the family. Cora came up beside Bettie, interlocking their arms. She gently gave Bettie a squeeze and asked, "Are you okay?"

"Yes. To be honest, I'm better than okay. I now feel like I can start living my life."

Cora looked at her with a strange expression. "Well, if you need anything, please call me."

"I will, but you know Thomas Jr. and Claudia have agreed to stay on at Bonnie Brae. And I know the rest of you are happy in your marriages. The only concern I have has to do with the execution of the will. Richard's nephew, Mack Ball, has been having some heated conversations with Thomas Jr. and Richard Jr. Apparently, Lucy's children aren't happy that Richard left my two sons as executors of the estate. They want to make sure they get, what they believe, they are entitled to. I hope everyone involved can come to a resolution without bringing in lawyers, but I'm not so sure."

"Well, I hate that, but I'm not surprised."

Helen walked up to the two women. "So, what are you two talking about?"

Bettie didn't want to discuss the estate with Helen. She had witnessed her daughter-in-law twisting the truth on occasion, and didn't want to fuel any unnecessary fire. "Helen, I hear you are planning a party in the near future."

"Yes, I am. It's for my friends from the country club. I want to show them what a beautiful home we have."

Bettie didn't miss the fact that she was excluded from the event.

"Well, I hope it goes well."

Richard Jr. called out, "Helen, come on. Everyone is waiting for us in the car."

Bettie turned and saw the last of the mourners getting into their vehicles to go back to a reception at Bonnie Brae. She returned to her assigned car and stepped inside. Peering out of the window, she watched the workers from the cemetery taking up the chairs and clearing the grounds. The casket was still on the platform, with the doors of the mausoleum swung open, beckoning for the next occupant to take its place inside. Her eyes were drawn upward to the inscription above the door, R.H. Wright. She almost laughed out loud. Richard, you're finally home.

The car slowly turned onto Chapel Hill Road, then turned left onto Duke Street. The driver slowed as they passed the mansions built by the Dukes and Hills. As the car drove down Main Street and passed Wright's Corner, Bettie smiled. Turning north, they went past the tobacco warehouses, with the sweet smell filling the air. Finally, the car pulled into the long driveway that led up to Bonnie Brae. A blanket of yellow daffodils swayed in the wind on each side of the drive, welcoming her home. And for the first time in her life, Bettie took in a deep breath, and was filled with an immense feeling of freedom that encapsulated every cell of her being.

Epilogue

Weeks before Richard's death, his nephew, Richard Jr., found the handwritten will that his uncle had written and placed it in the company's safe. Days after the burial, Richard's sister, Lucy, with the encouragement of her son, Dr. W.M. Ball, hired Congressman Charles L. Albernethy, to file a caveat to suspend the implementation of the will.

The litigation held the estate in bondage, not allowing funds to go toward the running of the Wright Refuge. Several newspaper articles in July 1929 reported the refuge's poor financial situation, and that civic groups were being asked to support it through this crisis.

The case went to court, and on November 6, 1929, Judge E.H. Crammer ruled, after both the caveators and propounders had come to a compromise. The section of the will that stated that all property would be held in trust for thirty years was found null and void.

Judge Crammer ruled that Richard's sister, Nannie, was to be given the deed to her late brother's home, Bonnie Brae. He also ruled that Nannie would immediately receive $100,000 for the sole purpose of donating it to the Wright Refuge.

After these initial contributions, the estate was divided into three parts. One-third went directly to Richard's sister, Lucy, to be divided among her and her children. The other two-thirds went into a trust at the First National Bank, from which Nannie Wright received interest on the money for the specific purpose of paying for the upkeep of Bonnie Brae. Upon her death, the trust was divided among the six living children of Richard's brother, Thomas Davenport Wright. There was no mention of Bettie in the will.

Weeks after Richard's death, newspapers reported his estate to be worth from $3,000,000 to upward of $10,000,000. Given that the estate contained large amounts of property, the actual dollar amount will forever be a mystery. Richard Wright will also be remembered for the number of times he crossed the oceans, during a time when travel was difficult and extremely uncomfortable. His obituary states that he crossed the Atlantic ninety-four times, the Pacific fourteen times, and around the world eight times. This would be an incredible feat for someone in today's world, but unheard of during the time in which Richard lived.

Printed in the USA
CPSIA information can be obtained
at www.ICGtesting.com
LVHW010241290224
772561LV00006B/22/J